"She acts as if she's the mistress here!"

Netta continued bitterly, "You made me marry you, but I'm still entitled to be treated—"

"Caroline is my guest here," Joss interrupted her curtly. "And as for entitlements, you don't get those without the obligations that go with them." She flinched away from the message in his eyes. "And surely *I* should be the one to complain? Oh, you needn't worry," he went on cuttingly as her eyes widened. "I won't disturb you. You can sleep in blissful solitude."

"Perhaps you'd prefer to go to Caroline?"

His face visibly blanched, and she drew a sharp breath of fear, immediately regretting her jealous retort. "I'm married to you, not to Caroline," he reminded her coldly.

Did he mean, not to Caroline—yet?

SUE PETERS
is also the author of these
Harlequin Romances

Many of these titles are available at your local bookseller.

For a free catalogue listing all available Harlequin Romances
and Harlequin Presents, send your name and address to:

HARLEQUIN READER SERVICE
M.P.O. Box 707, Niagara Falls, NY 14302
Canadian address: Stratford, Ontario N5A 6W2

Marriage in Haste

by

SUE PETERS

Harlequin Books

TORONTO • LONDON • LOS ANGELES • AMSTERDAM
SYDNEY • HAMBURG • PARIS • STOCKHOLM • ATHENS • TOKYO

Original hardcover edition published in 1980
by Mills & Boon Limited

ISBN 0-373-02410-X

Harlequin edition published June 1981

CHAPTER ONE

'I WOULDN'T marry you if you were the last man left on earth!'

Netta faced him defiantly, a tiny figure shaking with outrage, her spirit as fiery as the colour of her copper curls.

'The feeling's mutual,' he snapped back through tight lips. 'Don't imagine I enjoy the prospect of being saddled with you for a wife, for however short a time it may be.'

'Then let's forget the whole crazy idea.'

'There's nothing I'd like better,' he assured her grimly, 'except that I don't relish having the lives of the entire Embassy staff on my conscience for the rest of my days.' Anger rode him like a storm. It blazed through the strange, gold-coloured eyes that earned him the sobriquet 'le Renard' which she was to hear on many lips before she finally reached England, and tightened the lean, brown, pointed face with the wide forehead topped by close-cropped brown curly hair, that would instantly distinguish him in any crowd.

'I'm not responsible for the Embassy staff,' she retorted swiftly.

'Unfortunately I am,' he told her grimly. 'And I'm prepared to go to any lengths to get them away from Lak in safety.'

'Even to the extent of getting married?'

'Even to the extent of marrying you,' he told her with a singular lack of gallantry.

'Why can't you just get them away, and leave me behind?' she cried desperately. She felt blackmailed, trapped. 'I can look after myself.'

'The authorities in Lak don't think so.' His expression said, neither did he. 'They're stretching a point as it is, to allow a plane to land to evacuate the Embassy staff, and their wives and families.' He said 'their wives' with clipped emphasis. 'Their condition was that all the staff must go, or all must remain here in the Embassy, at the responsibility of the Ambassador. They refuse to be responsible themselves for individual stray foreigners, they've got quite enough on their plates as it is, coping with a civil uprising, without bothering with you,' he told her bluntly. 'If you got into difficulties, you'd have to get yourself out of them, and the authorities aren't prepared to accept blame for the consequences.'

'But why should they insist I get married, in order to come on the plane with you?' she demanded angrily. She would have liked to say, 'get married to you, of all people?' but she did not quite dare. The flaring light in those strange gold eyes stopped the words before they were uttered. 'Why can't I just go on the plane as one of the Embassy staff, and leave it at that?' she cried instead.

'Because the military have a list of all the bona fide Embassy staff.' He spoke with the barely controlled patience of someone explaining a point to a witless child.

'You could have told them I was a tourist.'

'And risked you getting shot?' He eyed her incredulously. 'Have you got no conception of the danger you've placed yourself in, by coming into the country in the first place?' he demanded. He looked as if he would like to shake some realisation into her, and Netta caught her breath, but with a supreme effort of self-control he desisted, and went on tautly, 'No one would believe you could be simply a tourist, because no tourist in their right mind would risk entering a country on the verge of civil war.' His tone questioned her own sanity, and she flushed angrily, but he went on before she could speak, 'If you even tried to use such an explanation, you'd immediately arouse suspicion that you were a political activator, here to stir up more unrest. And I don't need to point out the penalty for that kind of behaviour, in Lak,' he finished grimly.

'I came here on business,' she protested angrily.

'They wouldn't accept that, either.' He gave a short, harsh laugh, and his eyes raked Netta's slender figure, that remained daintily feminine in spite of her lightweight, tailored trouser suit. 'Their women don't conduct business. They have the sense to remain at home where they belong, and leave such matters to their menfolk.'

So as well as being an arrogant, overbearing bully, he was a self-confessed male chauvinist. How typical! she thought bitingly.

'I still don't understand why....' She tried to close her mind to the penalties he spoke of. She had heard tales, since she reached the Embassy....

'The only way I could possibly pass off your behaviour to the authorities, and still make it look convincing, was to tell them you were my fiancée, and you'd travelled out here on purpose to marry me. Surprisingly, even a war-ring army still believes in love.' Did his lips twitch ever so slightly as he said it? She could not be sure.

'You could have told them I was already your wife,' she persisted stubbornly, and his patience snapped.

'After nearly a year in the country, the authorities in Lak know me as well as they know Wendy and Harry Fraser,' he spoke of the Ambassador and his wife, whom Netta had long been friends with, and came to visit while she was in Lak. 'The authorities have got the records of the Embassy....'

'Stole the records, you mean,' she corrected him coldly.

'Have—stole—confiscated—call it what you like, they know I'm a single man.' His voice rose in angry exaspera-tion, and he took a quick step towards her.

Instinctively, Netta stepped backwards, trying to avoid him. In spite of her resolve not to be intimidated, she quailed before his furious glare, but her pace was no match for the length of his arm.

Lean brown fingers like steel bands reached out and circled her wrist. She tried to fling up her arm to free her-self, but she was no match for his strength, either. Six feet plus of masculine fury towered over her, provoked out of all patience by her stubborn refusal to obey his order.

And his order was—to marry him! A complete stranger....

'I still don't see why I should be made a sacrifice,' she

made one last frantic bid for her freedom. 'I'm not even on the Embassy staff. I'm only a chance visitor.'

'If you won't see reason,' he gritted, 'you can be the one to tell the Embassy staff just why you think the sacrifice of your maidenly status is worth risking their lives for.'

She had no option but to follow him. He pulled her along behind him with impatient force, through the door of the high-ceilinged Embassy study, and into the big drawing room beyond.

It was crowded with people. Everyone in the Embassy was gathered there, the men accompanied by their wives, and—Netta saw with dismay—a number of young children, ranging from an infant of about six months gurgling on its mother's lap, to a pair of six-year-olds who must be on the verge of being sent back home to school if circumstances had been normal. They all looked up as Jocelyn de Courcey thrust the door open without ceremony and dragged Netta through.

'Any news, Joss?' One of the men spoke up.

'Go on—tell them,' her tormentor grated harshly. 'Tell them—if you can.'

Netta never forgot the hush that followed his words. It was as if everyone in the room held their breath. Then one of the children wailed.

'Daddy, I'm frightened!'

She was about five years old, fair, with curly hair. Two large tears brimmed over, and rolled down her chubby cheeks, and her father reached down to pick her up in his arms, murmuring words of comfort. His eyes met Netta's over the child's head, imploring her....

He was one of the younger aides at the Embassy, the woman with the baby on her lap was his wife. Ordinarily, Netta supposed she would not have got to know them so well, her time would have been taken up with Wendy and Harry, but neither had been able to spare her more than an hour or two since she arrived, and she found herself thrown on the company of the junior staff. Acquaintanceship ripens quickly under the stress of danger, and she soon got to know them all, and their fears for the safety of their families.

'Daddy, I'm frightened,' the child sobbed.

Her father's gaze held Netta's, anguished, pleading. She could not meet it, could not bear it. It was sheer moral blackmail, but.... She spun to face Joss de Courcey.

'I'll marry you,' she gasped, before she could change her mind.

It was surely the strangest wedding she had ever attended.

'I'll have to go back to my hotel to change into a dress. I can't get married in a trouser suit.'

'There's no time,' Joss objected immediately.

'I shan't defect, if that's what you're afraid of,' she snapped.

'I'm not.' He looked straight at her as he said it, and oddly, she believed him. Believed he trusted her, even if he disliked her. 'There simply isn't time,' he said curtly. 'The plane's due to land just after sundown. We've only got a few hours, and the chief of the military is going to call here to collect me soon to arrange final clearance to release us.' Against her will, she decided he spoke the truth. She felt the same strange sense of trust in him. It was mutual, she decided, the same as their dislike.

'Come and tidy up.' Wendy rescued her, as if she sensed that Netta must have a few moments' respite before she was irretrievably committed. 'You look lovely, just as you are,' her friend comforted her, and Netta rounded on her in amazement.

'You actually approve of this, don't you?' she breathed incredulously. 'Wendy, you're hopeless!' Her knees collapsed as they reached her friend's bedroom, and she sat down on the bed with a rush, torn between a hysterical desire to laugh and cry at the same time. 'You haven't changed a scrap,' she managed at last.

'Well, darling, you must admit it's romantic.' Wendy tried her best to look ashamed, without success.

'Romance!' Netta scoffed. 'You're as bad as when we were teenagers together, at school.'

'Older, maybe,' Wendy conceded with a twinkle, 'but happy with it.' There was no mistaking the light in her eyes, and Netta's lips curved in spite of her own problems. Wendy's had been a whirlwind romance, with Harry posted to some out-of-the-way place at the other end of the earth, and Netta had some misgivings about the marriage lasting, but seven years later they still seemed just as much in love.

'*You* weren't exactly forced into marriage,' she reminded her friend tartly. 'If only I'd received your cable in time,' she exclaimed, 'I need never have come to Lak at all, and the whole wretched affair wouldn't have happened.'

'You must have wondered at my lack of welcome when you arrived,' Wendy answered ruefully.

'It was a bit of a shock,' Netta admitted. To her astonishment, instead of the effusive greeting she expected, Wendy received her with frank dismay when she presented herself at the Embassy.

'Oh, my goodness! Didn't you get my cable, warning you not to come?'

'No.' Netta looked puzzled for a moment, then enlightenment dawned. 'But I haven't been in touch with London for a couple of weeks or so. Dad's abroad, and when I had the chance to join a photographic safari it seemed too good an opportunity to miss. And as it was only a few days' journey from Lak, I came straight on from there.' Her friend's lack of response registered, and she added, 'If you've got a big reception or something on here, I'll explore by myself for a day or two, until you're free. We can spend some time catching up on each other's news afterwards, I needn't go home straight away, I'm not tied to any particular date of return.'

'You'll return with the Embassy staff the moment Harry can get clearance for a plane to land,' Wendy cut short her plans. 'And as for exploring, by yourself or otherwise, forget it,' she advised.

'But why? Is there an outbreak of the plague or something?' Wendy's face, as well as her tone, said she meant it, and the laugh died in Netta's throat. 'Or are diplomatic relations strained?' she asked resignedly.

'Neither.' Harry Fraser joined them, and Netta stared

at him, shocked beyond measure at the change in the likeable Scot since she last saw him. He looked exhausted, and desperately worried. 'Lak's asked our help, and we've given all we can, but their government still hasn't been able to contain the situation. You've arrived bang in the middle of a civil war,' he informed her baldly.

'So that's why everywhere was so deserted since I crossed the border.' She looked at her two friends, aghast. 'I thought it was probably a fast day, or something, and everyone was either indoors, or in the temples.' The real reason hit her like a blow, and she swallowed hard. 'The proprietor of the hotel was reluctant to give me a room. I wondered why the place was so empty.'

'Everyone who can go has already gone,' the Ambassador told her. 'Where are you booked in at?' he wanted to know.

'In the—that low white building round the corner. I didn't know whether you might have visiting dignitaries at the Embassy, so I got a room to be on the safe side.'

'You should be all right there, until we fly out,' Harry still looked unhappy. 'We'd prefer you to be with us in the Embassy itself, but ...?' He flashed an enquiring glance at his wife.

'There isn't an inch of room to spare here,' Wendy shook her head. 'The French are sharing the place with us until we leave,' she explained. 'Their Embassy up-country has been taken over by the insurgents, and the staff got out just in time, and managed to reach here. Even the bath's being used as a bed,' she wailed despairingly.

'I shall be fine where I am.' Netta hoped she sounded more confident than she felt. 'I'm only a stone's throw away from the Embassy, after all.' She did not know whether she was trying to reassure her friends, or herself.

'Just the same, you must eat your meals with us,' Harry insisted. 'Now you're here, we must keep in constant touch, so that you'll be au fait with any contingency plans we make for evacuating the country in the event the situation deteriorates suddenly.'

'How bad is it?'

'On the boil, but the lid hasn't actually blown off yet,' replied Harry graphically.

'When it does, I hope to goodness we're all on the plane, and on the way home,' Wendy interrupted fervently, and Netta noticed she said 'when' and not 'if'.

'If it were not for le Renard, I think we might not have succeeded in obtaining a plane at all,' one of their French refugee guests put in significantly, and Netta frowned.

'Le Renard?' She looked a question at the Ambassador. 'He sounds sinister, whoever he is,' and she shivered. The Fox. A creature of the night, who came and went with silent tread, along secret paths. 'Surely it isn't necessary for you to have recourse to such a person? A straight-forward request from you, to the authorities here....'

'Straightforward requests from an Embassy don't carry much weight in a country torn apart by civil strife,' Harry acknowledged wearily. 'And Jocelyn de Courcey, to give him his correct name, can employ lines of communication which are denied the Embassy.'

'He's not one of your staff, then?' In spite of herself, the peculiar nickname intrigued Netta.

'Officially, he's one of my aides,' Harry said evasively. 'But if you want anything while you're here, ask any of the other aides rather than Joss. He's got other things to do.'

'I think your French guest enjoys a flair for the drama-tic.' Netta feigned indifference. Harry obviously did not wish to discuss the mysterious Jocelyn de Courcey any further, and she knew better than to press him. Instead, she shrugged offhandedly. 'Le Renard, indeed!' she scoffed.

'Did you call me, *mademoiselle*?'

He spoke in faultless French, from just behind her. Netta spun round, startled, and found herself looking straight into the strange, golden eyes of the man they called the Fox.

It was like looking straight into the sun. Netta blinked, and had an urge to shut her own lids, as if the light was too bright. Or perhaps to use them as defences, to shut herself away behind them. Hide herself away, might be a better description. The stranger's eyes seemed to bore right through her, laying bare her very thoughts.

'*Non, monsi.* . . .' She stopped herself abruptly. 'I mean —no,' she said firmly, reverting to her own native language with a flash of quite unjustified irritation. Strain was making her edgy, and she felt in no mood to encounter mysterious strangers.

'Ah, Joss, I'm glad you've appeared again.'

Harry was at it now, she thought crossly. First the Frenchman, using such an odd nickname, and now the Ambassador himself saying, 'you've appeared again', instead of, 'you're back', as if the man was some kind of djinn, who could appear and disappear at will. Harry should know better, she thought impatiently, surprised that the normally down-to-earth Scot should succumb to his colleague's flair for drama.

'I want you to meet Netta Vaughan. She'll be coming back on the plane with us,' the Ambassador performed the introductions.

'Miss Vaughan.'

The newcomer acknowledged the introduction with a slight bow, and a look that seemed to pierce right through her. He did not smile, and he did not attempt to shake hands. Netta thrust her own unwanted hand back into the pocket of her jacket with angry force, piqued by the omission as he went on, speaking directly to the Ambassador, 'I told the military you had an all-male staff. I must contact them right away, to set things right.'

'Netta isn't on my staff,' Harry said. 'She came to Lak from holiday, to. . . .' He got no further. At the mention of the word holiday, the other man spun round on Netta, and his gold eyes lit with anger.

'You came on holiday—to a country on the verge of civil war?' he snapped incredulously. 'Are you mad?'

His unexpected fury hit her with a solid force, and she recoiled from his verbal attack.

'I—I——' she began, and then her chin came up, and the fiery temper that went with the colour of her hair rose to do battle in her own defence. She drew herself up to her admittedly not very great height, and looked up straight into his face. 'I came here *from* holiday, on a matter of business,' she said haughtily, and wished she was a foot taller, to make her nearer to his height. As it was, her tone failed to crush him as she intended it to, and he interrupted her impatiently.

'Whatever your reason, it can't be of such importance to bring you into Lak at a time like this,' he stormed. 'To risk your life for a triviality....'

'My business is *not* a triviality!' Against life itself, it was, she acknowledged honestly, but she would rather die than admit it to this overbearing stranger.

'Even so, it surely could have waited,' he dismissed her protest as of no consequence. 'To knowingly come across the border into a political cauldron....' Words seemed to fail him. She doubted if they failed him very often, she thought caustically.

'I wasn't aware....'

'The troubles here have been making headlines in every newspaper, television and wireless bulletin in this part of the globe for the past seven days.'

'And for the past fourteen days, I've been out of reach of all three,' she threw back at him triumphantly.

'You must have had to do some pretty convincing talking, to enable you to cross the border post,' he accused her, unimpressed. 'You can't claim ignorance of the situation after that.'

'There was no one manning the border post when I came through.' She had thought it peculiar at the time, but in the absence of anyone there to question, she had little alternative but to drive straight through.

'Surely that struck you as strange?' He gave her no quarter, and his persistence goaded her into an anger to match his own.

'It struck me that the border guards were either drunk, asleep, or had business of their own in the nearby village,' she flung at him rashly.

'They're defecting in droves,' Harry put in, but the other man was not to be diverted.

'No matter about the guards,' he dismissed them as

irrelevant. 'Now you're here, you're one more to be got away to safety.' His look, his tone, left her in no doubt he would have preferred there to be one less, and she flushed angrily, then went white.

'You needn't trouble yourself on my account,' she blazed back at him. 'I can look after myself.'

'You may do whatever you please, once you're over the border into peaceful territory,' he informed her icily, 'but while you're in Lak, you're the responsibility of the Embassy, and you'll do exactly as you're told. I'll go and warn the military,' he added to Harry, and spun on his heel.

Before Netta could get her breath back to reply, he was gone. One moment he was there, and the next he had vanished. She stared at where he had been standing, the defiant repudiation of his right to order her to do anything at all, dying on her lips. He was no longer there to defy.

When he returned, it was to tell her that she had to marry him.

CHAPTER TWO

'I'VE only got his word that he's not married already.' Netta wielded the hairbrush with nervous energy, and Wendy sat up, her eyes round.

'Of course he's not married!' she replied in a scandalised voice. 'Joss is an honourable man. He's one of the Mirshire de Courceys, from Long Minton,' she went on. 'Harry and I have known him for years.'

'He can be one of the de Courceys from Timbuctoo, for all I care,' retorted Netta waspishly.

'Oh, Joss is English enough,' her friend assured her. 'The de Courcey bit might be French—his family go back as far as Agincourt.' She ignored Netta's irreverent mutter, 'I wish they'd stayed there!' and went on, 'He owns Thimbles, now, since the old earl died.'

'Don't say he's got another title as well!' Netta groaned in despair, and Wendy laughed.

'No, the title didn't come down to him. Only Thimbles.'

'Wendy—Netta——' Harry's voice interrupted her discourse, 'Joss is waiting.'

'Let him wait,' Netta muttered, and then the young aide's imploring gaze swam before her mind's eye, and reminded her of the reason for Joss waiting, and she put the brush back on the dressing table.

'Coming!' she called, but her feet dragged as she followed Wendy downstairs, and back into the drawing room. As a concession to the occasion, someone had put two enormous jars of pale golden tua lilies in the room, and their perfume was almost overpowering. 'I think I'll always hate the smell of lilies,' she decided, as her eyes took in the members of the Embassy staff gathered to witness the ceremony. They had been joined by a figure in a strange military uniform, and an elderly man who had the stamp of officialdom indelibly upon him.

'He's the equivalent of a registrar,' Wendy murmured. 'We'd rather have had a priest from the mission, but. . . .'

'The mission?' Netta turned sharply, struck by a sudden idea. 'Couldn't I . . .?' she began, and Joss interrupted before she could go any further.

'No,' he refused her adamantly, 'you can't stay at the mission. You're coming back to England with me.' It was only afterwards she remembered he had said, 'with me', and not, 'with us', and wondered why. 'I don't even know your name.' He spoke as if he had thought about it for the first time. 'I take it Netta's short for something, the same as Joss?' There was a hint of humour in his face as he said it.

'It's short for Garnet,' she said stiffly. She could see nothing humorous in the situation.

He inclined his head. 'How appropriate,' he drawled.

Was he being sarcastic? She eyed him suspiciously.

'Harry's been telling me your background,' he said smoothly. So he had pumped Harry about her, just the same as she had pumped Wendy about him! They were even on that score, at least, she thought with a touch of malice. He would know, now, that her father was John Vaughan, the renowned jeweller and goldsmith. If he thought any further along the same lines, he might also guess what her business was in Lak, she realised uneasily. So long as he did not guess the details. As if in a dream she stood beside him in front of the elderly official, and heard his firm voice declare,

'I, Jocelyn, take thee, Garnet . . . for better, for worse. . . .'

'For better, for worse—but not for long,' Netta added a silent rider of her own. The moment they were back in England, and safe. . . .

'To love and to cherish. . . .' He could forget that, too, she thought fiercely. She would be his wife in name only until they reached safety. Because he was marrying her, it did not automatically give him any rights or privileges.

He turned and slid a slender gold ring from off his own little finger, and with a firm clasp raised her left hand and slipped it on. Amazingly, it fitted. His own fingers were

slender, and the exchange made a perfect match. The gold
band still felt warm from his own hand. Netta looked down
at the intricately chased surface, and her training under
her father told her the ring was very old. In all probability
it was a family heirloom. She would return it to Joss,
later. . . .

Without warning, the ring swam in front of her vision,
and her heart wept within her. No marriage should take
place like this, it protested. Marriage should not be a
thing of expediency, after a moment's acquaintance. It was
something precious, to be born from love, and tended by
time. Marriage was for ever. . . .

She had always planned to marry, if she did so at all, in
the little church they attended close to their London home,
with herself in white, and her father to give her away. Not
a cold, unemotional, civil ceremony like this. She blinked
hard and began to tremble, and then felt her hand clasped
between two firm brown ones, which closed about it, warm-
ing her fingers. It was as if Joss sensed what she might be
feeling, and gave her what reassurance he could. She
clutched his fingers convulsively, in a surge of unexpected gratitude, and heard the official say, 'I now
pronounce you man and wife.' And realised, with a dreadful sense of finality, what it was she had done.

'Try and look as if you're pleased, the military are
watching.'

He turned her towards him and growled a warning
under cover of claiming a bridegroom's privilege—his first
kiss. She supposed it should not have surprised her under
the circumstances, he had to make the ceremony look as
genuine as possible, but somehow it did. He bent his head
above her, and she raised her face dutifully, if reluctantly,
to meet the firm, hard pressure of his lips. An impersonal
pressure, placed there to satisfy tradition, and the watching soldiery.

But tradition did not demand that his lips should linger
on her own, exploring their untried sweetness. And then,
without warning, change, and become fired with an urgent,
demanding passion that took her completely by surprise. It

ran like lightning through her veins, tingling her every
nerve end into a startled awareness of the man who held
her in his arms. Her husband.... For a second or two she
lay quiescent in his embrace, and then the slumbering
womanhood that until this moment had lain dormant during all her twenty-six years burst forth into lovely blossom, warmed into life by the power of his kiss. She was
powerless to resist. Helplessly, she felt herself returning
kiss for kiss, drawn into a response she did not know it was
in her power to give until, in one brief, heart-stopping
moment, Joss de Courcey taught her how.

When at last he raised his head, she did not need to
dissemble to dupe the military. Her face glowed, and her
eyes shone, polished to brilliance by the solemn vows she
had just taken, and the crazy, wonderful, impossible conviction that she did not regret any one of them.

A full minute passed before Joss's warning came back to
her. A full minute in which he looked deep into her eyes,
reading her feelings as plainly as if he might read a book,
though she was unable to even try to interpret his own, because of the daze of conflicting emotions which she had
never experienced before, and did not know how to handle
now.

'The military are watching....' As if to underline his
warning, the figure in uniform approached them.

'Congratulations, Mrs de Courcey.'

She heard her married name spoken for the first time.
The soldier did not smile as he said it. His eyes regarded
her with a hard, unfriendly, official stare, and without
warning Netta went cold from head to foot. Not from
fear of the soldier, or the thought of the ceremony just behind her, and the fact that now she was Joss's wife, but at
the realisation of what Joss himself had done to her.

'Try and look as if you're pleased,' he told her. And to
add realism to the ceremony, he kissed her. Not because
he wanted to, but to impress the soldiers. The urgent
passion that awakened her response was nothing but play-
acting, on his part. It was done with consummate skill, and
bitter recrimination flooded her at his betrayal. He need

not have gone so far, even to convince the military. His over-enthusiasm had not only convinced the soldiers—momentarily, it had succeeded in convincing her, Netta, as well. And once a flower has opened to the sun, it can never again retreat into an unawakened bud. . . .

The realisation of what he had done extinguished the shine from her eyes and the glow from her face. It drained the newly awakened vitality from her heart, and left it as hollow as an empty cowrie shell, to be occupied by an agony of pain such as she had never known before. In a daze she felt Joss put his arm round her waist—the act of any normal bridegroom—and desperately she forced herself not to flinch away. The soldier was still watching. She leaned against her new husband, involuntarily adding realism to her own performance, but it was because her legs felt suddenly weak, not because she wanted to. She felt she would rather lean against any other person in the room, even the soldier, than rely on Joss for support.

'He shouldn't have done this to me.'

Out of the depths of pain and misery, a burning anger rose inside her against the man who had just made her his wife. She longed to tear off his ring and throw it back at him, deny her newly acquired status. Her right hand moved to do her bidding, and then her eyes caught the eyes of the soldier, still watching her, noting her every reaction, and drawing conclusions from it, and instead her shaking fingers turned the ring round and round on her finger, twisting it in an excess of nervous energy, but leaving it in place. She lowered her eyes, unable to stand the soldier's stare any longer, and found they looked down on her ring instead, so she raised them again, hating the thin gold circle, and forced herself to meet the stare without flinching.

'Wait for me here. I'll come back for you when the plane's ready to leave.'

She heard Joss speak to her, and then he kissed her again, lightly this time, playing the loving husband, she thought bitterly. She felt his lips brush her forehead, but the contact hardly registered through the turmoil of conflicting emotions that rocked the very fibre of her being.

'Go and finish packing.' Harry spoke to Wendy, reverting to mundane matters. The ceremony was over, the knot
tied—Netta felt as if it choked her—but everyday things
must be attended to. Her heart had just died within her,
but ... 'Go and finish packing....' A hysterical laugh
caught at her throat, and died as the soldier paused on his
way to the door with Joss.

'There will only be space in the plane for light hand
luggage,' he warned the room in general. 'No one must
take any more than is absolutely necessary for overnight,'
he instructed sternly, and gave Harry a significant look as
he added, 'All baggage will be searched, to make sure you
comply.'

'That means I can't take any office records with me.'
Harry frowned at the closing door, and turned swiftly to
his aide as soon as the soldier disappeared. 'Come, we've
no time to lose. All our files must be destroyed before we
leave.'

'I'll get what we need, right away.' Wendy moved too,
then turned back impulsively to Netta. 'This is criminal,
darling. Just as you're married!' she wailed.

'It was hardly a love match,' Netta reminded her tartly.
She stirred herself reluctantly into action, forcing herself
to appear as normal as possible. She heard her lips form
the lie, and a small, detached part of her mind wondered
how she could. Until now, she had never believed in love
at first sight. That was something which belonged to
magazine romances. Now, she knew it could happen—to
her, if not to Joss. It was Joss's fault, for rousing her.
There was no need for him to do this to her, even to convince the soldiers. In one moment of blinding revelation
she discovered what it was to love. And what it was to
hate....

'I'll go and get some things from the hotel,' she heard
herself respond to Wendy. She would want some overnight
things the same as the others. And she also wanted the
package she had collected when she first came to Lak,
the package which was the sole reason for her coming at

all. But Wendy was already on her way upstairs in Harry's
wake, and Netta did not know whether she had heard her
or not.

'Your baggage will be searched....'

The soldier's barb had been directed at Harry, but it
found a dual target, she thought grimly. At all costs she
was determined not to be parted from the contents of her
package. But how could she conceal them, to escape a
baggage search? It had all seemed so simple, when she
played hostess to her father's client in the tall Georgian
house in the quiet London square, less than a month
ago.

'I'll collect the pieces of jewellery you want re-set,
Ranjit.' Over the years her father's client had become his
friend, and they had long been on first name terms. 'You
say you aren't likely to be in England again until next
spring, and if I travel out for them it'll give me time to do
the work for you, and have them ready for when you come
again. How much work is there involved?' She glanced
across the tea table at her father.

'The same as before,' the white-haired goldsmith
answered her. 'We have to substitute synthetic stones for
the real gems, and use the original settings if we can. I'll
have to look at the settings to see what condition they're
in.' He turned to his client. 'You tell me some of the pieces
have been in your family for generations, and are much
worn. The enamelled pieces should be all right, but the
gold settings are softer, and may have become thin with
long use.'

'We can copy them for you,' Netta put in, with the un-
troubled confidence that only skill can bestow.

'If we have to,' her father nodded. 'Ranjit's brought some
excellent photographs, and full dimensions of the pieces. If
necessary we could make perfect copies, just from those.'
He looked an enquiry at his client.

'I should still want the jewellery to come to London,'
Ranjit objected. 'It has to be deposited in my bank here.'

'In that case,' Netta smiled, 'expect me in Lak shortly
after you get back home from your business trip here. I'll

collect the pieces and bring them back to London, and we can do all the rest for you here. I still think it's a pity, though,' she reflected.

It was a common enough commission nowadays, but she could not help regretting the necessity to hide the beauty of the real gems within the unappreciative walls of a bank vault. Even after the substitute synthetic gemstones were in place, the pieces of jewellery would still be extremely valuable. Modern laboratory-made gem crystals were costly imitations of nature's products, and the work involved in cutting and polishing was just as exacting as on the real stones. Nevertheless.... She sighed.

'It's a good deal safer to wear the synthetics,' her father reminded her, but in his eyes, too, there was a trace of lingering regret. Although he was world-renowned, and numbered royalty among his clients, he still retained a love for the basic materials of his trade that neither affluence nor familiarity could dispel.

'I don't feel too happy about you collecting those pieces from Ranjit, Netta,' to her surprise her father frowned concernedly after their client left that evening. 'There are rumours of unrest in Lak.'

'There's unrest everywhere, even in our own country.' Netta dismissed his fears lightly. 'There's always somebody disagreeing with somebody else over something,' she stated not too clearly. She often acted as her father's courier on such errands, and felt puzzled at his objection now. 'If it makes you any happier, I intend to contact Wendy and Harry Fraser at the Embassy when I get there —it's years since I saw them both, not since they were sent out to Lak from Paris.'

'In that case....' Her father's face cleared. 'You won't have a great deal to carry in the way of weight,' he went on more happily. 'From what Ranjit told me, most of the pieces consist of rings and pendants, with a few bracelets and hair ornaments. All of it's his wife's jewellery, and all fairly small.'

Even so, it was big enough to become a problem, now she was faced with a baggage search. She began to wish for the first time that she had not overridden Ranjit's objections when she called to see him to collect it soon after her arrival.

'I daren't give it to you,' he told her worriedly. 'With all this unrest in the country, it might put you at risk.' Endearingly, he was more concerned about the risk to her than to his possessions.

'There'll be no risk at all to me,' Netta persuaded. 'I'm travelling out with the Embassy staff. What better escort could your gems possibly have than a plane load of diplomats?' she pressed. 'And Harry Fraser says there's been widespread looting in the north. If the insurgents laid hands on your wife's jewellery....' She paused significantly.

'They would use it to fund their evil cause,' Ranjit finished for her, and his face grew stern. 'I'd do much to prevent that from happening.'

The alternative left him with no real choice. Which was how Netta came to have her present problem of smuggling the jewellery out of the country, a totally unnecessary subterfuge if times had been normal. She thought about confiding her problem to Harry, and enlisting his help, then decided against it.

'He's got enough worries of his own, without adding mine to them.'

The thought of Joss occurred to her, and she shook her head fiercely.

'Never!' she declared out loud. 'He'd simply make me take them back to Ranjit.' The very possibility hardened her resolve to find some way—any way—to keep the jewellery with her, and to convey it to safety in England as she had promised. She had never yet let down one of her father's clients, and she did not intend to do so now, Joss or no Joss, she determined.

She remembered as she sped through the eerily deserted streets that Joss had told her to remain at the Embassy until he came back for her. Well, Joss would have to lump it if he did not like her disobedience, she decided. She needed some overnight things, the same as the rest of the

Embassy staff, and the streets were empty, so there could be no immediate danger. The first person she saw, in fact, was the hotel proprietor, who left his task of boarding up his ground floor windows with obvious reluctance, to retrieve her package for her from his office safe.

'I'm leaving as soon as I've packed,' Netta told him briefly, and the relief on his face added to her disquiet. She knew, now, what it felt like to be a foreigner in a country at war. Neither side loved foreigners. They were a nuisance, in the way, and to be despatched out of that way with all possible speed. To his credit, the man tried to be helpful, but he had problems of his own, like the imminent danger of smashed windows, looters, and rapidly deserting staff. He could not hide his relief at the news of her departure.

'I'll.be half an hour,' Netta told him, and gained her room with a sigh of relief. She needed solitude in which to collect herself after the events of the last few hours. The sounds of a hammer and nails being wielded on boards to protect the downstairs windows of the building told her that her need could not be indulged. Rapidly she slit open the package that Ranjit had given to her and spread the contents on the bed. She fingered through the glittering heap with growing dismay.

'I can't possibly conceal all this lot!'

The soldier promised a baggage search, but she could not discount the possibility of a personal search as well. The jacket of her trouser suit had short sleeves and a shirt neckline, and she was wearing no jewellery except her watch during the marriage ceremony, something that could not have escaped the notice of the watching soldier. The big patch pockets of her jacket were too obvious to even be considered; they were the first places any searcher would look at. And to attempt to board the plane actually festooned with Ranjit's wife's jewellery would be simply asking for trouble. The settings were traditional, and worn by their owner to adorn her sari they would go unremarked except for their outstanding beauty. But worn by Netta, to accompany a safari suit? No, the idea was unthinkable. She knitted her brows in perplexity.

Finally she shrugged, then reached for her travelling manicure set, and blessed the makers for its stout construction. There was no help for it. It was sheer vandalism, but.... She set doggedly to work with one of the tools. Several times the sharp-pointed instrument slipped, but she gritted her teeth and ignored the welling scratches across her hands, and continued ruthlessly to uproot the gemstones from their lovely settings.

'Dad wanted to know what condition the settings were in,' she muttered. Their conversation returned to reproach her for wreaking such destruction. 'Now I'll be able to report that they're damaged beyond repair.' The gold settings did not present so much difficulty, they were softer, but the enamelled pieces were hard, and the gemstones consequently much more difficult to extricate, so that her struggles resulted in the settings suffering more from her hurried ministrations. At her work bench in London, with proper tools, and time at her disposal, they would not even have shown a scratch.

She winced as she looked at the discarded pile rapidly growing on the bed on the one side of her. 'Thank goodness Ranjit had the forethought to bring with him photographs and dimensions of the pieces, when he came to London,' she breathed thankfully. 'At least we'll be able to reproduce them accurately.'

'It's wicked, I know, but I can't help it,' she murmured at last, in apology to the long-dead jeweller whose hands had framed the beauty she now so wantonly wrecked.

'Thank goodness that's over!' She swept up the settings into a small pile at the back of a drawer, and covered them with clothes. There were not many to cover them with, she travelled light, but rumpled up they were sufficient to conceal the settings. She doubted if looters would bother with female fripperies, even if they managed to enter the barricaded building; and there was simply nowhere else she could conceal them. She had never realised before how bare a hotel room could be; even the wardrobe had no frontage on the top, it was completely flat, and would not conceal a fly.

'What on earth shall I do with these?'

She considered the small pile of gemstones that was left—rubies, emeralds, diamonds, of she dared not think what value. They winked back at her from the bed cover with solemn mockery, taunting her with their beauty—their priceless worth—and her own despairing inability to think of a single hiding place about her person, which seemed as lacking as the hotel room of reasonable possibilities that would not be immediately obvious to a suspicious soldier.

Her fingers fidgeted nervously with the waistband of her slacks. They felt damp with her recent efforts, and she rubbed them on the cloth to dry them. The dampness stuck to the material, moving it with her fingers, making the double cloth of the band rub up and down against itself, and she paused, struck by a sudden idea.

'The waistband of my slacks!' she breathed. 'Why didn't I think of that right away?' Indecision had already wasted precious minutes. The band was wide, and shaped, and in effect a continuous tube running right round her waist, the ends closed by the zip, and ideal for the purpose she had in mind.

She reached for her nail scissors and began snipping the end stitching of the belt. If she could slide the gemstones into the tube, they were small enough not to make too much of a bulge in the cloth, and might pass a perfunctory search. She tried the first one, and realised she would not get them in easily with her slacks still on. Quickly she wriggled out of them, and began pushing the gems one by one into the waistband with feverish haste, sliding them along, so that they were more or less evenly spaced, and did not bunch up together. She had told the hotelier she would be half an hour. She must have already been that, and more. If she did not hurry, he might come upstairs, demanding to know when she would be gone. As if to confirm her fears, a loud knocking on her bedroom door made her jump, and a voice demanded to know when she would be ready to go.

'Don't come in, I'm not dressed!' she called out, and after a slight pause she heard his feet shuffle away along the corridor, his voice muttering impatiently. It would not do to try his tolerance too far. The thought added impetus to her efforts. With fingers that shook, so that she had to make three attempts to thread the needle, she stitched the end of the waistband together again, careful to make a good job of it so that the stitches did not show, even if it took an extra two minutes to accomplish.

'These are the most valuable slacks I've ever worn,' she grinned suddenly as she put them on again, and paused in the act of tucking her shirt inside the band. If it was left outside, it would be an even better concealment, and it was fashionable, so it would not cause comment. She pulled the silk out again, then without hesitation stripped the shirt straight back over her head. The material was creased. It had obviously been tucked into the band, and the soldiers, suspicious already, might guess. Hurriedly she took another top from the drawer and slid it over her head. It was loose and clean, and uncreased, and long enough to come down to her hips, which was an added bonus, she saw with satisfaction.

'There's only my holiday film now.' She was reluctant to leave that behind. During the safari she had taken clips of many exotic flowers she had never seen before. They would give her inspiration for unusual brooch designs, a speciality which was making her almost as well known as her father. 'It's no good taking the camera, they're almost certain to confiscate that.' And she dared not take any clothes, either, or there would be nothing with which to conceal the jewel settings. She cast a reluctant look at her expensive photographic equipment, and turned her back resolutely on her undies as an imperative knocking sounded on her door. Hurriedly she thrust the clip of film underneath the loose change in her purse, picked up her shoulder bag, and opened the door to the proprietor's worried entreaties.

'You must go now, missie. Go quickly,' he urged. He looked very frightened, as if he wished he could take his own advice. 'Not that way,' he checked her as she made for the main stairway. 'Through the back. . . .' He chivvied her along a corridor and through what looked like kitchen quarters. She could not be sure what they were, in the dim light which was all the newly boarded windows allowed through. She had no clear idea in which direction she was heading, and then her guide unlocked a small door and shooed her through.

'Go quickly,' he urged again. 'They come....' And he slammed the door behind her. Netta heard the key turn in the lock, with a finality that told her there would be no going back.

She turned and looked about her apprehensively. She was in a narrow alley, presumably at the rear of the hotel that must, she judged, run parallel with the main street by which she had arrived. She would have to hurry. A quick glance at her watch told her it was not long to sundown, and she still had to get back to the Embassy. She could see the tip of its roof from where she stood, but it would take her a good ten minutes to get there along the streets, by which time she stood the risk of being caught by the curfew which Harry told her had been imposed during the emergency, and the even greater risk of keeping the others waiting for the plane.

CHAPTER THREE

WHICH way should she go?

Netta looked from side to side along the alleyway, undecided. One way seemed as good as the other. The alley twisted, so that she could not see either end. Without conscious choice, she turned right. If she was careful to skirt the sides of the hotel she should reach the main road eventually.

'If I'm wrong, I can always turn back,' she told herself.

There was not really time. She looked about her anxiously, hoping to find a short cut, but the properties that backed on to the alley all seemed to be enclosed by high walls, so that she had to keep to the pedestrian way, whether she wanted to or not. Nervously, she skirted the umpteenth deep, shadowed doorway, keeping to the middle of the alley, heart thumpingly conscious of the precious cargo she carried about her waist.

Her breath came in short pants, partly from haste, but mostly from tension, and perhaps a little, though she refused to admit it even to herself, perhaps a little from fear of what Joss might say if he returned to the Embassy and found her missing, when he had expressly instructed her to wait for him there.

She neared the end of the alley and sounds began to penetrate the high walls. She paused. Vehicle brakes squealed from somewhere ahead, and a man's voice rose in an unknown tongue.

'Even out here, they've got their share of careless drivers,' she grinned, and went on again, feeling more relaxed. Harry said most of the townspeople had fled, but there must be some still left. They were probably trying to do the same as she was herself, reach home before the curfew. Perhaps one of them might know of a short cut back to the Embassy. In another ten minutes it would be dark, with the sudden, total darkness of the tropical night, and she did not relish the thought of being out alone after that.

She reached the end of the alley, which led, as she suspected, back on to the main street, though slightly farther along, at the other side of a small square, which in peaceful times must make a pleasant promenade for the residents. The cause of the noise she had heard became immediately apparent. A number of lorries of doubtful make and vintage were drawn up in the square, higgledy-piggledy, with no attempt at orderly parking, and men were disembarking by the simple expedient of vaulting over the sides on to the ground. They must be estate workers, she judged, there were plantations on the edge of the town, and these must be the pickers returning after their day's labours.

'I wouldn't like to work for him!' One man, presumably their leader, harangued the others. Netta could not understand what he said, but he seemed to be urging speed, although the men in the lorries were wasting no time in vacating their transport. 'Bully!' she muttered, as he shouted again, and then he swung his arm, and her horrified eyes caught sight of what looked like a length of chain dangling from his hand. 'Surely he doesn't ...?' She stared at the group of workers crowding near him, but they did not appear to be in any way intimidated. Rather, his gestures seemed to arouse them to the same pitch of hysteria that he himself displayed. Several began to shout and gesticulate as well, and the group broke up and began to move across the square.

'They've all got weapons!'

The appalling truth broke upon her like a blast of cold water. They were not plantation pickers; they were a mob of insurgents. The maître d' hotel had said, when he thrust her through his door into the alley, 'They come. . . .'

'He's wrong,' she thought, panic-stricken, 'they've already arrived!'

Without hesitation, she turned and ran. Her heart beat with a terror that made its previous nervous palpitations seem like a gentle murmur, and she clutched at her side, doubled up by an unbearable stitch. The pain of it slowed her down, but the shouts of the men in the square drove her on until she rounded the bend of the alley.

'They've come in at both ends!' Her breath sobbed in her throat, and she stumbled to a terrified halt, leaning against the wall for support, and stared aghast at the shouting rabble that crowded into the entrance to the alleyway in front of her. Unknown to her, the narrow pedestrian passageway must describe a horseshoe round the back of the hotel, and both ends led on to the main street. And the rebels had entered it at either end.

She had often wondered what the word 'insurrection' really meant. She had glanced at it casually on the small print of insurance forms in clauses indemnifying the insurers from, '... the consequences of ... rebellion, revolution, insurrection, or military or usurped power....' Now she knew at first hand what those words implied. The mob was approaching her from both sides, incited to near-hysteria by the yells of their leader, and they were armed to the teeth, and intent on trouble. And she carried Ranjit's jewels around her waist. She was trapped.

'The door back into the hotel.' The mob had not seen her yet. Her sand-coloured trouser suit nearly matched the colour of the walls, and it made an excellent camouflage so long as she did not make any exaggerated movement to draw attention to herself.

She flattened herself against the wall and inched carefully back along the way she had come, round the bend, and out of sight, for the moment anyway, of the men coming towards her. She blessed the fact that the alley was so narrow, it slowed their pace as they crowded into the entrance. If she could reach the door into the back of the hotel.... Surely the proprietor would not refuse to let her in? He *must* let her in! The doorway loomed beside her, and she turned into the archway which sheltered it, and raised her fist to beat a tattoo on the wood.

'It's the wrong colour!'

She stared at the paintwork with numb disbelief. The

hotel door had been bright blue, and freshly painted. This one had peeling paint, of a colour long since faded into anonymity by age and neglect.

'It must be the next door,' she muttered.

It seemed like a hundred miles to the next door, although it could only have been a few yards in reality. The cries of the mob behind her grew louder, and she caught her breath, panic beginning to numb her mind, destroy her power to think. The threatening roar from the opposite end of the alley was getting louder, too. It only needed one of the rebels from either side of her to round the bend, and they could not fail to see her.

She sprang across to the other side of the alley, to hug the bend of the wall more closely. At least she would delay discovery as long as she could. It would be easy enough to cross back when she was opposite to the next doorway, she could see it a few yards along. There was a door on her side, as well, but she ignored it. The dark shadowed aperture of the archway held fewer terrors for her now than the approaching pincer movement of the insurgents. She reached the edge of the door arch on her side, and....

'Don't scream!'

An arm reached out of the darkness of the archway. It wrapped tentacle-like about her waist, and dragged her into the shadows. A hand clamped over her mouth, stifling the scream that rose to her lips regardless of his warning, which his hold rendered unnecessary anyhow. His hand clamped over her nose, too, so that she could not breathe. She started to struggle.

'Keep still,' a deep voice growled impatiently, 'unless you'd rather be caught by that mob out there.'

Shock immobilised her, not the order. The voice spoke in cultured English. And it belonged—she was sure it belonged to——

'Joss!' she whispered.

'Be quiet!' he ordered her tersely, in her ear, and lifted her bodily through the doorway, silently sliding the bolts to behind them the moment it was closed.

'But how—why ...?'

For answer, he kissed her. His lips closed on hers, parting them with a fierce urgent pressure, and she lost the desire to ask questions. The passionate woman inside her, whom Joss first aroused—was it only a few short hours ago?—and whom Netta herself had not yet even begun to know, came to life again at the touch of his lips. She tried to steel herself against him, but it was useless. Her senses throbbed with his nearness, and without conscious thought her arms rose to clasp his head, feeling the brown curls surprisingly soft under her stroking fingers.

From the other side of the wall, the clamour of the mob rose to deafening proportions as the two groups met in the narrow passageway, but it was as nothing to the clamour of her heart.

It sang inside her breast with a wild, vibrant song of uninhibited joy, that was at the same time as tender as a crooning lullaby. It hushed her fears and her protests and her questions, and she melted into his arms, turning her face upwards to meet his kisses with an eagerness that matched the fierce passion of his lips, uncaring that the shouts rose to a crescendo on the other side of the wall, and then grew dim and finally died away as the mob, finding nothing but an empty alley, surged off in search of more likely prey.

'Joss. . . .' Her voice was a soft whisper when at last he let her go.

'That's the only way I know to keep a woman quiet,' he said. And he laughed.

The merciful darkness hid her face. It sheltered the stunned shock that blanched her cheeks and lips, and left her eyes bleak with the bleakness of someone who in a few short hours has been awakened for the first time to the full, wondrous glory of love—and learned as well to feel the destroying corrosion of hate. And come by the same road to the bitter knowledge that, far from being two separate emotions, the two could well be one.

'I hate you!'

She felt him pause, and look down at her in the darkness.

'It didn't feel like that a few minutes ago.' His voice mocked her, a disembodied taunt from somewhere over her head. It stung her into impulsive action, and she pushed against him with all her strength, freeing herself from his arms. Loathing his touch.

'Go away,' she cried. 'Leave me alone!'

'Keep your voice down!' His own voice hissed like a whip through the darkness, lashing her into silence. 'D'you want to bring that mob howling at our heels?' he growled angrily. His hands left her waist and gripped her by her wrists, cruelly tight.

'Stop it! Let me go!' She whispered the words, the threat of tears as much as the threat of the mob choking back her voice.

'I'll do nothing of the kind.' His voice tightened, and so did his grip. 'You're coming with me.'

'You can't make me.'

He proceeded to demonstrate that he could. He loosened her one wrist, but kept tight hold of the other, and pulled her with him through what appeared to be a courtyard, then paused at another door to whisper back, 'Whether you love me or loathe me is quite irrelevant. Every moment the plane remains on the airstrip waiting for us increases the danger of its being taken by the rebels. I won't have the other passengers put at risk because of you,' he told her sternly, then broke off, and against the paler wall she could faintly see his head raised in a listening attitude. She held her breath and listened, too. 'In case you don't know, that's gunfire,' he enlightened her grimly as the distant popping sounds continued. 'And it's coming this way. It's time we left.'

She might as well try to resist a tornado, she thought despairingly, then another burst of gunfire split the night, and voices began to shout. Someone screamed.

All thoughts of resisting Joss vanished. She sped alongside him, conscious that his grip on her wrist slackened, as if he sensed she would comply now, and follow him, simply using his hold to guide her. He led her with silent speed across a bewildering number of walled courtyards;

through endless doors and along alleyways until she lost all sense of direction. Joss seemed to know exactly where he was, and the way he wanted to go, and in spite of the almost total darkness he did not hesitate once. He found his way with an uncanny exactitude, unhampered by the lack of light, like a wild creature that dons the cloak of the dark for protection.

'Le Renard.' He lived up to his odd nickname.

'What is it?' He paused, and she panted to a stop beside him.

'Nothing—never mind.' She did not realise she had spoken out loud.

'Then keep up with me. And keep quiet.'

More doors. More courtyards. More alleyways, until——

'Down!'

Even as he flung her to the ground, she felt the vibration through the earth, seconds before she heard the bang. Joss's mercurial reaction saved them. He threw her under the shelter of the nearest wall, and himself on top of her, and the blast of the explosion whistled harmlessly past above their heads. It must have met resistance further along the alley, because sounds of crashing masonry and splintering glass echoed back to them, a grim reminder of what their own fate could have been if Joss had not....

'Are you hurt?' He pulled her to her feet without ceremony.

'No.' She shook her head, too shaken to talk.

'Then come.' He waited for no more, but he let go of her hand.

'Joss....' She held it out to him, appealingly, suddenly desperate for the reassurance of his touch, but he ignored it, and grasped her round the waist, supporting her, but also, she realised, forcing her to keep up with his now much greater pace. The stitch returned to her side, but a spreading glow from the fire against the sky was sufficient to anaesthetise the pain. She ran beside him until, just as she began to fear she could not go on any longer, a breeze stroked her face, and Joss slackened his pace to a walk. She lifted her face to the welcome breath. True, it carried the acrid taint of burning, but it was better than the stifling, airless heat of the alleys. Those lay behind them, she could see the outline of the high walls making strange, geometric patterns against the glow in the sky. A flat expanse of open land lay before them.

'The airstrip.' Joss located their whereabouts for her.

'Thank goodness!' she breathed. Soon they would be on their way to safety.

'Keep low, and stay by me.' Joss ducked and turned into the rough scrub bordering the edge of the airstrip, using it as a cover to prevent their figures from showing up against the glow from the fires in the town, which seemed to Netta to grow alarmingly brighter with every minute.

'There's no need to push me into the ground!' she snapped. He had chosen a route that would enable them to run side by side, and his arm pressed relentlessly against her back, forcing her to crouch double as she ran.

'Wait!'

He dropped down on one knee, obliging her to do the same, and the thorny scrub pierced the thin stuff through the knees of her slacks.

'Ouch!'

'Silence!' he hissed. 'Look. . . .'

She heard the engines burst into life even as he turned her, in time to see the aircraft itself, a pale shape in the darkness ahead of them, begin to move across the open airstrip.

'That's our plane.' The one that was waiting for them. The one that should take them to safety.

'The pilot probably got tired of waiting,' Joss retorted sharply. 'Under the circumstances, I can't say I blame him.' His tone blamed Netta. 'Get ready to run,' he warned her before she could speak, 'he'll probably taxi out this way, and if we can manage to attract his attention. . . .'

'You mean, we flag him down, like a bus?' A sharp giggle rose in her throat at the incongruity of his suggestion, and she stifled it hastily. If the pilot did not see them, if he left them behind, there would be nothing to giggle about. She tensed herself to rise, and then everything seemed to happen at once.

'Down!'

Joss's hand on her back thrust her flat with a force that knocked the breath from her lungs. A loud barrage of shots from somewhere on the other side of the plane drowned her angry protest. They were quickly followed by a flash, and an explosion, and Joss half rose to his knees.

'Take off, you fool! Take off,' he begged of the pilot.

Engines roared to a crescendo as if in answer to his bidding. Men shouted. A fusillade of shots rang out, and the pale shape of the aircraft thundered towards them with a deafening roar. Netta ducked, convinced it could not rise in time, and then the wheels left the ground in an almost vertical take-off that brought a desperate mutter from Joss.

'He's got to make it! He's got to....'

The engines screamed with the strain, but somehow, miraculously, they held, and gradually the pale cylinder gained height, and rose out of gunshot range above their heads, into the safety of the sky.

'Phew!' Joss subsided into the scrub beside her. 'That was a close call.'

'They've left us behind.' Her voice was a thin thread of fear.

'It's your own fault,' he rounded on her harshly. 'I told you to remain at the Embassy until I came back for you.'

'I'd have been back there before dark if it hadn't been for the mob in town,' she retorted defiantly, refusing to accept his blame.

'If you'd remained at the Embassy, you'd have been there when the news came that the insurgents had already reached the town.'

'Harry said they were forty miles away.'

'Harry didn't know then that they'd commandeered a fleet of trucks which made short work of your forty miles,' he enlightened her grimly. 'The moment the news came through, the Embassy was evacuated. Fortunately, Wendy remembered you saying something about going to collect some clothes from the hotel, otherwise I wouldn't have known where you'd gone. As it was, I wasted a good deal of timing in looking for you. From now on,' he ordered brusquely, 'you'll remain with me, and do exactly what I tell you to.'

'There's no earthly reason why I should.' Even in her present plight she resented his overbearing attitude, and her tone said so plainly.

'In case you've forgotten,' he reminded her in a hard voice, 'a few hours ago you promised to love, honour, and obey me. And until we're safely away from Lak, I intend to see you do just that,' he stated uncompromisingly.

Love, honour—and obey. He meant the latter, of course. The love and honour part did not count; he had not married her for love.

Slow tears invaded her defences. They scalded her cheeks in the darkness, and she turned away so that Joss should not see and dropped her head wearily on to her arms, careless of the thorny shrubs that surrounded them. The thorns could not inflict any greater pain than the desolation which tore at her heart.

The receding sound of the aircraft droned away into the distance, heading towards the border. It mocked her plight, and mocked the bitter realisation that, now the plane had left without them, she need not have married Joss in the first place.

CHAPTER FOUR

'I FEEL as if I've begun to take root here!'

Netta groaned and eased herself stiffly on to her knees, following Joss's lead. She felt cramped, and cold, and sore all over, particularly around her waist, and she blamed Joss bitterly for being the cause of her discomfort.

'We've only been here for an hour or two.' To her chagrin he remained completely unmoved by her plight.

'He's incapable of feeling,' she told herself angrily, incensed by the fact that Joss himself showed no signs of suffering from any discomfort. 'It doesn't feel like that to me,' she said aloud. They seemed to have lain flat in the scrub for days instead of just hours. She shivered, and eased her fingers under her slacks belt. The gemstones she had so ruthlessly extracted from their settings were small and fairly flat to look at, but they felt just the reverse to lie on, she thought ruefully.

'What's the matter with your waist?'

'Nothing.' She had not realised he might notice her movement. She would have to be careful, he must not guess. 'I'm tightening my belt,' she answered him tartly. She felt both cold and very hungry.

'It's your own fault you've gone without food,' he offered her scant sympathy. 'If you'd waited at the Embassy as I told you to, you'd probably be sitting down to a good meal on the plane by now.'

'You'll blame me for the uprising next,' she accused him hotly, stung by his tone.

'I don't blame you for that,' he conceded, and amazingly she detected a note of amusement in his voice, 'though it was probably a woman who started it.'

'You....'

'There's no point in starting another war,' he checked her furious retort. 'You can't win, and it's bad policy to go

40

into battle on an empty stomach,' he taunted. He rose to his feet, and his head turned, his eyes searching the surrounding darkness. 'There's no sign of the mob now, and they don't seem to have left a guard of any sort on the airstrip. Come on, it's time for us to go.'

'The last of the mob left hours ago.' Netta was not inclined to forgive him for what she regarded as a totally unnecessary safety margin which Joss insisted on, and which left her frozen to the bone, and more physically wretched than she had ever felt in her life before.

'They might have turned back.' His voice was hard, uncaring for the way she felt. 'I'm responsible for your safety.'

'I'm responsible for myself.' She faced him with what dignity she could muster under the circumstances. 'I'm not....'

'As my wife, you're in my charge,' he reminded her curtly, 'so come with me and don't argue.' He did not leave her enough breath to argue, she thought furiously, he took her along with him willy-nilly, by the same expedient as before. He grasped her wrist and pulled her behind him straight back towards the town.

'Surely you're not going to go back there?' She pulled back fiercely as he made to enter the nearest high-walled alley. 'It's insane!' she protested. 'We should be going the other way, towards the border.' The way the plane went. She tried not to think about the plane.

'We'll make for the border later,' he tugged her remorselessly forward again. 'First, we must have food. Enough to eat now, and enough to take with us. The country between here and the border is desolate, and we can't travel a hundred miles without eating.'

'There must be villages,' she argued.

'Which we will have to avoid,' he told her sharply. Just as he avoided the bands of roaming insurgents who appeared with breath-stopping suddenness out of the darkness ahead and behind them as they crossed the town, until Netta began to despair of them remaining undiscovered. But beyond pausing to draw her into a doorway, or against a wall now and then, Joss did not stop. With a catlike silence of tread he followed a route of his own until at last he came to a halt in what appeared to be the garden of a large house. The high walls rose out of the darkness ahead of them, and Netta could distinguish bushes of some kind grouped together in a small shrubbery. She brushed against one of them, and the aromatic smell from the bruised leaves reached her nose in pungent protest at her carelessness.

'This way.' He forced her right into the middle of the shrubbery, ignoring the scratching twigs himself, and obliging her to do the same, until,

'Oh!' She cried out as the ground fell sharply from beneath her feet and she stumbled forward, knocking against him.

'Steady,' he admonished her sharply, and set her on her feet again. 'Look where you're going.'

'How can I look? It's as black as a mineshaft here,' she flared resentfully.

'You're entering a passageway that runs underground,' he informed her briefly. 'That's why it slopes away from your feet. Keep your hands on my waist, and walk behind me.' He guided her hands to his belt and held them there with his own, and started forward again with a flat-hipped stride that made no concession to her own unsteady progress. She stumbled behind him, incensed by his lack of consideration, but not daring to let go, not daring to lose contact with him in the darkness.

'You can let go of me now, we've arrived.' He let go of her hands as the floor flattened out under their feet, and she reluctantly withdrew them. Contrarily, she did not want to let go of him now. A tingling awareness of him flowed through her finger ends like molten fire, driven by the wild, uneven beating of her heart. His nearness worked on her senses with the potency of vintage wine, until the heady excitement of it made her sway.

'Sit down.' He guided her to a bench of sorts, and she sat. She brushed a hand across her eyes, trying desperately to still the clamour of emotion inside her. She resented its hold on her, but she could not control it, and she took a deep breath, trying to appear normal as he spoke.

'Do you feel faint?' For the first time, a hint of concern for her showed in his voice. He must have taken her plea of hunger seriously, she thought caustically.

'No,' she shook her head, 'it's something in my eye.'

'Let me have your handkerchief, and I'll get it out for you. It's light enough in here to see if you come over to the grating.' She became aware for the first time of daylight filtering through bars somewhere above their heads.

'I thought I had my hanky.' She fumbled in her pocket, reluctant to give it to him, unwilling for him to discover that there was nothing at all the matter with her eye. 'I can't find it,' she discovered. 'I must have dropped it somewhere. It doesn't matter anyhow—whatever it was has gone. It was probably only an inturned eyelash.' She dared not allow him to touch her again, his nearness evoked feelings that she must not allow to show in her face, for fear they betrayed themselves to him. Feelings that she dared not acknowledge, even to herself. . . .

'Do you remember when you had your handkerchief last?' His look was keen, his tone sharp, and his interest in her eye forgotten.

'I don't know.' She wrinkled her forehead. 'I think it was while we lay in the scrub at the side of the airstrip.' She remembered quite distinctly when she last used it, to mop up the tears that she refused to let Joss see. She had not needed it since, and now it was gone. What did a handkerchief matter? 'Where are we?' She dismissed it, and looked about her curiously. They appeared to be in some kind of cellar.

'We're in the safest possible place.' Unexpectedly he grinned. It gave his face a puckish look that took years from his age, and drew her own lips up in a reluctant answering smile. 'We're in the vaults below the Embassy,' he enlightened her.

'What?' She sat up with a suddenness that set the bench underneath her rocking dangerously.

'Shhh! Not so loud,' he cautioned swiftly, and grabbed

the bench in time to prevent it from crashing to the floor.

'I thought you said the Embassy had been evacuated?' Instinctively she whispered, reacting to his mood. 'I can hear someone talking.' The sounds came from above their heads, in what must be one of the ground floor rooms.

'The Embassy staff were evacuated,' he confirmed, 'the insurgents have taken over the Embassy as their head-quarters,' he added casually.

'You mean ...?' Shock stopped further utterance, and she swallowed convulsively. 'You knew that, and you deliberately came back here? Brought me here?'

'If you can't beat them, join them,' he quipped, then more seriously, 'This is the last place they'll think to look for the opposition,' he assured her with beautiful sim-plicity.

'Opposition?' Her stunned senses latched on to the last word. 'Surely you're not going to remain here and organise a resistance?'

'No,' to her relief he shook his head, and his face grew grave. 'My assignment in Lak has ended.' He spoke with-out regret. 'Any resistance the insurgents meet must come via the Lak Government forces. I've finished the job I came for.'

'What was your job?' She rounded on him suddenly, goaded out of her desire to appear indifferent to him. 'Who are you—what are you?' she demanded. 'I've got a right to know who I married.' The aura of mystery that surrounded him both intrigued and repelled her, in spite of the fact that Harry Fraser had vouched for him.

'I came out to Lak at the instigation of their Govern-ment and our own, for the sole purpose of making sure the Lak Royal Family escaped with their lives, in the event the unrest became an uprising.' He joined her on the bench and spoke quietly, without emphasis, as if such an assign-ment was an everyday, unremarkable affair to him. Netta expected him to argue, perhaps tell her to mind her own business. To her surprise he did neither, but treated her demand as if it was an eminently reasonable one.

'The Lak Royal Family?' she breathed, taken aback by

the sheer unexpectedness of his answer. She did not question that he told her the truth. She sensed that with Joss, he would tell the truth or not tell at all. 'No wonder Harry wouldn't talk about you,' she remembered the Ambassador's evasiveness. 'He told me you were one of his aides.'

'It was a useful cover,' Joss conceded, 'and the Frasers were very helpful. But I had ways open to me that were denied the Embassy.'

Secret ways, she thought. 'The ways of a fox?'

'If you like,' he smiled again. 'The people who call me that are not the only ones to see the likeness,' he commented obliquely. 'But I must go,' he rose to his feet abruptly. 'We must have food.'

'Don't leave me here alone.' Her fear rose anew, not of Joss so much now, but of being left on her own. What if he did not come back?

'I'll be back, never fear. Don't move from here until I come.' His voice hardened into sternness, and his steely glance demanded her promise.

'I'll wait.' She hated the submission, but she would not dare to venture on to the streets on her own for a second time. 'How long——?' she began, but Joss was gone. One moment he was standing by her side, the next the vault was empty, except for herself and—she caught her breath as a rustling sound came from the darkness of the far corner, then she relaxed and gave a shaky laugh. 'It's only a rat.' By contrast with the present occupants of the Embassy, a rat could not raise even a tremor in her.

'How will this suit you, for breakfast?'

She did not hear him come back. He reappeared beside her with the same silent step that had taken him away, but this time his arms were loaded, and he handed over his booty with an almost boyish pride.

'A loaf—cheese, meat, cake, fruit—a bottle of wine?' She accepted his treasures with growing wonder. 'Where on earth did you get these from? You must have looted the nearest grocer's shop,' she accused him.

'On the contrary, my foray was quite legal and above

board,' he told her loftily. 'I got them from the Embassy pantry upstairs. As a member of the staff, I've got every right.'

'You shouldn't have taken the risk. What if, ...' She raised dismayed eyes to his, unable to go on.

'The squatters upstairs don't know all the ins and outs of the building yet,' he quietened her fears. 'They've mainly occupied the downstairs rooms, they haven't had a lot of time to explore. They weren't to know there's an upstairs pantry to serve the banqueting suite. Fortunately, I did,' he grinned. 'Oh, by the way, while I was about it, I purloined one of Wendy's handkerchiefs for you. Don't lose this one,' he warned her, 'I may not be able to get another replacement.'

She took his offering, and tried not to think of the danger he had risked in order to get it for her. 'Come and eat.' She turned to the food, unwilling that he should see her expression. 'You've even brought paper cups.' Her voice wobbled slightly out of control, and Joss gave her a keen glance.

'Let me fill them.' He opened the bottle of wine, and poured.

'Not too much,' she held up a cautionary hand. 'I don't drink wine very often except at Christmas and birthdays. It always makes me feel sleepy.'

She was too late to stop him, or else he did not hear her, because he handed her a paper cup brim full.

'Try it,' he urged when she hesitated, 'it won't hurt you. It's a local wine, and very good.'

Encouraged by Joss, she sipped cautiously. The liquid was sweet, and light, and seemed more like a cordial. Her fears allayed she drank thirstily, and the warm glow of it ran through her, taking away the stiffness and the cold of the night. The food revitalised her flagging energy, and suddenly their impromptu picnic became a feast. Quite how it happened she did not know, but soon she and Joss were talking together as if no antagonism had ever existed between them. True, they kept their voices to a whisper, a necessary concession to the constant tramp of feet across the grating above their heads, that would not allow them to forget their position as refugees, but in spite of the danger, the conspiratorial atmosphere added a spice to the food—to the company. . . .

'Did you manage to get them away in the end? The Lak Royal Family, I mean?' Resolutely she turned her thoughts in another direction, and shook her head at his offer of more food.

'Yes, they all went on the plane along with the Embassy staff.'

The plane that she and Joss should have been on. That they would have been on, if she had remained at the Embassy, as he told her to. If he had not come to find her. If the insurgents had not arrived when they did, and blocked her way back. Joss blamed her, but it was not her fault. She checked her mind again, with another question.

'Will you come back to Lak, afterwards?' She spoke without thinking, as if they were casual acquaintances, as if there was no tie between them. Then she remembered, and her fingers twisted the slender gold ring round and round, nervously, until she caught his glance, watching her, and stopped abruptly. Perhaps he already had a girl waiting for him in England. He would probably start proceedings to have their marriage annulled the moment they reached home, and safety.

'I'm glad,' she told herself fiercely. 'I'll give him his ring back the very moment we dock. I'll be free, the same as before.' But while her mind exulted at the prospect, a small corner of her heart traitorously died within her at the inevitability of it all, at the knowledge that it could never be quite as it had been before, and she had to steel herself to listen when he answered,

'No, I shan't return to Lak. Thimbles needs me now. It's time for the fox to return to his lair,' he said quietly, and smiled, as if he found the prospect good.

'Thimbles?' Surely that was the name of his home. She remembered Wendy telling her. It was an odd sort of name for a home, she thought, and fought down a desire to giggle. Joss might be offended if she laughed at the name of his home. To stop the giggle she picked up her cup and raised it to her lips, then paused with a frown. 'That's funny, it's full!' She could have sworn she had already drunk at least half of her wine.

'Drink it up while I put the rest of the food away for later,' Joss said casually. He did not answer her questioning look, but continued to pack the remains of their meal carefully back into its wrapping. His voice seemed to reach her from a long way away, and when she looked at him his features were curiously blurred. Why did his face look blurred? She blinked, trying to bring it into focus, and was surprised by a yawn.

'I—feel—shleepy....'

'Good,' Joss approved, and turned towards her. 'Don't try to fight against it,' he advised her calmly. 'Just let go.' He caught her in his arms as she attempted to stand, and swayed dizzily. 'The wine will make sure you sleep soundly until I get back,' he said, and there was a wealth of satisfaction in his voice. She felt him wrap her in something warm and soft, it must be a blanket of some kind, and although she struggled to keep on her feet, her arms were pinioned inside its folds, and she was unable to offer any resistance when he picked her up easily and laid her down like a child, and her cheek encountered—surely, one of Wendy's pillows? Joss must have purloined the blanket and pillow on purpose, intending to ply her with the wine until she was drowsy. Through the mists that fogged her mind she realised, dimly, that she had not seen him drink more than sparingly of his own cup.

'This time I'll make sure you stay in the Embassy until I get back,' he said. And he laughed.

Through the drugged drowsiness that clawed her irresistibly into the maw of sleep, her last conscious feeling was one of burning anger against Joss, and the unscrupulous methods he had adopted to bend her to his will. First, he kissed her to keep her quiet. She would never forgive him for that kiss. Never! she vowed. Now he plied her with wine, that he must have known was potent, even if it seemed to her to be mild, until she had drunk deeply, and discovered its treachery—Joss's treachery—too late. Through the growing darkness she heard his laugh, and hated him for it. Desperately she struggled to stay awake, to tell him that she hated him. . . .

She slept.

She awoke to the sound of voices. Someone was close by, talking in low tones. Talking about her. She opened her eyes and stared straight up into the olive-skinned face of a man in the act of bending over to touch her hair. She sat up abruptly, her eyes widening with alarm, and Joss said,

'Don't panic. He's a friend.'

'How was I to know that?' she snapped, anger following on the heels of fright. 'He doesn't wear a label.'

The stranger spoke, to Joss, not to her.

'You would pass all but a close inspection, if you adopted native dress, but the woman would not.'

'Woman, indeed!' Netta spluttered indignantly, and a fleeting grin lightened Joss's face as the stranger continued,

'Her hair would give her away. And so would her temper. Our women are submissive.'

'Well, I'm not!' Netta tossed the blanket aside and gained her feet in one angry movement.

'You see?' The man shrugged helplessly. 'It would help, of course, if her hair was black. I'll bring you dye.'

'Dye my hair? Never!' Netta's hands rose to her head in defence of her copper curls.

'No,' Joss was equally decisive. 'We'll travel by night instead. The darkness will act as a cloak.'

Netta stared at him in surprise. She did not expect him to uphold her. Rather, she thought he would take a perverse pleasure in making her change the colour of her hair. She stiffened, prepared to do battle with him over the issue, and now he left her with nothing to fight against. Deliberately, to provoke her, she felt certain. She let her breath out in a deflated puff, but before she could think of anything to say, another voice joined in the conversation, and a man appeared out of the shadows from the other end of the vault.

'You'll need speed, as well as a cloak, to save you now.'

He gave Netta a peculiar look, and beckoned to the other two men. 'I wish to speak,' he insisted, and led Joss and his companion aside, away from Netta.

Really, the men were impossible! All three of them, she fumed. They treated her as if she was of no account, not even there, in fact, though it soon became obvious that she was the subject of their conversation. Several times the last comer gesticulated fiercely in her direction, and although the men kept their voices low they appeared to be arguing among themselves. Netta watched them with growing unease. The two strangers argued in a language she was unfamiliar with, doubtless so that she should not understand what they said, since they had both spoken to Joss in good English earlier. He seemed to have no difficulty in understanding them, and joined in the conversation in the same tongue. She would give a great deal to know what they were talking about, she thought uneasily, but the temptation to butt in and demand to know evaporated swiftly when she glanced at Joss's face.

In response to a particularly violent gesture from the second of the two men, he turned and looked across at Netta, and his eyes were flint hard. She caught her breath sharply. What were the two strangers saying, to make him look at her like that? His eyes seemed to bore right through her. And then, just as abruptly, he looked away, back to the other two men. He shook his head and spoke sharply to them, stilling whatever argument it was they were pressing. At first, Netta thought, they looked nonplussed, then the first man shrugged as if giving up, and without more ado they both melted back into the shadows towards where the tunnel from the garden led into the vaults.

'What was that all about?'

She tried to sound casual, but tension showed in her voice, and in the tautness of her slender figure as she faced Joss defensively. Defending herself against what she did not know, unless it was against the cold anger that hardened his eyes and his expression as he turned to confront her, and stood for what seemed endless minutes looking down at her with a close, searching scrutiny that made her eyes falter nervously under his stare. He noticed them falter, and an ominous frown darkened his forehead as he spoke.

'What have you done with the jewels you stole?' he demanded harshly. 'The ones you took from their settings that you hid in your hotel room?'

CHAPTER FIVE

'THE jewels I stole?' She stared at him, stunned. 'I didn't steal them,' she denied hotly, 'I....'

'Don't lie to me,' he snapped. 'Those two men who've just gone are reliable contacts of mine. The second one who came in brought the news that the mob had raided the hotel, and found a pile of jewel settings—without the jewels,' he stressed harshly. 'The settings were hidden underneath a pile of women's clothing in a guest's bedroom. The guest could only have been you.'

So that was why the newcomer had looked at her in such a peculiar fashion.

'Is that what you were arguing about?'

'I was arguing to prevent them from straightaway handing you over to the authorities to deal with,' he told her bluntly, 'which means, at the moment, the rebels themselves.'

'They can't!' She stared at him, horrified. 'They wouldn't—I thought you said they were contacts of yours?' Surely they could not be in sympathy with the rebels too?

'The jewel settings which the looters found were all traditional to Lak,' Joss reminded her grimly. 'And while the two men you saw here have no sympathy with the uprising, they have even less with foreigners who try to steal their national wealth.'

'I didn't steal them,' she cried angrily. She knew, even better than Joss, what the settings were like. Somehow she must convince him of her right to the jewels, make him convince the two strangers. While they were with him, Joss had prevailed, but once they were out of earshot, away from the influence of his stronger personality, they might have second thoughts about handing her over to the rebels. Fear paralysed her at the very thought. She must not let Joss know where she had hidden the gems. He would undoubtedly force her to hand them over, to buy her safety, and she had promised Ranjit.... Nothing would make her go back on that promise, she vowed stubbornly. Where she went, the jewels would go with her, until they reached the safety of their client's bank in London.

'Well?' Joss took her by the shoulders and gave her a shake, misconstruing her silence. 'Is that why you came to Lak in the first place? Tell me the truth,' he demanded fiercely. 'I've got a right to know who I married, as well as you,' he used her own words against her, 'and I want to know whether or not I've married a....'

'Jewel thief?' She drew herself up proudly. 'You can set your mind at rest on that score,' she assured him coldly. 'And before you decide to act as judge, jury and executioner, you might do me the courtesy of listening to my side of the story.'

'Go on.' His face did not relent, and he kept hold of her by the shoulders still. 'As if I might make off with the loot,' she thought bitterly, and resisted an urge to slide her fingers round her slacks belt to make sure the jewels were still there. With an effort she took control of herself, and went on more quietly,

'You already know who my father is.' There could be few who did not know John Vaughan, at least by reputation, and she blessed the fact now. 'I came to Lak to collect some jewels from a client, to take back with me to be remodelled.' She mentioned Ranjit's name, and could see from the quick interest on Joss's face that he knew who she meant. 'I often act as a courier between my father and his clients, but this is the first time I've been accused of stealing the jewels I come to collect,' she finished bitterly.

'Are you in the habit of extracting the gems from their settings after you've collected them?' he enquired sarcastically, and she flushed.

'I usually wait until I get them home,' her own voice reflected the bite in his, 'but I'm not usually faced with the prospect of a mob of looting insurgents on the one hand, and a threat of a baggage search by soldiers I don't trust

any more than I trust the rebels, on the other,' she retorted with spirit, and had the satisfaction of feeling his
fingers lessen their grip on her shoulders. She half put up
her hand to rub the place where they had been, it tingled
still with the force of his hold, but she refused to allow
him to see that it hurt, and resolutely thrust her hand into
her slacks pocket instead. 'The gemstones themselves were
the really valuable part of the jewellery, and I was responsible for their safety, so I had no option but to hide
them. If you want to check my story, you can always ask
Ranjit,' she hurried on for fear he might ask her whereabouts she had hidden them. 'He'll vouch for what I say,'
she finished triumphantly.

Joss stared down at her for long minutes, his strange
gold eyes probing deep into her own, and she met his
look without flinching.

'You'll have to leave the gems wherever they are, and
risk them being found,' he said at last. 'You can't go back
for them now, the rebels will be on the lookout for you to
return to the hotel and try to retrieve them.'

'He hasn't guessed!' Relief surged through her. 'He
thinks I hid the gemstones in the hotel, as well as the
settings.' She lowered her eyes hastily for fear they might
reflect her jubilation, and give her away.

'That accounts for the jewels, but it doesn't explain the
missing film.'

'What about the film?' She had completely forgotten
about it until now. 'At least I've got that with me.' Where
did I learn to be devious? she asked herself, astonished,
her normally truthful self looking on amazed at the ease
with which the inferred lie came out. 'I've got that with
me.' Saying without words that she had left the jewels behind. Confirming Joss's supposition that she had done just
that. 'It's only holiday snaps I took on safari,' she told him
guilelessly. 'You can have the film by all means, if you
want it, it's in my bag somewhere.' She bent to get it for
him, and he checked her movement with his hand.

'Don't bother, you might need it to convince the
authorities if we're unlucky enough to be caught.'

'Why should a holiday film bother them? It wasn't even taken in Lak.' She was genuinely puzzled now, and showed it, and the stern set of his features relaxed a little.

'Only a blameless life could make you so naïve.' The way he said it, it did not sound like a compliment, and she eyed him warily. 'Try and look at it from the point of view of the people who raided your room,' he dropped his hands from her shoulders and spoke with barely controlled patience, 'They found you and the jewels missing, and as if that wasn't enough, they discovered some extremely expensive photographic equipment apparently abandoned without a second thought, and the clip of films was gone. What conclusion could they come to, but that the film was as valuable to you as the jewels?' he asked her impatiently.

'So?' She shrugged, unable to see the point he was driving at.

'Give me patience!'

Joss's plea went unheard, and his own evaporated.

'Can't you see?' he asked her, tensely. 'The stuff you left behind in the hotel not only brands you as a jewel thief, but as a possible spy as well.'

'A spy?' He sounded like a paperback thriller, she thought scornfully. 'You're talking nonsense! If we're unlucky enough to get caught by the rebels, I can easily explain....'

'Do you imagine they'd wait long enough to listen to your explanation?' he interrupted her roughly. 'In the mood the mob's in now, they'd act first and think afterwards.'

'They'll think I've escaped on the plane.'

'They know differently,' he disillusioned her. 'They found your handkerchief in the scrub bordering the airstrip. It was caught on a twig, and waving at them like a flag. They couldn't miss it,' he accused her tersely.

'I didn't leave it there on purpose.' She refused to be pilloried for something else that was not her fault.

'If you had, it couldn't have served as a clearer guide.' He refused to relent. 'It took no time at all for the rebels to put two and two together, and realise you'd missed the plane, and must therefore be still somewhere in Lak.'

'That means. . . .' She stared at him, silenced by the implications of what he had just told her.

'That means the rebels would dearly like to discover where you're hiding.' He did not mince words, and she shivered. 'They'd give a great deal to get their hands on the jewels you hid, and only you are in the position to tell them where they are.'

'What shall we do?' she asked in a dry whisper. Visions of the man with the chain rose frighteningly before her.

'We'll travel by night,' Joss answered briefly. 'Very soon one of my contacts will return with two night cloaks. They'll serve as a disguise enough in the darkness unless we have the ill luck to be actually confronted by someone.'

He did not suggest what they might do then. Netta swallowed. Night cloaks were a good idea, but. . . . She thought longingly of the safety of the airplane, and then resolutely thrust the thought aside. It was no good wishing. The ankle-length night cloaks would have to do. They were a reasonable enough disguise, as Joss said, because they were a common article of clothing worn by the Lak people who used them as a simple solution to the problem of the severe variance in temperature between day and night, which fluctuated between sub-tropical at noon and sub-zero after dark, occasioned by the high altitude of the country.

Her own cloak trailed on the floor forlornly when she tried it on. She did not expect the two men to return, but Joss's faith in them proved to be justified, and shortly after dark they came with two bundles of clothing, and left again immediately.

'They haven't . . . ?' She raised apprehensive eyes to Joss.

'They won't betray you,' he answered the question she dared not ask. 'Try this on,' he thrust the smaller of the two bundles towards her.

'It's too long.'

'Of course it is, if you wear it across your shoulders. The men wear theirs that way.' He slung his own cloak across his shoulders in a manner that told her he had worn one before, probably for the same purpose, as a disguise. It gave him a brigandy sort of look, she decided critically, and felt her heart begin to thump uncomfortably hard. It made him look even more handsome, if anything.

'The women of Lak keep their heads covered.' He removed her cloak from about her shoulders and draped it across her hair. 'That's better.' He surveyed the length of it critically. 'It's free from the floor, so you can walk without tripping over it. Or run, if you have to,' he added significantly.

'It feels like a nun's habit.'

'You don't look a bit like a nun.'

Unexpectedly he reached out and caught her to him. She raised her head, startled, and the cloak slipped from off her hair, framing her face in its soft woollen folds, and Joss cupped his hands round her head and tipped her face up towards him.

'You weren't meant to be a nun,' he affirmed softly, and lowered his head until his lips trailed lightly across the delicate softness of her cheek. They explored the fine bone line to where a dimple showed at the corner of her mouth when she laughed. She was not laughing now, but he found the spot where the dimple lay with unerring accuracy.

Netta quivered under his touch, and went deathly still. She tried to steel herself against him, valiantly trying not to respond, but her heart hammered against her ribs in a wild tattoo, and the urge to put her arms round his neck became irresistible, until she tried to raise them, and found them trapped beneath the enmeshing folds of the cloak. Joss drew it even more closely round her, and laughed down into her face, enjoying her predicament.

'The cloaks serve more than one useful purpose,' he murmured. 'The Lak men like their women submissive.'

'I'm not a Lak woman,' she denied hotly, stung into anger by his amusement. She hated him, when he laughed at her. 'And I'm not submissive, either.'

'If you hope to pass as a Lak woman, you'll have to learn how.'

His lips left her dimple and sought her mouth. They

parted her lips with a firm pressure that stilled the angry words they were forming, until the words no longer wanted to come. She tried in vain to stiffen herself away from him, terrified by the ease with which he was able to bend her to his will. Her mind cried out to her to resist, but her heart treacherously refused her the ability.

'I can't fight you. I can't,' she moaned when at last he let her go, and she leaned trembling and defeated against him.

'For your first try at being submissive, that wasn't bad,' he approved. 'Keep it up, and you'll pass as a Lak woman yet.'

She recoiled from him as if she had been stung.

'You—you——' she choked into silence on a sob. Once again he had tricked her into responding to his kisses, playing on her feelings as a harpist plucks the strings of his instrument, cynically drawing out the notes for his amusement. And she had provided the tune.

'Don't ever touch me again,' she cried fiercely. 'Never, do you hear me? Never—never. . . .' In a frenzy of anger she thrust the folds of the cloak from her and raised her hand to strike him.

'It's time to go.'

Joss fielded her hand neatly and spun them both round as a voice spoke from the shadows behind them. A figure stood at the entrance to the tunnel into the shrubbery.

'We're ready.' Joss released her hand, contemptuously indifferent to her anger, and the possibility that she might again attempt to hit him.

'Keep your hair covered,' he commanded her curtly, 'or it'll betray us both.' For a dreadful second or two she felt she did not care, until he added, 'jewels aren't worth risking your life for.' His comment stilled her. Had he guessed? She shook herself mentally. There was no way in which he could possibly know. But the doubt was sufficient to keep her still when he turned and pulled her cloak over her head with an impatient tug, before he put his arm round her shoulders and swung her with him to join the man who waited for them. His cloak swirled about him as he turned, faintly theatrical in the gloom, and it added to Netta's sense of unreality as she went with him, feeling as if she was taking part in a bizarre play.

'There's no need to pull me along as if I'm on a lead,' she protested angrily, stumbling in her efforts to keep pace with the long strides of the men as they emerged through the shrubbery, and out once more into the dreaded alley-ways.

'You must keep up with us,' he said curtly, but just the same he added something in the same strange tongue she had heard him use with the men before, and the one who led them slackened his pace slightly. It was a relief, but Netta still found she had to trot to keep up with them.

'The men of Lak must train their women like race-horses, if this is the pace they expect them to walk at,' she panted resentfully when they paused at the exit from the alley they were traversing, and which emerged, she saw with dismay, on to the central square of the town near to the front of the hotel which had been her recent abode.

'Their women are wise, they remain in their homes,' Joss retorted. Netta scowled at this implied criticism, but before she could reply he went on unsympathetically, 'Only ladies of doubtful virtue venture abroad after dark.' She saw his teeth flash white in the guttering light of the flares that threw a mixture of flame and smoke among the groups of figures, cloaked like themselves, who moved restlessly in the broken darkness around the edges of the square.

'Well, they needn't think that about me,' she whispered, furious at his jibe.

'I hope that's just what they will think if we're un-lucky enough to be confronted by any of the rebels,' Joss answered unfeelingly, and raised his hand to their guide in a dismissive gesture.

'What are you signalling to him for?' Netta demanded to know uneasily.

'His job's finished,' Joss told her as the guide turned the corner into the square and mingled unobtrusively with the groups of rebels. 'From now on, we're on our own.'

She despised herself for the thrill his words sent through

her, and conflicting emotions made her voice sharp as she replied fervently,

'I wish we were on our own, miles away from here.' She eyed the knots of cloaked men fearfully. 'We'll have to go some other way. We can't go through that crowd, or we're sure to be discovered. There isn't a woman among them,' she discovered, and checked, appalled. Joss did not just hope what they would think when they saw a woman with him. He had known, before he brought her here.

'I'm not going to cross the square. You can't make me!'

'You must. All roads lead into the square, and the way to the border is on the other side.'

He made her. He caught her by the shoulders as she tried to escape past him, back into the darkness of the alleyway, and propelled her forcibly into the square. A group of rebels strolled towards them, and called out something to her, and ribald laughter rose at whatever it was they said, from others of their kind nearby. Joss snarled something back in the same tongue, and grabbed her roughly to him. One arm went round her waist, the other held the cloak over her head, over her face. She felt trapped, stifled, and something inside her snapped. Throwing caution to the winds, she beat against him with her fists, suddenly terrified, frantic to be free.

'Let me....' She did not get as far as the word 'go'. He silenced her with a kiss of such force that it pressed her lips back against her teeth, bruising, agonisingly painful. Momentarily, shock stilled her. And then a wave of pure fury flooded through her at his brutality. She had warned him not to touch her again, and this was his answer. He was behaving like an animal—a savage! The sheer primitive ferocity of his attack—it could not be called a kiss—goaded her into retaliating.

Unable to speak, because his face pressed down over her own like a mask, she lashed out with her feet and fists, careless now of the rebels around them, fighting like a tigress in a personal rebellion of her own that made the other war seem tame by comparison. Her nails scored deeply across his face, and he jerked his head sharply upwards with a quickly checked curse. Several voices rose from the watching rebels, offering him jeering advice. Netta could not understand the words, but there was no mistaking the tone. She longed to shout back at them, denying that she was what they thought her to be, but her lips were numb with the cruel pressure upon them, and would not form the words.

Without warning, the shouts and jeers grew dim, and she swayed, half fainting. She felt Joss's arm move from behind her waist and grasp her under the knees, and he lifted her bodily, holding her tightly against him so that her face was buried in the folds of his own cloak. He pulled it round her and she lay against him, spent, longing to cry, and yet terrified of making a sound. A confusion of shouts broke out round them, and rough hands grasped at her. She shrank against Joss, too petrified to cry out, and the rumble of his ferocious answering shout resounded through his chest against her ear. He swung round and her feet, sticking out horizontally as he carried her, struck something soft and yielding. He was using her as a club! She risked a peep, and saw the ring of men around them fall back, giving way, and Joss loped through the gap, carrying her easily, as if she was some kind of prey he had fought for and won, and then the shouts died away behind them, and the guttering light and smoke from the flares gave way to blessed darkness. Still Joss travelled on, unspeaking, until at last she felt him slow his pace, and she became conscious of cold; biting cold that gripped her feet where her cloak had fallen away from them. She stirred in his arms and shivered, and Joss stopped and stood her down on the ground, holding her against him for support.

'We're nearly there.'

She was too exhausted to ask where 'there' might be.

'Can you stand?' He hardly waited for her nod. 'Then walk,' he commanded her, 'it'll warm you.' She stumbled, but he forced her to go on. The flow of blood returning to her numbed feet brought pins and needles, and excruciating pain, and the bitter cold of the pre-dawn made her gasp. The ground they were traversing was rough and

steep, and thickly dotted with scrub, similar to the peri-
meter of the airstrip.

'I can't go on.' She sank weakly to her knees.

'Walk!' he commanded her harshly, and pulled her upright again, relentlessly forcing her forward. 'We've got to
reach the cave before daylight.'

'Cave?' His callous treatment had the effect he intended.
Warmth began to seep through her as he forced her forward. It steadied her shaking limbs, and enabled her to
place her feet with greater surety, so that she did not
stumble so often.

'It's a hole in the rocks. It runs off the hillside,' he told
her briefly. 'The locals know of it, but the rebels won't.
The two men you saw at the Embassy have left us more
food there, and blankets.'

Blankets. Blessed warmth. The urge to sleep was almost
overwhelming, aided by the intense cold. She felt too tired
to feel hunger, or even surprise when the thorns of the
dense scrub released their clutching hold on her cloak, and
they walked free, on rock. Jumbled, tumbled rock, remains
of some prehistoric eruption, that received them into its
jagged midst, and straightway deprived her of——

'Joss!' Panic caught her as he vanished.

'Follow me.' His arm reappeared round what looked at
first glance to be a solid rock face, but upon following his
guiding grasp she discovered a fissure just wide enough to
allow the passage of her body. She eased herself sideways
through the slit, and her feet stumbled on something soft.
She put out her arms to save herself, and Joss caught her
as she fell.

'They've done us proud!'

He lowered her on to the pile of dark blankets on the
cave floor, and she looked up, dazedly surprised that she
could see his face clearly.

'It's light!' she exclaimed.

'We've made it just in time.'

The sun rose with the same abruptness with which it
had set the night before. One moment they were groping
in darkness, the next, it was broad daylight.

'Your face is bleeding,' Netta realised.

'From where you scratched me.'

He reached up slim brown fingers and traced the score lines across his cheek. He slanted a look at her across the heap of blankets, and latent anger glowed deep in the gold eyes.

'You're an excellent actress,' he congratulated her icily, 'but you needn't have made your performance quite so realistic.' His look, his tone, told her she would pay for her temerity.

'My performance?' She gasped at his effrontery. 'What about your own?' she flared angrily. The scratches she had put on his cheek—the thought that it was her nails that had inflicted them made her feel sick—were as nothing to the weals his own play-acting had scored across her heart, not once, but several times.

'I had to silence you somehow,' he shrugged her accusation aside. 'You cried out in English.'

'And that's the best way you know, to silence a woman!' she threw his own taunt back at him with bitter emphasis.

'It worked,' he pointed out irrefutably. 'I wouldn't have bothered, otherwise,' he added in a hard voice, and Netta flinched as if he had struck her. She loathed him, she told herself fiercely, so she did not care. But she could not help the fact that she was feminine enough to feel his indifference as an insult.

'First food, and then sleep.' Joss bent his mind to what he obviously considered more important. How like a man, she thought bitingly.

'I'm not hungry.' She refused the proffered food.

'Nevertheless, you will eat.' He pressed the flat dark bread and strangely spiced meat into her hands, and she ate, reluctantly, but too weary to defy him further, until at last, satisfied, he relented, and spread the blankets flat across what appeared to be a deep bed of twigs on the farther side of the cave floor.

'Are there thorns?' She carried smarting evidence on her legs and hands of the variety carried by the scrub outside.

'No, these are rushes from the river banks just beyond

the cave.' He held the top blanket back, waiting for her to settle herself on the makeshift bed.

'Where are you going to sleep?' Belated compunction caught up with her, and she raised questioning eyes from her couch, which to her surprise felt remarkably comfortable.

'With you, of course.' He watched her eyes widen with startled dismay, and added impatiently, 'It's quite in order. We're married—remember?'

CHAPTER SIX

THE smell of smoke wakened her.

She could not believe that she had slept. She did not think it was possible, when Joss lowered himself on to the rush bed beside her, that she could hope to sleep. She shrank as far away from him as the limited space would allow, and drew her cloak closely, defensively, around her, and felt his look pierce through her like a knife. To avoid it, she turned on her side, away from him, only to discover that it bored through her back until it felt as if it must surely burn a hole through her spine. She lay tense and rigid as he drew the rough woollen blanket over them both and lay down beside her, but he made no attempt to touch her, no attempt to bridge the gap which she put between them by rolling on her side away from him, and she felt unaccountably resentful when, a few minutes later, his even breathing told her he slept.

Sleep seemed far away from Netta, the turmoil of her mind denied that she could ever rest again, but without her being conscious of it, exhaustion took its toll, and the warmth emanating from the blankets and Joss's close proximity to her had their effect, and unaware, she surrendered to oblivion.

The smoke made her cough. It swirled through the cave in thickening clouds, smarting her eyes into tears, and her rested body into alarmed activity.

'Joss, wake up!' She turned and sat up, and discovered the place beside her was unoccupied. She looked round wildly.

'I'm here.' He spoke softly from beside the narrow entrance in the rock. She could just make out his figure in the choking gloom.

'Get out, quick, before we're trapped!' Terror urged her to his side, and the entrance, with the promise of clean air outside the cave.

'The fire's outside, not in here.' He caught and held her back, pulling her to one side of the gap in the rocks.

'But....' She struggled to be free.

'Look outside.' He shook her roughly to make her comply, and retained his tight hold on her jacket, preventing her from moving away from him.

'What are they doing?' Reluctantly she obeyed. It was becoming difficult to breathe, and she held her handkerchief—Wendy's handkerchief, the one he had taken such a risk to obtain for her—over her nose and mouth. Men's figures moved among the smoke outside, and flames crackled hungrily through the wide sweep of tinder-dry thorn and scrub visible from their vantage point among the rocks.

'We've got to get out. We'll be trapped!' It was obvious the unknown men were fighting a losing battle. The whole area appeared to be ablaze, and it was evident that it was beyond the powers of the twenty or so men outside to control it.

'Stay where you are,' he ordered her curtly.

'I can't,' she choked. 'I can't breathe.'

'If it gets more than you can bear, lie face downwards on the floor. Smoke rises, and there'll be an inch or two of clear air at ground level. You can breathe from that.' Joss remained standing himself, his eyes on the activities of the men outside.

'They're not much good at fire-fighting. They're making it worse.' She remained upright as well, unwilling to give in unless Joss did. Unwilling to show weakness in front of him.

'They're not trying to put out the flames. They're deliberately fanning them, to make them spread.'

'But why?' she asked, bewildered. She had seen farmers fire the stubble fields after the harvest in England, but there seemed no point in this. The fire was consuming growing bushes. 'Oh, look, the poor thing's terrified!' she exclaimed pityingly, as a small gazelle-like creature darted out of the scrub, fleeing for its life from the flames.

'That's what they're hoping to do to us—flush us out of

hiding,' Joss told her grimly. 'They must think we're lying out in the scrub somewhere. And they want those gems you hid.' He ignored her involuntary gasp, and went on, 'They can't have found them yet, or they wouldn't be doing this now,' he deduced.

The rebels were a lot closer to the gems than they realised. Instinctively her fingers found her slacks belt, and she checked herself sharply. Joss must not guess, either.

'They're coming closer.' Netta eyed the approaching men uneasily. They had formed themselves into a line, like beaters, and were fanning the flames in front of them, aided by the prevailing wind which blew the smoke away from them, and straight towards the cave.

'They can't know about the cave, otherwise they'd have investigated it before they set fire to the scrub,' Joss returned confidently.

'They might discover it by chance, if they cross the rocks.' She refused to be reassured, and the knowledge of what she carried in her slacks belt added to her anxiety.

'With a bit of luck they'll go round the outcrop of rock,' Joss replied. 'It's cool enough in here, but the sun's hot out there, and the fire will make them hotter still. The rocks make for rough walking, and they're more likely to take the easier route round them. Providing we keep quiet, we stand a good chance of remaining undiscovered,' he added, and his tone held a warning. Twice he had taken drastic measures to silence her.

'I'll be quiet, don't worry,' Netta assured him in a bitter whisper, and anger flared in her as she saw his lips twitch. Resolutely she swallowed a cough as she took her handkerchief from in front of her face for a second or two to brush away an outbreak of irritating tickles that persisted against her neck and arms. It could not be perspiration, in spite of the smoke the cave felt uncomfortably cold, and she had jettisoned her cloak when she rose.

'Ugh!' she muttered.

'Sssh!'

'I can't help it. It's a huge spider,' she whispered back angrily, and brushed it aside with shuddering aversion.

'And another. They must have come from the rushes.'
She regarded the insects with horror. 'No, they're coming
from the roof,' she realised as a dark blob scurried across
her shoulder, and she raised her eyes in shrinking disbelief.
'There's hundreds of them!' Spiders were dropping from
the cave roof; swinging down on webs; crawling down
the walls; doing, in fact, what Joss had told her to do,
seeking the few inches of clear air on the cave floor as the
smoke thickened and rose, and made their shadowy
habitat untenable. 'Great heavens! There's an army of the
creatures!'

A monster of a size and hairiness such as she had never
seen even in her wildest nightmares dropped on the end
of its web, and swung in front of Netta's face like a black,
leggy pendulum. She opened her mouth to scream.

'Quiet!'

Joss's hand clamped over her face with desperate speed,
stifling her cry before it was uttered. His other hand tossed
aside the spider with a savage thrust, and a careless indifference to its horrific appearance that Netta could not
help but envy.

'The spiders won't hurt you. They're not the poisonous
kind.'

She could not care less whether they were poisonous or
not, their looks were enough for her, but with an immense
effort of will she remained silent when at last he removed
his hand from over her mouth with slow caution. When he
was satisfied she would stay quiet he picked her up in his
arms, away from the crawling activity on the cave floor,
and she shuddered, and buried her face in his shirt. With
careful steps he carried her across to the rush bed, and
held her high with one arm while he reached down with his
hand and shook the blankets, ridding them of any stray
spiders that might be lurking there.

'Forget the spiders,' he whispered in her ear. 'Forget the
smoke.' He lowered her gently down on to the rush couch,
and drew the blanket over her, over them both. 'Soon, very
soon, all this will be over, and you can forget,' he promised
her softly, with an un-Joss-like tenderness that made her

wonder if she was dreaming. His lips stopped speaking, and started to blot out the memory for her there and then. Not cruelly, as they had done before, but gently caressing, pressing on her eyelids to shut them against the spiders, wandering from there to the tiptilted end of her nose to tell it not to smell the smoke, trailing rapture behind them as they slowly found their way to the spot where her dimple lay, and lingered there until it deepened into a smile, and then coaxed the hesitant smile into tender, lovely life.

With a sigh she surrendered to his arms, giving herself up to his caress, returning it as it grew urgent, compelling, sweeping her away with an upsurging passion so over-whelming that it was beyond her power to control. It blotted out the danger that threatened them from the rebels outside; drew a veil across the past, and the future, and lit her whole being with a fire that paled the brush fire outside into insignificance by comparison, an all-consuming flame of ecstasy that burned like lightning, and that for the rest of her days would endow the stark cave with a secret beauty of its own, known only to her—and to Joss.

She was alone when she woke up. She looked round her warily, but there was no sign of the spiders. The smoke had vanished, and the insects had retreated to their preferred haunts in the crannies of the cave roof. Netta brushed a hand across her face, clearing her hair from her eyes, and her palm came away showing a black sooty streak.

'I feel filthy!' she groaned.

The smoke had dispersed, but it had left behind marks of its presence in a rash of sooty smudges over her clothes and person, and her thoughts turned longingly towards hot water, and delicately perfumed soap.

She tossed aside the blankets, and stretched. Joss was gone, but he would not be far away. The euphoria of last night remained with her still, boosting her confidence. Everything seemed different this morning. Life itself was different, after last night. She rose to her feet, feeling sur-prisingly refreshed, and blessed the rushes for their hospitality. Tonight, she and Joss would be gone. She bent automatically to fold the blankets in a neat pile, baring the dry, reedy stems of their makeshift bed, and paused, struck by a sudden thought.

Rushes. That meant water. Joss said they had been gathered from a river bank close by. Perhaps that was where he had gone now, maybe to have a swim. The rebels must have departed, for him to risk such a thing. The prospect of cool water, even without soap, proved irresistible. She left the blankets and slid through the slit in the rock, and took a cautious look out over the surrounding terrain. The rebels had indeed gone. There was no sign of human life on the burned-out slopes. The arsonists had unwittingly done her a good turn, in that their vandalism had left them with no place to hide themselves. All that remained of the growing thorn bushes was charred and blackened stumps, incapable of concealing a rabbit, let alone a person. She turned and looked in the other direction. The same black desolation met her eyes, but beyond it the river gleamed, coolly inviting. She hesitated no longer.

'I shan't be away for very long,' she excused her conscience for not waiting for Joss to come back. He could hardly shout at her for leaving the cave on the same errand as himself, she consoled herself. She could not see him by the river, but perhaps he was swimming further along the watercourse.

'I need a wash more than ever now.' She surveyed her feet and legs ruefully as she neared the bank. The charred remains of the scrub had seeped into her shoes on the way, and blackened her slacks as high as her knees, and even without the scrubby thorn growth to contend with, the walking was rough. The day was far advanced, but the sun was still intensely hot, and perspiration streaked her face and stuck her hair damply to her forehead, and she gained the bank with a gasp of relief. It turned into a groan of disappointment as her eyes took in what from a distance had looked to be cool, inviting water.

'Surely Joss isn't swimming in that?' she muttered incredulously. The slow-moving river was an uninviting, dirty yellow colour, more nearly resembling thick soup than the clear, bright streams of home, its surface marred by an unidentifiable collection of debris that jostled for room in the opaque water.

'I'll just damp my hanky, and sponge my face and hands,' she decided. A side eddy made a patch of clearer water near to the bank. It was flanked by a strip of dried mud, punctuated by deep holes that looked as if they had been made by the hooves of animals. She remembered the gazelle. She had probably stumbled on the favourite watering place of the local fauna. She saw Joss in the distance as she stepped to the edge of the mud patch.

'Netta, don't....'

'Netta, *do*,' she contradicted him crossly as his shout reached her. The rest of what he said drifted away, and she set her lips mutinously. Being with Joss was worse than being at school, she decided, heat and discomfort making her irritable. Whatever she wanted to do, he seemed to find a good reason why she should not. 'I'm not a child, and the sooner Joss realises it the better,' she said to herself rebelliously, and stepped forward deliberately, ignoring his second shout. 'If he yells like that, all the rebels in the state will know we're here—oh!'

Without warning the deceptively firm-looking crust on top of the mud bank gave way beneath her feet. Black, evil-smelling slime welled over the tops of her shoes.

'Joss!'

Frantically she tried to backstep, but the mud gave her no firm footing, and she sank even deeper.

'Joss!'

'Keep still! Don't struggle!' Through a haze of panic she heard him shout, heard his feet thunder along the sun-baked earth towards her. He caught her flailing hands in a firm grasp, and pulled. With a reluctant squelch the mud released her, and she blessed the fact that her shoes were sturdy lace-ups. They remained on her feet. She staggered off balance, unable to keep her footing because of the layer of mud adhering to the soles, and she scuffed her shoes hard on the ground to try and clear it.

Joss grabbed her by the shoulders, and stood her on her feet none too gently. 'Didn't you hear me shout?' he demanded angrily. 'I told you not to....'

'I'm not obliged to do as you tell me,' she retorted angrily. If they were going to have a showdown, it might as well be now, she decided. 'I'm an adult, not a child, and I won't be ordered about by you!' she stormed defiantly. It was a pity he towered so far above her, having to look up at him took away some of the force from her defiance, but it was not something she could alter. 'I'm tired of the whole business,' she exclaimed. 'First I get a plague of spiders down my neck, and now I've got fish in my socks!' Exasperation overcame her as she shook a thin, silver, eel-like creature from the inside of her shoe.

'Fish? Where?' Joss stopped glowering, and bent swiftly to grab her foot. Without ceremony he snatched the one shoe from her hand, and swinging her off the ground he tugged her other shoe from her foot.

'There's no need to undress me!' She grabbed back her shoes angrily. 'It's only one small fish.' She had no aversion to fish, only to spiders. 'I'll put it back in the river, it's still alive, if that's what's worrying you.' Really, you could take concern for the environment too far, she thought impatiently, and bent to pick up the wriggling silver body.

'Put it down,' Joss ordered her urgently. 'Drop it!' he shouted when she did not immediately comply, and without waiting to see if his order was obeyed he brushed it from out of her fingers with a hard hand.

'Don't shout at me like that!' She turned on him stormily.

'——!' He swore sharply, and shook his hand violently, ignoring her indignation. For a brief second the creature seemed to cling to his fingers, then with a further violent shake Joss dislodged it, and it described a bright arc and landed back in its own element with hardly a splash.

'It's bitten me!' His face turned colour underneath its tan, and Netta stared at him in surprise. Men were peculiar. The bigger and tougher they were, the bigger babies they seemed to be, she thought scornfully.

'It's nothing to make a fuss about. Good heavens,' she exclaimed, 'the fish isn't as big as a minnow.' She laughed derisively.

'Its bite's deadly poisonous.' He wiped the smile from her face abruptly. 'Help me to pull the heads from these rushes.' He reached out and hurriedly bent the tall stems from across the firm part of the bank, and began snapping off the feathery heads with frantic haste.

'What do you want rush heads for?' Had he gone mad? she wondered impatiently. 'Let me look at that bite,' she insisted.

'There's no time.' He split open one of the rush heads and rubbed it with desperate speed across the place where the creature had bitten him. Netta saw with dismay that his hand was already beginning to turn purple round the bite, and swelling alarmingly. 'The sap contains an antidote,' he explained his actions tersely.

She needed no second bidding to help him. She tore at the rush heads with shaking fingers. The tough fibres of them split her nails, and the juice stained her hands almost as brown as Joss's own, but she did not care. It was her fault he had been bitten in the first place. If only she'd listened. . . .

'I didn't know.' Her whisper begged his forgiveness.

'I shouted, to try and stop you from getting near the water.'

'It looked like an animals' watering place. I thought if the wild things went there to drink, it must be safe.'

'The animals are safe. The fish can't bite through the horns of their hooves, or penetrate the tough hairs on their legs. People haven't got that kind of protection.'

The rapidly spreading swelling along his arm underlined the truth of what he said, and Netta pulled at the rush heads with the speed of fear.

'Help me back to the cave,' Joss said at last, in a breathless kind of voice, and she turned to him sharply.

Help him? An icicle of terror speared through her, and her eyes searched his face. It had gone grey, and—was it her imagination, or did his voice sound slurred? Hurriedly she stuffed a handful of rush heads into her jacket pocket and grasped him round the waist.

'Lean on me,' she bade him, and immediately felt terrified when he did. Joss, who was so strong, who took charge of everything. And now he leaned on her. The slope back to the cave was steep, the going underfoot rough, and Joss's weight was almost more than her slender frame could bear. Rivulets of perspiration stuck her clothes to her body in a clammy embrace.

'If only I'd listened! If only I'd done as he said.' Remorse propped up her flagging reserves of energy when she felt as if her legs must surely give way under her, and she staggered the last few yards to the cave mouth and almost lifted Joss through the entrance as he slumped, barely conscious, in her hold.

'Did you see anyone....' His blurring mind still ran on the rebels.

'No, the slopes are empty.' She searched them with desperate eyes, willing someone to be there. She would even welcome the insurgents, if only they would bring medical aid to Joss. But the blackened terrain surrounding their hideout offered her no support. Even the gazelle had gone.

Somehow she managed to keep upright until they reached the rush bed, and the blankets she had started to fold earlier. The lower one still remained in place, covering the rushes, and she sank on to it on her knees, and lowered Joss down as gently as she could. He collapsed in a limp heap, his eyes half closed, and with a supreme effort she managed to roll him on his back, and pulled the top blanket closely round him. The rush heads dropped from her pocket as she tucked it under him.

'Give me your hand.'

She doubted if he heard her. His eyes were half open, and looked vaguely in her direction, but they had a glazed appearance, as if he did not really see her, their clear bright gold as dull as the waters of the river.

'Stay....' he muttered.

'I'll stay with you, don't worry.' She had no intention

of leaving him. For the first time, she thought wryly, she intended to obey his orders even before they were uttered. She sat back on her heels and hurriedly split open the extra supply of rush heads. If the sap contained an antidote to the poison, then more of the same thing could do nothing but good, she reasoned.

Throughout the endless night she massaged his arm with the brown juice pressing it into the site of the bite, and all the while Joss tossed restlessly on his makeshift bed, muttering with ever rising fever.

At first Netta did not comprehend the words, she was too busy with the rush heads to listen closely to what he said, but in the end the persistent mutter penetrated the daze of exhaustion that, as the long hours passed, turned her movements into automatic reflexes, dictated by subconscious reaction rather than by conscious thought, and she sat back on her heels and listened more closely. Perhaps he wanted something, was trying to tell her to do something for him. She ran out of rush heads, but by now his arm, and the site of the bite, were dyed almost black with their juice, and it was doubtful if more would help.

'Tara ... stay....'

He shook with cold, and she cradled him to her, holding him in her arms, lying beside him in a vain attempt to warm him with the warmth from her own body. Then the heat of the fever burned him, and he tried to throw off the blanket, and she strained to hold it round him for fear that the cold would return. And all the time he tossed restlessly, calling in delirium for,

'Tara ... Tara ... stay....'

She knitted her forehead in a frown. Who was Tara?

When he first begged, 'Stay,' she thought he meant herself; thought he wanted her to remain with him, to help him. Desolation washed over her in a cold wave. It was not her, Netta, Joss wanted at all. It was the unknown Tara.

The name sounded Irish. Visions rose to taunt her, of a black-haired, black-eyed colleen, a lissom fair-skinned girl, endowed with the loveliness born of clear cool air, and the soft benediction of gentle rain.

'Tara ... stay....'

Why had she left him in the first place? Netta wondered dully. Wondered how she could, ignoring the fact that until last night she herself wanted to do the same. But not since last night. Impulsively she pressed her lips to his unconscious mouth, striving to stop the persistent entreaty that pierced her like a knife; striving to make him recognise her own presence beside him, and forget his need for the other girl.

'Joss, it's me, Netta. I'll stay with you. I won't leave you.'

'I'm jealous,' she acknowledged, but without surprise or shame. She felt she hated the unknown Tara, almost as much as she first hated Joss. As fiercely, she realised, as she now loved him.

'I'll stay with you.' She stroked his hair back from his damp forehead. 'I'll never leave you. Never.'

'Tara . . . stay. . . .'

He could not hear her. He did not want her. He only wanted Tara.

'Joss, I love you.' Sudden tears scalded her eyes, cascaded down her cheeks. She pressed her face against his unresponsive lips, that only called for someone else. Willing him to recognise her—to want her. . . .

'Joss, I'm your wife.' The gold of the ring on her finger, the ring that such a short while ago had rested on his, gleamed a silent mockery of her anguish. 'I'm your wife in every way, now,' she whispered, and her trembling lips suddenly firmed in a determined line. 'Nothing can alter that. Nothing—and nobody—will.' Not even the absent Tara, she vowed to herself. Not even she could undo what had passed between herself and Joss, last night.

Unless. . . .

Sudden icy doubt pierced her heart, until it felt as if the pain must surely stop it from beating. Unless Joss had made love to her, simply in order to force her to forget the spiders and the smoke.

Simply—once again—to keep her quiet.

CHAPTER SEVEN

'Who's Tara?'

She had not meant to ask him. She spent the night torn between doubt, uncertainty, and a white-hot rage that built up inside her to frightening proportions, so that she alternately longed to strike out at Joss and at the unknown girl he was begging to stay. At last she came to a decision as daylight penetrated the gloom of the cave, and told herself resolutely,

'I won't ask him. I won't let him know I'm even interested. As soon as we reach England I'll give him his ring back, and we'll go our different ways. He can have his Tara, and I'll be free.'

And then, after what seemed a lifetime of agony until the sap from the rushes began its healing work, and Joss at last stopped tossing and calling, and dropped into a deep, natural sleep, and at daylight opened clear eyes that recognised her again, she was unable to stop herself, and straight away blurted out,

'Who's Tara?'

She could have bitten off her tongue the moment the words were uttered, but it was too late to retract now. Joss's hearing, as well as his sight, was restored to normal. He turned his head and looked up at her with a bright, alert gaze, and asked interestedly,

'What do you know about Tara?'

'Nothing,' she responded shortly, and when he continued to look at her, his eyes probing, curious, probably guessing, she added reluctantly,

'You were lightheaded last night, and you kept calling for Tara—whoever she is.' She shrugged, and turned away, and tried to appear indifferent, tried not to see the sudden comprehension, and then the dawning amusement in his eyes as he replied unexpectedly,

77

'You've both got the same coloured hair, you and Tara. Only hers is flat, and yours is curly.'

'Flat? You mean straight, I suppose?'

'Something like that.' He grinned suddenly, and his eyes lit up with a mischievous light. 'It's the same thing.'

'It probably is, to a man.' She cast him a withering look. 'Flat!' she ejaculated scornfully, and turned away so that he should not notice how her lips suddenly trembled, moved out of control by a vision of a regal beauty with straight auburn hair piled high. . . .

'You must have some food. You'll need your strength for when we travel.' She fumbled with fingers that shook at the leather pouch that contained the rest of the food that Joss had purloined from the Embassy kitchen.

'We travel tonight,' he told her.

'You can't be serious?' She spun round in protest, the vision thrust aside by shock. 'You won't be fit enough by tonight to even think of travelling.'

'Fit or unfit, we travel tonight,' he insisted. He pushed himself upright on the rush bed and ran a hand through his hair, rumpling it into wild disorder round his head.

'You can't possibly walk after a fever like that,' she cried. 'At least leave it for another twenty-four hours. The rebels don't know we're here, and we've got enough food to last us if we're careful.'

'We can't leave it,' he told her flatly. 'And I shan't need to walk far, only to the river bank.'

'Not there? Not again!' Netta shuddered.

'We travel by water.' Joss was as unmoved by her aversion as he seemed to be by his own unpleasant experience on the river bank. 'The rush-cutters come with skiffs once a week, and tonight is their night. If we miss it, we'll have to wait another week, and we daren't risk that.'

'Surely men don't cut rushes from the river, and risk being bitten by those awful fish?' She raised a disbelieving face to his.

'That's why they have to come by night,' Joss explained patiently. 'During the hours of darkness, the fish burrow deep into the mud to escape the cold after sundown, so that the river is safe until daylight.'

Even so, Netta's heart thumped uncomfortably against her ribs as she picked her way cautiously downhill beside Joss towards where smoking flares outlined a scene of purposeful activity on the river banks, as the rush-cutters worked methodically felling and loading the rushes into the long, shallow draft boats lined up against the bank.

'What if the rebels are there, among the rush-cutters?' she whispered nervously.

'We should have been warned, if they were,' Joss assured her quietly. 'Keep your cloak over your head, and remember to walk a few paces behind me.' His teeth flashed in a quick grin as he said it, and she retorted waspishly,

'You needn't rub it in! The Lak women are submissive....'

'They know better than to answer back when their menfolk speak,' Joss returned, 'so whatever happens,' he warned, 'keep quiet.' His voice was a command, and Netta subsided into resentful silence. Joss lengthened his stride, which automatically put her in the desired position of a few paces behind him, since her shorter legs could not keep up, and she muttered furiously to herself as she trotted in his wake.

He turned. He must have caught her mutter, and he sent her a quelling glance as a figure cloaked in a similar manner to themselves detached himself from among the rush-cutters on the river bank, and came towards them. Netta stifled a gasp. A machete gleamed wickedly in the stranger's hand. A tool—or a weapon? She froze, and then Joss spoke, using the same strange tongue with which he had addressed the men who came to see him at the Embassy. The stranger replied in kind, and Joss instructed Netta over his shoulder,

'Follow me.'

He did not bother to turn round as he said it. And he did not bother to say 'please'. Netta glared at his tall, retreating back. Arrogant back. She fumed, silently, but she had to follow him. There was no option. It was either do

as he bade her, or be left behind, and the possibility of a
further encounter with the silver fish was even more
daunting than the thought of meeting the rebels.

With one hand she pulled her cloak over her hair and
face, and her other fumbled with her slacks belt. The gemstones felt as large as boulders under her nervous fingers,
and her heightened imagination made them glitter even
through the layers of enshrouding cloth. Cloaked figures
were all around them, but to Netta's relief they took little
notice of either Joss or herself, being too intent on cutting
as many rushes as possible and layering them in the
bottoms of their boats drawn up close against the river
bank.

Their guide gestured to them, and approached one of
the skiffs that had as yet no rushes in it. Without pausing
Joss murmured something to him in a low voice, then
stepped straight off the edge of the bank and into the boat
—and lay down flat in the bottom. Netta stared at him
nonplussed. Had the fever made him so very weak? she
wondered, dismayed. He had shown no sign of lack of
strength while he was walking from the cave, and the
track was rough, even if it was downhill.

'Follow me.' His firm injunction was reassuring, but
what he asked her to do was not. She eyed the gap between
the bank and the boat with growing trepidation.

'I c-can't!' Deep shadows thrown by the guttering light
of the rush-cutters' flares made the extent of the gap in-
distinct. What if she misjudged the distance, and stepped
into the river? What if the light from the flares brought
those terrible fish to the surface, misled into thinking it
was no longer night? Her legs were shorter than Joss's,
and felt distinctly unsure of themselves. It was easy enough
for him to straddle the gap, she thought angrily as she
teetered nervously at the very edge of the water.

'Come on!' His voice from the boat waxed impatient.
'What are you waiting for?'

'I'm waiting for you to help me in,' she whispered
furiously. 'Any gentleman would. . . .'

'The Laks don't behave like gentlemen to women who

wander abroad at night. They're expected to look after themselves.'

'You...!' Sheer fury goaded her into action. 'How dare you!' she breathed, and took a quick, angry step. Too late, she realised that she was stepping over water, that the boat was farther away than she had imagined. 'Help!' Desperately she tried to lengthen her stride in mid-air. She would never make it. She would fall in. The fish.... A hand came out of the bottom of the boat—Joss's hand. It grasped her foot and pulled. Another hand thrust hard against the small of her back, and she fell forward in an undignified heap, and landed in the bottom of the boat on top of Joss. She tried to struggle up, and hard arms went round her and pulled her down beside him.

'Lie still!' he hissed urgently, and pulled her close against him, tugging her cloak over her face and head.

'Let me go!' She started to struggle. 'They'll smother us!' Her voice rose as a shower of rushes descended on top of them.

'Be quiet,' he commanded her harshly. 'They're covering us over, to hide us.'

The sense of what he said penetrated her daze of panic, and with a beating heart she lay tense, but still, in his arms.

'You could have helped me into the boat,' she whispered resentfully when at last the shower of rushes stopped, and he whispered back against her ear,

'If I'd treated you any differently, it would have caused immediate comment, and might have betrayed us. The rebels would love to know where you hid those gems,' he reminded her grimly.

'You said there weren't any rebels among the rush-cutters, otherwise we'd have been warned,' she responded sharply, still smarting from his cavalier treatment.

'So far as we know there aren't, but there might be an informer among them,' Joss replied. 'It's a risk we daren't take, so lie still, and *keep quiet.*'

'There's something sharp digging in my ribs.' She tried to wriggle to a more comfortable position.

'Whatever it is, it's better than a gun barrel,' he said

unfeelingly, and she winced into silence as yet more rushes descended on top of them.

'It's a good job they're rushes, and not anything heavier,' was her last conscious thought before, unbelievably, she slept. It might have been the aftermath of the sleepless night before, or the result of strain and fright, or just the gentle rocking of the boat on the slow-moving waters of the river, that lulled her into slumber. Or it could have been the warm, safe feeling, of lying in Joss's arms. . . .

She opened her eyes, and for a wild moment thought she was back in her student days, lying in a punt on the Isis, with her latest admirer poling. Something soft lay under her head, and whatever it was that had stuck in her ribs didn't any more. She sat up and surveyed her surroundings. Nothing could be further from the cool green trees and daisy-starred banks of the Oxford stream. Barren, rocky landscape greeted her from either bank, and in front. . . .

'It's the sea?'

'Not quite,' Joss replied. 'We're approaching the mouth of the river, though, the sea lies a mile or two further on.' He continued to pole, his bare arms flexing with a whipcord ripple of hard muscle that proclaimed him to be far from the days of callow studenthood.

'It's daylight,' she realised, her fear returning. 'We must find somewhere to hide. I can see boats ahead of us.' That meant people.

She glanced nervously at the distant activity on the rapidly widening watercourse. To get so far, and be discovered now, would be the last straw.

'Relax,' Joss bade her. 'We crossed the Lak border during the night. We're out of danger of pursuit now.'

'You mean . . . but the border was. . . .' The way the plane went, the border was a hundred miles away. Surely Joss could not have poled them so far during one night? And after a bout of fever, the night before? She stared at him with something approaching awe.

'We've come about fifty miles in all, the waterway takes

a short cut through swamp land where the roads can't go,'
he offered her the information laconically.

'Just the same, fifty miles. . . .' She found it hard to grasp
that he could even contemplate getting the skiff so far in
one night. 'You should have rested,' she began, and then
looking at him she realised it was ridiculous to suggest
that he should rest. His easy balance, the lithe sway of his
body as he wielded the long pole and drove the skiff with
sure speed and tireless energy, made rest the last thing he
would contemplate.

'One of the rush-cutters poled us for the first mile or
two.'

She looked down, and saw that the rushes were under
her now, not on top, and they were covered by a cloak—
Joss's cloak; her own was still wrapped round her, carefully tucked in to keep her warm during the long night on
the river, and Joss had kept himself warm by poling the
skiff. She watched him curiously. He was a strange mixture
of harshness and gentleness, this man they called the Fox.
This man who was her husband. . . . First of all he had refused to help her into the boat. Although his reason was for
the sake of their own safety, illogically she still resented his
lack of chivalry. And afterwards, he had stopped to make
her a comfortable bed while she slept, covering the rushes
with his own cloak, and deprived of its warmth himself,
poled them fifty miles across the Lak border to the coast.

'The current helped a lot, fortunately it was going the
same way that we were,' he made light of his efforts with
a shrug.

Which way were they going? she wondered suddenly—
bleakly. She and Joss? She looked up at him, searching his
face, trying to probe the thoughts that lay behind those
strange, gold-coloured eyes. Were they perhaps of England
—and Tara? And maybe the means by which he might
most easily rid himself of a marriage of convenience to
one girl with hair that was auburn and curly, in order to
marry another with hair that was auburn and straight? Flat,
he called it.

Since she intended to return his ring—looked forward to

returning it, she told herself fiercely—it should not matter what he was thinking. Or of whom.

So why should her heart whisper entreatingly of ways by which, if only she wanted to, she might continue to wear Joss's ring? Might make him *want* her to wear it?

CHAPTER EIGHT

NETTA was seasick during the voyage home.

After their traumatic flight from Lak, it was almost ridiculously easy to obtain a berth when they at last reached the docks. In spite of their disreputable appearance and total lack of luggage, Joss's name once more seemed to work some kind of magic, and it seemed to Netta they had no sooner found the shipping agents than they were on board a vessel, and heading on the long trek towards England. True, it was not a palatial liner.

'It's a cargo vessel, with limited passenger accommodation,' Joss told her when he rejoined her outside the shipping agents with the tickets in his hand, 'but it's better that we leave on the first available boat.' So he did not think, even now, that they were completely safe, Netta deduced shrewdly, and kept her thoughts to herself when she surveyed the single-berth cabin that was to be her home for the voyage. Limited passenger accommodation exactly described it, she thought disparagingly, but she carefully refrained from saying so out loud. Instead,

'Where...?' she began, and stopped. She had asked him the same question in the cave, but the answer this time had to be very different. The bunk was narrow, functional, and definitely only meant to hold one. She was glad it was only meant to hold one, she told herself fiercely.

'Accommodation for ladies is to the fore of the vessel, the men's cabins are aft,' Joss read her thoughts with ease, and grinned at her rapidly rising colour.

'I only wanted to know,' she started sharply, and he interrupted her easily.

'Well, now you do. I shan't be very far away, don't worry.'

That was the least of her worries, she decided tartly, and was quickly to discover another, bigger one that occupied

85

the whole of her attention, even to the exclusion of the gemstones round her waist. It was soon evident that the cargo vessel did not ride like a liner, either. What cargo it carried, she never discovered. Within less than an hour after they got under way, she lost interest completely. It could have been coconuts or car parts, for all she cared. The first squall—Joss casually called them summer storms —hit them shortly after they had eaten lunch. For a cargo ship the food was very good, and Netta ate hungrily, savouring familiar cooking once again, only to confess ruefully soon afterwards,

'I wish I hadn't eaten that trifle for dessert. I think it's beginning to disagree with me.'

Joss showed no signs of discomfort, she thought resentfully, but aided by the wildly bucking motion of their makeshift transport on the roughening sea, the disagreement turned into a raging battle inside her, in which the soup and the main course joined with unseemly enthusiasm. Netta fled for her cabin, and barely managed to reach its blessed privacy before she and her recent lunch parted company on the very worst of terms.

'Red hair and a green face go with one another quite well,' Joss observed interestedly from the doorway of her cabin.

'Go away,' she groaned.

'There's no place much I can go,' he answered consideringly, and remained where he was. 'The deck's mostly taken up with cargo.'

'Go anywhere. Overboard, if you like. But leave me alone!' she wailed. She choked, gagged, and turned desperately away from him, but instead of following her uncharitable suggestion he stepped the rest of the way into the cabin and held her head with expert hands until the worst was over. Then he lifted her into the bunk and sponged her face with blessedly cool water before he went out. She heard the cabin door close softly behind him, and hoped guiltily that he would be careful if he walked on deck. She would never forgive herself if he did fall overboard....

He came back again later. She did not know how much later, and she was too spent to care. She only wished he would go away and leave her alone. Overriding even the misery of seasickness was the fear paramount in her mind that Joss might discover the gemstones in her waistband. She felt him lift her up and lay her down again on fresh pillows, and whispered weakly,

'Leave me alone. I'll manage for myself.' Bitterly now she rued her promise to Ranjit, to deliver the jewels safely to his bank in London. Without them she could have sunk into merciful oblivion. Without them she might even have endured Joss's ministrations. Under other circumstances, her traitorous heart whispered, she might even have enjoyed them. She steeled herself to the feel of his arms about her as he lifted her up, despising herself for the longing that almost overwhelmed her, to turn her face into his shoulder, and let Ranjit and the jewels, indeed the rest of the world, pass her by.

It's the result of the weakness, it will pass, her weary mind insisted.

Give in, her equally weary heart begged, but she turned her face away, and stiffened her body against his hands, and somehow managed to stem the tears that longed to flow, because she was too proud to let Joss see them if they did. She refused to allow her heart to want a husband who had married her for expediency, and not for love. Who loved someone else. He had used her heart as a sacrifice to buy the safety of others, and then carelessly thrown that sacrifice away, unneeded, because the plane, after all, had gone without them.

'I'm thirsty.' Perhaps he would go away, if only to find someone to send with a drink. He went, but her relief was shortlived, because he returned with the drink himself.

'Sip this.' He held a glass of iced fruit juice to her lips, and she drank reluctantly. It was cold, and sweet, but it did little to revive her flagging energy. She fumbled at the neckband of her top, trying to ease the zip open in a bid to let in some cooler air, but her weakened fingers refused even this simple task, and her arms fell limply back on to the bunk.

'I'll do it for you.' Joss reduced the zip to instant obedience, and pulled the damp material loosely away from her burning skin. 'You'd be more comfortable if your waistband was loosened as well, it's far too tight in this heat,' he said critically, and reached down.

'No, leave it.' She tried to push his hands away, but they had not got sufficient strength for that, either. He put them aside with ease.

'Don't be silly,' he admonished her impatiently. 'I'm only loosening the zip, I'm not going to undress you.' He ignored her frantic, 'Please—don't....' and loosened the zip. Then he slid his fingers under the waistband, easing it away from her skin. 'You'll be cooler,' he began, then paused.

'He's found them!' Even before his fingers slid the rest of the way round her waistband, pausing at each hard bump on the way, she knew he had found them. He fingered the bumps under the cloth at first thoughtfully, and then with dawning comprehension and anger flicking across his face.

'You had the gemstones on you, all the time!' His eyes were as hard as the gold settings from which she had extracted the jewels. Hard, and accusing. 'You let me think you'd hidden them in the hotel,' he said harshly. 'You risked your life to bring them out. You should have told me.'

'And let you barter them to the rebels for my freedom?' she interrupted him shrilly. In spite of her weakness, she struggled upright on her pillows, and faced him with determined defiance. 'You assumed I'd left them in the hotel, I didn't tell you I'd done so. And I didn't tell you where they were, because it wasn't your concern,' she said firmly. 'The jewels are my responsibility, not yours.'

'They're my responsibility as well, now.' For a second a fleeting, unreadable expression displaced the anger deep in his eyes, but she was too occupied in shoring up her own crumbling defences to notice, and the next moment it had gone, and the anger returned, and a determination stronger than her own.

'The moment we dock you'll be free of any responsibility towards me,' she retorted with spirit. 'You can have your ring back the second we step ashore. For that matter, you can have it back now.' Her hand moved to take it off.

'Keep it where it is.' His fingers closed over hers in a grip that made her wince. She tried to pull her fingers away. She could not bear his touch. It sabotaged her determination, undermined her strength of mind. Her heart raced with choking speed, but Joss held on to her with ease, the force of his grip reflecting the inflexible line of his jaw. 'Until those gems are deposited in a safe place, you're not moving an inch from my side,' he gritted, 'and while you're with me, you'll wear my ring. I have a right. . . .'

'You took your rights in the cave!' she flung back at him passionately, perilously close to tears. With a supreme effort she controlled them, though she could not control the shake in her voice. He had taken her, used her, when all he wanted was Tara. She would never forgive him for that. Any more than she would forgive herself for responding, for believing him, for being gullible enough to commit herself before she gave a thought that there might be an ulterior motive behind his lovemaking. She might yet have to pay the penalty for her trust. She blanched at the thought, and thrust it from her. She had enough problems to contend with, she thought wearily, without adding another one that might never arise. Joss unexpectedly added one himself.

'It's a good job I've already radioed the Home Office, and warned them we're on our way.'

'What have the Home Office got to do with us?' She had forgotten for the moment the nature of Joss's business in Lak.

'They've warned the Customs people to expect us.'

'Customs?' She raised dismayed eyes to his, their clash of wills temporarily forgotten. She had not given the Customs check a thought.

'In case it hadn't occurred to you,' he could see it had not, she thought wrathfully, 'we'll be entering England without luggage, without papers, and without any means of identification. The Customs people will want answers to all sorts of questions.'

'Will the Home Office clear us?' If she was searched, who would believe she had a right to the gems? Fear rose in Netta, and she swallowed convulsively. With Lak in a state of siege, no one would be able to contact Ranjit. And even Joss, she suspected uneasily, might still not be entirely convinced of her right to the jewels.

'The Home Office will clear me,' he laid emphasis on the latter word, and her momentary relief died a swift death. 'I hope that as my wife you'll get the same free passage through.' He removed his hand from her fingers as he spoke, and his glance rested significantly on the ring. It winked back, deriding her helplessness, daring her to continue to defy him. 'Think about it,' Joss advised her coldly, and went out, leaving her mind in such a turmoil that she was scarcely capable of thinking about anything at all, except that as soon as she was free of the gems, she would also be free of her ring—and of Joss. Rebellion seemed to be in the fashion, she acknowledged drearily, because while her mind rejoiced at the prospect of all three, her heart told her mutinously it only wanted to be rid of the gems.

Later, she joined Joss at the rail, and watched the familiar white cliffs approaching with a trepidation they had never aroused in her before. Her legs felt curiously weak, and she told herself stoutly that it was the result of the rough passage they had had, but each time she thought of the coming Customs check she had qualms worse than anything the sea could produce. Even the rebels had not been able to rouse her to such a state of nerves, and when Joss told her curtly, 'When we reach the Customs, stay close to me, and leave me to do the talking,' for once she did as he bade her without protest.

'He won't need to kiss me to keep me quiet this time,' she told herself bitterly, and swallowed the lump that rose in her throat to mourn the omission. Her tongue clove to the roof of her mouth in parched paralysis, and she could not have spoken if she had wanted to when Joss sought out the first Customs and Excise uniform they encountered when they landed.

'Why does he have to attract attention?' she asked herself with frightened exasperation. 'Why can't we just file through, like any other passengers?' And all the time she knew they could not. Their bedraggled appearance, as well as their lack of papers and luggage, would attract attention of itself.

'We were warned you'd be coming, Mr de Courcey,' the uniformed man accompanying Joss bent a kindly eye on Netta's white face. If he did but realise it, his own presence had more to do with its lack of colour than her recent ordeals, but he went on, happily unaware, 'Your wife looks as if she's had a rough time, what with the sea voyage and all. You stay here, sir, and I'll go and see if your car's come.' He courteously handed Netta into a hard wooden chair, and bustled out, to return a few minutes later with the news, 'Your chauffeur's waiting for you, right outside the door. You'll soon be home,' he consoled with a smile, and Netta returned it weakly, her relief tempered by the unspoken question,

'Which home?'

'In London, as always,' her mind told her staunchly. 'At Thimbles, with Joss,' her heart implored.

'Ranjit's bank is in Chelsea,' she compromised with them both as she walked to the car with Joss.

'I'm afraid you're too late for the bank today, madam,' the chauffeur volunteered, 'and it's Bank Holiday weekend, too.'

'That means they'll be closed until Wednesday,' Joss observed.

'My father's safe is quite adequate,' Netta said shortly, which answered her heart, as well as her need for security for the gems, and wondered at the bleak depression that settled on her as she preceded Joss into the rear seat of the luxurious limousine, and heard him give her address to the chauffeur.

The housekeeper answered their knock, and her face reflected the same disconcerting dismay with which Wendy had greeted her arrival at the Embassy in Lak.

'I wasn't expecting you home for a while, Miss Netta.'

'What's going on?' Netta surveyed the bare hall, and the open door leading into what looked like an equally bare drawing room, with a puzzled frown.

'It's dry rot, miss,' came the gloomy answer.

'Dry rot? I thought we were having the house decorated?'

'We were. I mean, we are, when the boards have been seen to,' the housekeeper explained, 'but the men found the dry rot downstairs, and your father decided to have the house stripped and thoroughly checked over, and rewired at the same time. All the furniture's been sent into store except for the pieces in my room, and they'll be moving me out of that by the morning, I expect,' she predicted unhappily.

'That means the safe's gone, too?'

'The safe went to the bank, miss. Your father's going to be away for another few weeks, he's accepted an invitation to read his paper on diamonds to the Amsterdam Conference, after he's finished his business there, so he'll be away....'

'For another few weeks. You said.' Netta nodded in a preoccupied fashion. Her mind reeled. She could scarcely believe her evil luck. After coming all this way, now they had at last reached England she still could not rid herself of the burdensome gems. 'My clothes?' More than anything else, she needed a change of clothes. Surely not all of those had gone, as well?

'Your clothes all went along with your furniture, into store, miss. You won't be able to get at them until your father comes home and gives instructions for the furniture to come back. We didn't expect you yet, you see,' the housekeeper reiterated maddeningly.

Netta stared at her, stunned. Even in England, she was still a refugee. She not only had nowhere to put the gems, but she herself had neither a change of clothing, nor a roof under which she could find reasonable shelter.

'I'll find a hotel somewhere close by.' She paused, struck by another thought. She could not go into a hotel in her present dilapidated state, and without luggage. And if she had clothes, she would not dare to change them and leave her slacks and their priceless waistband in a hotel wardrobe.

'I don't know what to suggest, I'm sure,' the housekeeper began worriedly. 'It's a problem, with no furniture in the house.'

'It's no problem,' Joss assured her crisply, 'my wife will be coming home with me.'

'Your—wife?'

Netta could have slapped him. The housekeeper's shocked eyes flew to her left hand, and Netta resisted an urge to thrust it into her slacks pocket, out of sight.

'We were married in Lak. It's a long story,' she intervened hastily.

'It sounds remarkably short notice to me,' the older woman said disapprovingly. 'Does your father know, Miss Netta?' she asked, in a voice that Netta recognised from when she was very small, and wont to bring home stray puppies at inconvenient moments. An hysterical giggle rose inside her at the thought of likening Joss to a stray puppy, and she stifled it hastily. Now was not the time for hilarity.

'Mr Vaughan will be told when he returns from abroad,' Joss said smoothly, in a tone that made it plain he had no intention of giving explanations to a housekeeper, however valued a member of the household she might be. 'In the meantime, I think food is indicated.' He gave the older woman a polite nod, took Netta by the arm, and steered her firmly towards the car.

'Where shall I contact you, if your father rings, Miss Netta?' the housekeeper called after them.

'Thimbles, at Long Minton,' Joss said firmly.

'I'll let you know when I find a hotel,' Netta called back.

Twin daggers of determination and defiance flashed between them as their eyes met, and Netta ducked hastily

into the car as the chauffeur held open the back door.
Lunch would give her a reprieve, she thought thankfully.
With a sense of surprise she realised she felt hungry. Food
in a relaxed atmosphere might give her the inspiration she
needed to circumvent Joss, and solve her difficulty at the
same time.

She eased herself into the far corner of the back seat,
deliberately putting as much distance between them as
possible. A tab protruded from the top of the hide cushion,
and she pulled it experimentally. As she expected, it
brought down a central armrest, and she slid it out to its
full extent across the seat between them. It was just the
barrier she needed, she thought with satisfaction. She felt
Joss's glance slide coldly across at her, but she refused to
meet it. She was in England now, and their 'honeymoon',
if such it could be called, she thought bitterly, was over,
as were the humiliations and the trials of her dependence
upon him. Now she was home she could return to her old,
free independence. She owed no allegiance to Joss, rather
it was the other way around; he had blackmailed her into
marrying him. She used the phrase deliberately, keeping
her anger alive. And now it was over. She ignored the pang
that shot through her at the thought, although she could
not ignore the inescapable fact that the unawakened, heartwhole girl who had journeyed outward so lightheartedly
would never again inhabit the empty, aching shell of her
former self, which was all she had returned to England
with.

'Where had you in mind to eat, sir?' The chauffeur spoke
as if they were dressed in their best clothes, and out for a
social occasion, and Netta's desire to giggle returned. Suddenly, everything seemed unreal. The rebels, the burning
brush, the gunshots and the plane roaring out of reach over
their heads. The cave—she did not want to think about the
cave—and the river and the rough sea. And now, in complete contrast, the sleek car bowling smoothly between
quiet fields, which stretched out in front of the long
hood in a seemingly endless procession, the streets of
London already left behind.

'We'll throw ourselves on Mrs Berry's mercy, I think,' Joss answered, and the chauffeur's peaked cap nodded.

'She'll be prepared for you, sir. I phoned her when we set off, just in case.'

Joss seemed to attract the same sort of instant service at home that he had done abroad, and Netta hoped uneasily that it was not a big restaurant they were going to. In her present state of dress she did not feel like inviting stares from the other diners. But the 'Mrs Berry' sounded reassuring. It was probably some small country pub which Joss frequented, and where he was well enough known to gain special attention, she consoled herself.

Perhaps she could get a room there for herself, over the period of the holiday weekend? The possibility sharpened her attention, and she sat up. It would solve her problem beautifully. Then she could return to London and deposit the gems in Ranjit's bank, get herself some decent clothes, and go to a hotel in town until her father returned home. Of course! That would provide the ideal solution. Her flagging spirits revived miraculously at the ease with which her problems could be settled.

'If only I'd given myself time to think, I needn't have got into such a state about it in the first place,' she berated herself scornfully. The nervous strain of the last weeks had affected her more than she realised, dulling her usual clarity of mind. It seemed like a good omen that her powers of thought were already reasserting themselves.

The problem of her marriage would no doubt be solved just as easily, she told herself with new-found optimism. All that she needed to do, once she was rid of the gems, was to return Joss's ring, go back to London, and instigate proceedings for an annulment. She need not wait for Joss to take the initiative. If she started the proceedings herself, it would show him she did not care. She could unburden herself, and leave the whole disastrous episode behind her.

As well as her heart?

She blinked at the sudden stinging sensation at the back of her eyes, and turned hastily to look out of the car window.

'It's probably a cold coming,' she sought feebly for an excuse for her optic discomfort. 'It's probably the change in climate.'

But the fields outside the car windows lay basking in warm summer sunshine, and even in her light safari suit she felt not the slightest chill. Only a cold, gripping pain in the region of her heart that seemed to have become a constant companion from the time she promised, reluctantly, 'I will.'

The fields went on, and on. At last she turned to Joss and forced herself to speak.

'We've come a long way out of town, just to get a meal. How far away is this Mrs Berry of yours?'

She sensed the answer even before it came. It spoke to her from his easy assurance, from the cool authority in the glance that he turned on her, and it ignited an explosive anger inside her that took away the hunger, and the tiredness, and even the ache about her heart.

'Mrs Berry is the housekeeper at Thimbles,' he said coolly. 'We're going home for an early dinner.'

'Your home....'

She choked on the words, fury depriving her momentarily of the power of speech. She swallowed hard, and tried again, but remembered, just in time, the chauffeur sitting quietly, but alert, in front of them. Pride forbade her to argue in front of a servant. As Joss knew it would, she realised, even further incensed. He had timed it with beautiful accuracy so that she would not realise where she was going until it was too late to do anything about it. Virtually kidnapping her.

'How dare you!'

She bit her lip savagely to stem the tirade of condemnation that boiled up inside her—would have boiled over, but for the presence of the chauffeur.

'Thimbles is more comfortable than a hotel,' he said calmly, 'you'll be better looked after there.' He meant the gems would be better looked after, she thought furiously, and blanched as a fresh, more personal implication of their destination dawned upon her seething mind.

She had not got a stitch of clothing with her except for the battered, mud-stained, disreputable outfit that she stood up in. And she was on her way to Thimbles, as Joss's wife, to meet Joss's family.

And Tara....

CHAPTER NINE

'THERE'S Thimbles.'

Joss's voice reached Netta across a wall of silence. She retreated behind it like a protective barrier, vibrant with suppressed emotion. She resented him breaking through. It was a liberty, an intrusion of her privacy.

'Over there, through that gap in the trees.'

Joss stepped across the barrier as if it was not there, and the anger inside her erupted, tearing aside the flimsy remnants of her self-control. She stiffened, then rounded on him, and opened her mouth to let the angry words pour out.

'I'll stop the car for you for a minute or two, madam. The view of the house from here is particularly fine.' The chauffeur spoke first, unaware of the impending storm his words had interrupted. His hand moved, and he pressed a button on the console which slid the car window down on Netta's side until it disappeared into the door aperture, leaving her with an uninterrupted view.

She did not want to look at the view. She would much rather have done without the chauffeur's consideration and gone straight on to Thimbles, and got the ordeal over as quickly as possible. Her nerves crackled with tension at the mere thought of meeting Joss's people. She did not even know if they lived at Thimbles. He had never spoken to her of his family. Only of Tara. . . .

'It smells good.' Joss took a deep, satisfied breath as a warm breeze wafted through the window, bringing with it the scents of high summer to mingle with the leather smell of the car upholstery. He leaned across to look out of the window with her. The armrest got in his way, and he flicked it upwards, back into the slot from whence it had come, so that there was no longer any physical barrier between them. He slid along the seat into the space that the armrest had occupied, and Netta felt him press against her shoulder, not hard, just touching, too intent on catching the first glimpse of his home to notice that he was crowding her. To notice that she was there at all.

She moved uneasily, wishing there was more space between her and the side of the car, to allow her to move away from him. Wishing he had left the armrest where it was, that the house stood on his side of the car. The touch of his shoulder against her own set her pulses racing with a clamorous awareness of him that she thought she had conquered when they left the cave. Now it broke through her frail defences with a terrifying ease that warned her she had not left the battle behind her when she left Lak.

'You can see the house more clearly in the winter, when the trees are bare.'

They framed it now. Unwillingly, her eyes followed his pointing finger, across the low hedge that flanked the climbing lane in a wild tangle of honeysuckle and foxgloves. She caught her breath. Why did the foxglove spots have to remind her so sharply of the exotic velvet blobs which broke the bright gold of the tua lilies in the drawing room at the Embassy, during the mockery that was her wedding ceremony?

The high-standing corn beyond the hedge wavered suddenly across her vision, and she blinked hard, willing the curve of the river below it to remain still. The waters danced crystal clear in the sunlight—no sluggish poisoned river this—and led her eyes upwards again from the opposite bank across green parkland to the gap in the trees that formed the end of a graceful ride.

'They were planted when my great-grandfather was born.' Joss spoke matter-of-factly, accepting the caring that planted for generations still to come. A caring that even through her anger Netta sensed he would carry on. The hand that planted the parallel rows of widely spaced, venerable park giants had done so with an eye to pleasing the senses, as well as providing shade, she saw. No unimaginative rank of swiftly maturing poplars, these. Limes abounded, she could smell their perfume mingling with the scent of honeysuckle from the hedge, and hear the low-toned hum of their attendant bees even from this distance. There were chestnuts, too, that must look glorious in their spring blossom, but now bore a prickly weight of swelling fruit. Conkers, such as children love to gather. Joss's children. His—and Tara's? Her anger sharpened, shoring up her defences, so that her voice sounded almost normal when she spoke.

'It's Tudor period.' No one, however angry, could remain indifferent to such gracious loveliness, and her eyes feasted on the low lines of the manor house that was her destination. The dark timber framing dissected the herringbone pattern of red brick-like veins in an old hand, warmly coloured in the sunshine, and serene in its sylvan setting. Joss must have sensed her reluctant interest, because he volunteered,

'The first Jocelyn de Courcey started it, when he came back from the wars. His son carried on the building, and since then, like Topsy, it's "just growed".' Joss smiled, but the smile was for his home, and not for her, and Netta thrust down an unwelcome pang. At least she had been right about the period, she thought with satisfaction. She remembered Wendy saying that Joss's family went back to Agincourt.

'It's "growed", as you call it, very nicely,' she commented drily as the car swung on to a wide gravel sweep, and drew to a halt in front of the house, and she was able to inspect it at close quarters. Age had matured the various periods of building into one harmonious whole, helped by the sensitive care with which the original concept had been enlarged and extended by subsequent owners, using similar materials and pattern of architecture. 'It's beautiful,' she breathed, unable to hide her admiration.

'I didn't know you were interested in architecture.' Joss half turned towards her, then broke off as a wild barking sounded from somewhere inside what looked like a stable block standing away to the side of the house. A weather vane glinted in the sun from the centre of the roof, pointing the breeze from the south.

There were a lot of things Joss did not know about her, Netta thought dispiritedly. There was one vital thing he must never learn, and that was the secret longing locked deep in her heart, to which she only had the key. 'And I've thrown that away, for good,' she told herself with conviction. She felt in control of herself again, now that she was free from the confinement of the car, free from immediate contact with Joss. He stood a foot or two away from her on the gravel, his head raised, listening.

'I wonder if she remembers?' he murmured, almost to himself.

'Dogs don't forget, sir, even if they're young,' the chauffeur spoke with assurance. 'Will Dyer carried on training her for you when you went abroad, and normally a word from him will quieten her.' The man smiled tolerantly. 'From the noise she's making now, she must have heard your voice, and recognised it.'

'Let's try her.' Joss whistled once, and waited. The barking stopped, then started again on an almost hysterical note, until someone's hand appeared over the stable door and pushed it open. Without waiting for it to swing fully ajar, a slim russet body hurtled through the opening and made towards Joss at top speed. There was no question that the dog remembered. Joss went down on one knee with a low delighted laugh that had in it a sudden catch. He held out his arms, and the young Irish setter dived headlong into them, with threshing tail and licking tongue, and gruff little whimpers that left no doubt who it acknowledged as its master. Netta felt a sudden lump rise in her throat, and swallowed hard. This was a side of Joss she had not seen before, a warm, affectionate side, so different from the tough, self-sufficient shell which was all he had ever presented towards herself, and against which she had hammered in vain, only to fall back bruised and defeated. A swift stab of pure jealousy speared through her as she watched him wind his arms about the dog, fondling it with unashamed affection. He had held her in his arms too, but his affection then had been feigned, aimed only at silencing her. And she had basked in the warmth of its illusion, until the sun went in and left her shrinking from the bitter wind of reality. For her, there was no joyous homecoming.

'Let's see how well she's taken Will's training.' Joss caught at Netta's hand and drew her away from the dog towards the house. His touch was indifferent, impersonal, his attention solely on the red setter. 'Stay!' he commanded, and Netta raised her head, startled. Where had she heard him say that before?

Joss drew her with him across the gravel, but she only half saw where she was going, her mind was busily seeking backwards, teased by the elusive memory, and then the dog whined sharply, bringing her back to her surroundings. Joss paused, and looked back over his shoulder, to where the young setter stood beside the car, quivering, begging him to let her come to him.

'Stay, Tara. Stay!' he ordered firmly.

'Tara? Did you call her—Tara?' Netta spun round, and snatched her hand away from his. She knew, now, where she had heard the order before. For a second or two, a mist seemed to dance in front of her eyes.

'That's her name,' Joss laughed down at her, enjoying his bombshell. 'Who did you think Tara was?' he asked her. 'If you remember, I told you her hair was the same colour as yours.' He said her hair was flat. The setter had a flat coat. She understood, now, the amusement she had seen in his eyes when he told her. A tight band of fury seemed to constrict her chest, making it difficult for her to breathe. Once again Joss had deliberately deceived her, cruelly inflicted on her a night of misery and uncertainty and torment that returned in a wave to wash over her.

'How could you?' she gasped in a strangled whisper. 'How could. . . .'

'Joss! How marvellous, darling!'

First the chauffeur saved him from her anger, then the girl. A member of his family? A sister, perhaps? She ran from the front door of the house, not with quite the same speed as the red setter, but with the same singleness of purpose. She ignored Netta and the chauffeur as if they were not there, and made straight for Joss, though Netta had an uncanny feeling that the pale blue eyes missed no detail of her own person, nor her clothes, which immediately felt ten times more bedraggled than before in contrast with the undeniable chic of the other girl's appearance. She exuded expensive grooming, from her pale green linen dress and dainty high-heeled matching sandals to the tip of her flaxen hair, which was done up in a French roll, with not a wisp out of place.

'Masses of lacquer,' Netta judged ill-humouredly, and fought down a flood of possessive fury which rose inside her as the newcomer flung both her arms round Joss's neck and swung her feet from off the floor. She had to return them to terra firma fairly rapidly, Netta saw with malicious satisfaction, since Joss did not wrap his arms round her and hold her up, as she obviously hoped he would. It would have taken quite a bit of doing anyway, Netta decided uncharitably, since the fair-haired girl was almost as tall as Joss, although she was slim to the point of being angular. Joss's response seemed somewhat tardy, and she thought he looked decidedly surprised at the newcomer's appearance, though he kissed her warmly enough to send another stab through Netta, and she stirred restlessly. She did not want Joss herself, so why should she bother who he kissed? she asked herself defiantly, but she could not shrug off the blanketing weight of depression that settled on her as her head and her heart gave her two different answers at once.

'It's marvellous to be back,' Joss agreed enthusiastically, and turned to Netta. 'Come and say hello to my cousin Caroline,' he bade her.

So she was his cousin, not his sister. And although she told herself she had no right to feel possessive about Joss, she could not help the grudging reluctance with which she joined the pair.

'Oh—hello.' The fair-haired girl swivelled a look in Netta's direction as if she noticed her for the first time, and Netta's lips tightened. The family all seemed to be tarred with the same brush, she thought censoriously. Joss had not offered to shake hands with her when they were first introduced, and neither did Caroline, and his first greeting to her had had about it the same lack of cordiality as his cousin's. She gave the other girl a cool nod, and resolutely kept her own small fist firmly in her jacket pocket.

'Come on in home, do,' Caroline returned Netta's greeting in kind, and turned back to Joss immediately, still clinging closely to his arm.

So Caroline called Thimbles 'home', Netta noted, and wondered if the word had been used deliberately for her benefit, to make her feel an outsider. She needn't have bothered, she thought abrasively. I couldn't feel more of an outsider in this family, if I tried. Not that it mattered. As soon as her father returned home, she would be able to leave Thimbles, and Joss. Leave them to Caroline? An upsurge of revulsion at the prospect caught her by surprise, and impulsively she stepped out so as not to be left behind as the two set off towards the house, leaving her to follow or not as she wished.

'Come!' She snapped her fingers to the red setter. At least the dog wagged its tail to her, she thought, and felt unaccountably comforted when it answered her summons, and stopped long enough for her to caress its soft ears as it passed.

'Tara seems to have taken to you, madam,' the chauffeur smiled. 'I've never known her to take notice of anyone before, except Will Dyer and the master.'

'She doesn't want to let him out of her sight, that's all.' Caroline's look challenged Netta's right to give an order to Joss's dog. 'Down, Tara! She's over-excited.' She flapped a beautifully manicured hand at the setter, which considering she had just said it was over-excited was not the most sensible thing to do. The young animal took it to be a signal for play, and with a joyful bark it jumped up against Caroline with both front paws on her dress. 'Get down!' Caroline staggered back against Joss as if the dog had been a fully grown St Bernard pushing against her, instead of a lightweight setter, and Netta's lips curled. Joss's cousin was missing no opportunity to demonstrate that she belonged at Thimbles. And Joss belonged to her?

'Down, Tara!' Joss quietened the dog sternly.

'Look at my dress,' his cousin wailed, 'it's marked all down the front! I'll have to go in and change.'

'It'll brush off, it's only dry dust.' The gravel was bone dry, and the slight mark would shake off the linen with ease, Netta judged.

'You should have left the dog where it was until I called her.' Joss turned on Netta with a frown of displeasure.

'Eh, Mr Joss, but it's good to have you home again!' A buxom, beaming figure appeared in the house doorway, and Joss's face lit up with pleasure, chasing the frown away.

'Mrs Berry!' At least she knew who Mrs Berry was, Netta thought, and realised suddenly that she felt desperately hungry.

Joss kissed the white-haired woman soundly on both cheeks, in a manner that made Netta suspect—correctly, she afterwards discovered—that the housekeeper had at one time been his nurse, and she forgot some of her ire at his manner towards herself as she watched him. Back home, among his own people, he appeared in an entirely different light, a warmer, more human one, than the 'Renard' she knew.

'I'm starving!' he echoed her own thoughts, and the housekeeper's smile grew even broader, if that were possible.

'I've got your favourite for you,' she announced in a pleased voice, 'it'll be ready just as soon as you are. A nice mixed grill, some fresh picked mushrooms ... I'll go and see how the cooking's getting on, while Johnson brings your luggage up to your room.'

'We haven't got any luggage for him to bring up,' Joss said ruefully. 'We got away from Lak with our lives, and just what we stood up in, and lucky to do that. I wonder, Caroline,' he turned to his cousin, 'could you fit Netta out with some clothes until she can get to the shops after the Bank Holiday?' Manlike, it did not occur to him that there might be any difficulty in that direction.

'I'll make do until I can get something for myself,'

Netta refused promptly. She would rather wear rags than put on anything belonging to Caroline, she thought mutinously. Even if it would fit, which it wouldn't, since the other girl was very much taller, and a good deal broader in build.

'We're the wrong size for one another.' Caroline somehow managed to sound regretful, Netta thought cynically, and it flashed across her mind that the other girl would make a formidable opponent. And then she wondered why she should regard Caroline as an opponent, when she had nothing she wanted to contest possession of. Certainly not Joss, she told herself stoutly.

'Your little friend is rather small,' Caroline went on smoothly, and Netta's lips tightened. The girl made her sound as if she was stunted, she thought angrily, but before she could think of a suitable retort, Mrs Berry intervened.

'Miss Rosemary's clothes would be a better fit than Miss Healey-Smythe's,' she suggested comfortably. 'They're about the same dainty build.' So much for Caroline's spite, Netta thought with a grateful glance at the housekeeper. 'I'll instruct Mary what to get for you, and we'll soon fit you out in something pretty,' she went on in a friendly voice, and Netta warmed to the first real welcome she had received at Thimbles, except from Tara. 'I'm sure Miss Rosemary wouldn't mind. If you'd like to come along with me, Miss—er——' she invited.

'What a good idea,' Caroline enthused, 'and while you're away, Joss and I can have a nice long talk. Take your time, Miss—er——' she ran into the same difficulty as the housekeeper.

'I'm not "Miss" anything,' Netta stated flatly. Since Joss did not offer to introduce her, she thought furiously, it was high time she made herself known. Maybe she should have waited for him to speak. He opened his mouth as if he was about to, but she rushed on regardless, silencing him effectively. Maybe it was the backlash of anger because of the way he had deceived her over Tara; over many other things, which she preferred not to think about now. Perhaps Caroline's manner goaded her into it. But whatever it was that drove her, she had no cause for complaint about the effect of her announcement on the others.

'I'm Mrs de Courcey,' she introduced herself bluntly. 'Joss's wife,' she underlined her status in a clear voice.

'Joss's—*what*?'

It was the reverse of congratulatory—and slightly overdone. Caroline's artistically painted eyebrows rose in a haughty arc, but Netta sensed her surprise was not as genuine as she would have liked her audience to believe. She turned to Joss with a deeply wounded expression.

'You didn't tell me you were thinking of getting married, Joss darling. You didn't let me know.'

As an exhibition of hurt feelings, it was well done, except for the faintly calculating gleam in the other girl's pale blue eyes that Netta detected easily enough, but thought wryly that Joss, being a man, probably would not.

'We didn't know ourselves until half an hour before the ceremony,' she stated evenly, without giving him a second in which to explain. She did not see any reason why she should hide his conduct, she thought mutinously, nor her own false position as his wife. Making it plain to other people helped to bolster up her own determination to remedy that position at the earliest opportunity, and she could see no logical reason for the sudden sick feeling that assailed her, of having burned her boats behind her. 'After we were married,' she carried on deliberately in a firm voice, 'we were too busy keeping one step ahead of the rebels who were hunting for us to have time to post announcements.'

Let them make what they pleased of her announcement now! she thought uncaringly, and kept her chin high, facing Caroline's hostility with fierce pride. She had her back to Joss, so she did not see the quick gleam that came into his eyes, that might or might not have been anger towards her for taking the situation into her own hands, without giving him the opportunity to make his own explanation. He had done the same thing with her father's housekeeper, Netta thought with satisfaction, so this was simply tit for tat.

'I expect Mr Joss will tell you all about it, while I take

Mrs de Courcey upstairs and find her a change of clothes.'
Mrs Berry's voice cut across the sudden crackling silence
that dropped between them, and Netta looked across at her
suspiciously. Was there just a hint of laughter in the warm,
kindly voice, as she spoke to Caroline? 'Perhaps you'd like
to come with me now, madam?' She offered Netta an
avenue of escape. 'You'll be able to put all those awful
things behind you, now you're home, and you can relax
and be comfortable,' the housekeeper went on hospitably.

'I shan't be staying for long,' Netta announced in a
clipped voice. 'Only during the Bank Holiday weekend,
then I'll be returning to London.' She had already made her
position as Joss's wife abundantly clear, she decided hardly,
so she might as well make her future intentions even
clearer, to Joss, as well as to Mrs Berry and Caroline.

With her head held high she followed the motherly
figure through the doorway. She did not look at either
Joss or Caroline as she passed them. She did not dare to
look at Joss, although she was warmly conscious that the
red setter padded behind her across the tiled floor of the
hall, accompanying her to the foot of the wide, curving
staircase that wound upwards to a balcony landing above
and disappeared into what seemed to be a wing of the
house away to the left.

'Stay!' she told Tara, automatically forbidding the dog
access to the upstairs rooms, and immediately winced as
she heard her own voice repeat Joss's order. She wished
she could feel some satisfaction that Tara obeyed her, she
thought forlornly, the setter sat obediently at the foot of
the stairs, and watched her with liquid eyes as she
mounted, but instead of jubilation all she felt was a weariness of spirit descend on her like a grey blanket, so that
her usual fleetness of foot deserted her, and she had to
reach for the banister rail to help pull herself upwards.
Luckily, Mrs Berry's ample girth made her slow in ascend-
ing, so it did not look unnatural that Netta paused as well
when they reached the landing and looked over the carved
rails into the hall below—and gasped as Joss's eyes
speared her to the spot across the cool, shadowed distance.

'Let's go into the drawing room, darling, we can talk in comfort there.'

Vaguely she heard Caroline speak, felt irritation rise in her at the girl's persistent use of the word 'darling' which, coming from Caroline, had in it a showbiz kind of emptiness that repelled her. She watched the pale green dress disappear through a doorway leading off the hall, and saw Joss start to follow her. He was half way across the hall in his cousin's wake, and Netta thought herself safe from observation, when he suddenly paused, as if he sensed she was watching him. He stopped and raised his head, and looked up straight at her.

She caught her breath and a thrill of something like fear ran through her veins. Her legs longed to run, to flee to some sanctuary where she need not meet the compelling glow in those strange, golden eyes. But she could not move. His look rooted her to the spot. Her legs would not run, and her eyes could not look away. And the expression in his narrowed glance told her that, far from returning to London as soon as the Bank Holiday weekend was over, she would leave Thimbles only when he—Joss—decided he would let her go.

CHAPTER TEN

It seemed a hundred years before he turned away.

When at last he dropped his eyes, and followed his cousin into the drawing room, and the heavy door shut behind him cutting him off, Netta held on to the banister and shook all over. The palms of her hands felt wet, and for a dreadful minute she thought she was going to faint. She clung on to the carved wood as if it were a lifeline, while the landing, and the hall below, spun in a crazy dance in front of her blurred vision.

'The rooms in the master suite are lovely and bright. They face the morning sun.'

Mrs Berry's voice steadied her, and she turned as the housekeeper opened a door further along the landing and beckoned Netta to follow her inside.

Sanctuary! The bedroom welcomed her like a light at the end of a dark tunnel, and she stumbled towards it; relief keeping her on her feet. To have privacy—a room of her own. . . . She was through the door before the sense of what the housekeeper said penetrated her mind.

The master suite?

She had expected to be placed in a small guest bedroom, and her knees nearly failed her altogether when she viewed the accommodation which she was being offered. The room was huge, and as the housekeeper said, it was light, with long, leaded windows on two walls. Her feet sank into a soft embossed carpet, and at any other time she would have delighted in the beauty of the furnishings, which blended in a perfectly chosen admixture of antique and modern to offer aesthetic pleasure and luxurious comfort to the fortunate occupant.

'Your bathroom's through this door, madam,' Mrs Berry drew her into the room with obvious pride, 'and Mr Joss's bathroom leads off his dressing room, through here.'

110

Netta hardly heard her. The bed drew her eyes like a magnet. It was large, like the room, an amply proportioned double-sized fourposter—and it was made up for two. There would be no need for her to ask this time where Joss would sleep. It was perfectly obvious where Mrs Berry thought they were both going to sleep.

'No!'

'I beg your pardon, madam?'

'Oh—er—nothing.' Netta gathered her scattered wits with difficulty. Mrs Berry was not to know. Until the chauffeur telephoned her, she could not know that they were even on their way. But in that case, how had the chauffeur found out? He had been there at the docks to meet them. Perhaps the Home Office had. . . .

'It's good to have the master suite in use again,' Mrs Berry beamed at her happily. 'The old Earl never used it —being a bachelor, he didn't bother. He used to keep it ready for Mr Joss's parents to use when they came, but that didn't last long, poor souls.' She shook her head sadly, then brightened. 'It's time Thimbles had a bride again.' Her eyes were soft as she turned them on Netta. 'Eh, but it was wonderful news when we had Mr Joss's cable from the ship, to tell us he was on his way home at last, and bringing his wife with him, and would we open up the master suite for you both.'

'Joss cabled you?' Netta's voice was a choked whisper. He had not said a word to herself about what he had done. She shrugged aside the fact that for the greater part of the voyage she had been prostrate with seasickness. The moment she was on her feet again Joss should have told her. No, asked her. As it was, he acted on the high-handed assumption that she would fall in with whatever plans he had in mind, whether she was willing or otherwise, and she writhed impotently under the ease with which he had succeeded. So far! she told herself angrily, and turned her back on the bed.

'Well now, didn't he tell you?' the housekeeper asked her in a surprised voice. 'It's not like Mr Joss to be secretive. But perhaps he wanted to surprise you.'

The Joss she knew would probably surprise Mrs Berry, thought Netta acidly, but she did not say so out loud. There was no point in causing any more dissent in the house, particularly as she did not intend to remain there for more than a few days, however attractive her surroundings. It was sufficient to ward off Caroline's hostility, without incurring Mrs Berry's displeasure as well. Joss was obviously the apple of her eye.

'It's a good thing you were a week or two on the way. It gave us more time to prepare for you.'

'We were on a cargo ship,' Netta replied absently. Talking helped to restore her poise, and she carried on in a firmer voice, 'The vessel called in at most of the major ports on the way back, loading and unloading cargo, which was why the journey took so long.' It had taken weeks, and seemed like years. 'The room is quite beautiful,' she added, with an obvious sincerity that brightened the housekeeper's smile. At least she could be truthful about that, she thought thankfully as the elderly woman told her helpfully,

'Mary's bringing you some clothes, and you'll find all you need in the bathroom. Miss Rosemary always keeps it stocked for when she comes to stay here.'

'Miss Rosemary?' Joss should have at least sketched in an outline of his family for her, since he had virtually brought her to his home by force, and she blamed him resentfully for her lack of knowledge, which must make the housekeeper wonder. She smarted under the necessity of gaining information about his people in such a manner, though Mrs Berry did not seem to think it was at all untoward, and went on placidly,

'Miss Rosemary is Mr Joss's sister. She's married, and living abroad now, but she comes home every year to visit. The old Earl brought them both up, after their parents were killed in a car smash when they were very young. They were like his own, to him. And since he never married, they were the only family he had who were really close to him.'

Which probably explained why Joss had inherited Thimbles, and not the title. Netta had only the vaguest of notions about the rules governing such matters, but she knew a profound thankfulness that she was free from the entanglements such a position would have brought in its train. As plain Mrs de Courcey she could take steps to have their marriage annulled without attracting unwelcome publicity.

'That sounds like Mary now. Come on in and show Mrs de Courcey what you've brought for her,' Mrs Berry instructed the fresh-faced country girl of about nineteen, who appeared through the door with her arms full of clothes, and regarded Netta with a friendly smile and frank interest.

'Look after Mrs de Courcey while I go and supervise the cooking,' the housekeeper bade her, and turned to Netta. 'I'll call you in about three quarters of an hour,' she promised, and bustled away.

'You must be feeling hungry by now,' Mary said sympathetically. 'But Mrs Berry's cooking's worth waiting for,' she added with disarming frankness, and Netta smiled.

'I'm starving,' she confessed, 'but I need a bath even more than I need food.' The ablutionary provisions on board the cargo vessel had been adequate but spartan, and her longing for perfumed soap had not diminished since her night in the cave.

'I'll go and run your bath for you, while you get undressed,' Mary offered obligingly. 'There's a robe here,' she laid it carefully across the bed, and put a selection of dresses beside it for choice, and a pile of dainty underwear. The robe and one of the dresses were in a pale, creamy primrose, the former daisy-sprigged, and the latter plain.

'They're lovely,' Netta smiled her thanks. 'Primrose is one of my favourite colours.'

'Mrs Berry said as how you'd got red hair, miss—I mean ma'am—and the two don't shout at one another, do they? You has to be careful, with red hair.'

'They go beautifully together,' Netta laughed out loud, the tensions of the past hours finding an unexpected safety valve in amusement at Mary's unorthodox view of fashion. 'Your gardener must think along the same lines,' she remembered. 'I noticed a lovely clump of yellow holly-hocks set against a corner of the house, as we rounded the drive.' The red herringbone-patterned brick made a per-fect foil for the tall, old-fashioned loveliness of the papery powderpuff flowers, which were just at their peak of blooming, and gave the ancient house a warm, homely touch as if to welcome anyone approaching.

'Yes, but hollyhocks aren't just for colour, are they?' Mary said practically.

'Surely you don't use them for culinary purposes? For cooking?' Netta elucidated, as Mary turned on her a look of puzzled incomprehension. She had heard of a lot of peculiar plants being used in such a way, but never holly-hocks before.

'Lor' no, you'd be poisoned for sure,' Mary laughed merrily. 'But you've got to have a clump of hollyhocks, haven't you? They say as it keeps love in the house, does a clump of hollyhocks,' she imparted her simple wisdom as she opened the bathroom door, and Netta heard her hum-ming happily to herself over the sound of running water.

'It keeps love in the house. . . .'

Maybe it did, but not for herself and Joss. For Caroline and Joss, perhaps. For Caroline and Joss, certainly, if Caroline had her way. Netta sat down on the edge of the bed rather suddenly. The couch she had just vowed to herself she would not go near, but her knees refused to hold her, and she had no choice. Her fingers trembled so that they fumbled on the buttons of her shirtwaister top, and it was only the increased volume of Mary's rendering of '. . . 'tis love, and love alone, my heart is seeking,' sung with more enthusiasm than regard for tune, that made her realise the taps had stopped running. Hurriedly she dis-robed, and slipped on the pretty cotton robe, and mentally blessed her unknown sister-in-law's taste for clothing which, like her size, exactly accorded with Netta's own. Without having met Rosemary, she knew they would like one another. Which was not of much use—sharp pain pierced her at the thought—since they would never have the opportunity to get to know one another.

'I've run the water nice and deep for you.' It was plain that Mary liked her bath that way, and could think of no greater favour to bestow on someone—Netta realised with a sense of shock—someone whom the young maid must regard as the new mistress of Thimbles. She considered her position. For some reason, it was something she had not thought about before—and must not think of now. Mary would learn the true situation soon enough, she thought grimly, and found herself envying the young maid's uncomplicated outlook on life, and hoping that no one would ever spoil her simple trust. It would be like trampling on a daisy. She herself had trusted Joss....

'I'll take your clothes downstairs with me when I go, and give them a good wash for you,' her young helper offered generously, and jolted Netta back to a sense of reality like an electric shock. Mary must not be allowed to touch her safari suit. No one must be allowed to touch that. Being at Thimbles had given her a false sense of security, but it did not alter the priceless value of the gemstones in her waistband. Mary eyed her slacks critically. 'My, but they've had a bad time!' She regarded the stains left by the river mud, and which would probably never come out of the material now. 'I'll try and get it clean for you, otherwise the only way would be to dye the whole suit,' and reached for it across the bed.

'Never mind the suit,' Netta grabbed it from her hastily. 'I washed it on the boat coming over, so it's clean, though as you say the stains probably won't ever come out now.' She became aware that the homely little face opposite was regarding her with hurt surprise. 'It's no reflection on your capabilities,' she hastened to assure Mary, 'but the suit itself isn't worth a lot of work.' It was worth a fortune, and the possibility of even one of the smallest of Ranjit's diamonds disappearing down a washing machine waste pipe filled her with horror. 'It's just that—just that——' she searched desperately for an explanation that would satisfy the young girl, and salve her pride at the same time. 'It's just that I want to keep my suit as a souvenir,' she finished lamely, and went weak with relief as Mary's face brightened.

'Of course you do, how silly of me. Anyone would want to keep the clothes they were married in.'

How mistaken could she get? Netta wondered drearily, and came to the conclusion that marriage was turning her into an accomplished liar. Hastily, she built upon the accidental impression she had conveyed.

'I certainly do,' she murmured, and hated herself for the deception. She touched the cloth of her slacks sentimentally against her cheek. The stones in the belt felt reassuringly hard and lumpy. 'No one washes the stains from a wedding dress, do they?' she asked softly, and blessed the fact that the maid had a romantic streak.

'Of course they don't,' Mary sounded quite indignant. 'And there was me, going to wash out all those memories!'

If only soap and water would wash the memories away. Wash away the whole episode, and return her to the carefree, heartwhole person she was before she went to Lak. She suddenly felt immeasurably older than Mary, although there were only a few years between them. And there was still the problem of where to put her safari suit.

'It'll be perfectly all right in the chest of drawers, until I come back from my bath,' she told herself firmly. The last few weeks had made her ultra-nervous. 'I'm in a private house, not an hotel,' she convinced herself she was over-reacting to strain. There was no danger of anyone touching her safari suit, now she had successfully diverted Mary's attention. Mrs Berry was the only other person likely to have designs on her laundry, and she was busy in the kitchen. 'Just the same, I'll tuck it into a drawer.' She waited until the door closed behind Mary before she chose the bottom drawer of the dressing table, and was vividly reminded of the last time she had hidden something at the back of a drawer. 'There's nothing I can do about the jewel settings now,' she shrugged philosophically. She had salvaged the really valuable part of the jewels, and Ranjit was wealthy enough to stand the loss of the rest. She tested the temperature of the bathwater with an experimental toe.

'Bless Mary, it's just right!'

She gave a sigh of pure bliss, and sank into the relaxing warmth of soft water. She reached out and captured a bottle of shampoo that matched the fresh sweetness of the jasmine soap, and luxuriated in foaming perfume. 'I'll shower off,' she decided at last reluctantly, and pulled the plug from the bath, and wriggled under the hissing cold water that tingled her into a liveliness she had not felt for weeks. The receding bath water gurgled, and the shower sang, and——

'Surely that's someone talking?' She tensed and went still as a low-toned hum came from the bedroom next door. It went on, and she fumbled for the shower switch and reached for a towel. The water in the bath gave a final prolonged sucking gurgle, and went silent, and the strains of, 'Ah, 'tis love, and love alone ...' rose softly in the ensuing silence.

'It's only Mary come back.' Netta gave a sigh of relief and started to towel her hair dry. 'I'll really have to calm down,' she scolded herself. 'If I keep on like this, I'll soon be a nervous wreck!' It was infinitely soothing to feel the fresh silk of her borrowed undies against her skin, and to lie back in the chair in front of the dressing table and give in to Mary's plea to be allowed to brush her hair.

'Mrs Berry says you need to rest, now you're home.'

'I'll do that a lot better when I know how the people from the Embassy got on.' Joss had not mentioned them, and a sudden fear assailed Netta. Surely he would have told her if he had heard any news of Wendy and Harry Fraser? But he had kept his own counsel on other matters that affected her, so it was just possible he had done the same on this. She bit her lip, torn between anxiety and anger.

'They're all safe, didn't you know?' Mary looked astonished at her ignorance. 'It was in all the papers. Mrs Berry showed it to me. She kept a copy to show to Mr Joss when he got home, I know. There's a picture of him in it, and one of the Ambassador and his wife.'

'We haven't seen any English papers since we left the Embassy,' Netta forestalled the inevitable question of why her own photograph did not accompany that of Joss. Now she knew her friends were safe, she felt free to attend to her own problems. . . .

'That's how we knew you were married in the first place,' Mary prattled on. 'It said as how the Embassy people, and the Lak Royal Family, had landed safely in Italy. Fancy Mr Joss knowing the Lak Royal Family!' she marvelled. 'But they said there was no news of Mr and Mrs de Courcey, and we were that worried. And then, of course, we had Mr Joss's cable from the boat, and that put everything right again.'

It might have put everything right for the staff at Thimbles. So far as she was concerned, it put everything wrong, Netta thought wryly, but all she said aloud was,

'It must have come as a shock to Mrs Berry, to hear the news of our marriage like that.' Not half such a shock as it had been to herself, but she refrained from commenting on that as well.

'Not a lot upsets Mrs Berry,' the young maid twinkled suddenly. 'Though it came as a shock to Miss Caroline, I reckon.' Her voice held a wealth of satisfaction. 'She came hotfoot down here the same morning as the newspapers came out, and then tried to make out she didn't know anything about it. And her with a copy of the *Gazette* in her luggage, and the pictures and the story all over the front page!' The young voice was scornful. So her intuition about Caroline had been correct, Netta thought.

'Miss Caroline doesn't live here permanently, then?' she asked in a disinterested voice.

'Not her,' Mary exclaimed ungrammatically. ' 'Tisn't smart enough, down here, for her. She'd rather live in London, and have the bright lights.'

'That will be all, Mary. You can go now.'

Netta jumped as Joss's voice spoke from just behind them. I should be used to him by now, she thought vexedly, indignation rising in her on the heels of fright.

'I'll come and clear up in here for you, while you're downstairs having your dinner, Mrs de Courcey.' Mary did not seem at all disconcerted by Joss's silent approach.

'Don't touch my safari suit,' Netta began urgently as Mary made for the door, and she turned back again and replied happily,

'I gave your trouser suit to Mr Joss, ma'am. He came up and asked for it while you were having your bath. He said as how he'd keep it safe for you, since you wanted it as a souvenir.' She beamed at Joss, obviously applauding his sentiment.

'How dare you take possession of my suit?' The anger that smouldered inside Netta spilled over as the door closed behind the maid. It must have been Joss's voice she had heard when she was showering off after her bath. If only she had opened the door into the bedroom and investigated, instead of being content just to listen, she could have prevented him from taking it.

'Where have you put it?' she cried furiously.

'It's in my safe, where it will remain until your father comes home.'

'That might be weeks!' Netta stared at him in disbelief. 'I can take the jewels to the bank on Wednesday, they'll be open then.' Her chin came up. 'I intend to take them to the bank on Wednesday.'

'Since they're in my safe, you won't be able to,' Joss replied with a calm deliberation that served to incense her further. 'It's no good arguing,' his voice hardened as she raised hers in protest, 'I shall hand the jewels over to your father myself. I won't have you wandering around carrying valuables worth half the price of the Crown Jewels,' he told her bluntly. His estimate of their possible value was not far wrong, but Netta was too angry to appreciate his inspired guesswork. 'It isn't safe for a girl to have such things in her possession.' He did not say anything about it being unsafe for a man, she thought bitingly. It was typical of his chauvinistic attitude, she told herself furiously, but before she could speak he went on, 'Anything could happen while you'd got them in your possession, and I intend to have a word with your father as soon as he comes back, about allowing you to act as his courier on such errands,' he added grimly.

'What I do for my father is none of your business,' Netta blazed, goaded out of control by his overbearing attitude. 'I'm over twenty-one, and I'll please myself what I do,' she asserted her independence.

'Before we were married, it wasn't any of my business,' Joss conceded, and she gave a disbelieving hiss. It simply wasn't possible that Joss should admit something was not his concern, she thought sarcastically, and the next minute he spoiled it by adding, 'now you're married to me I intend to make it my business.' And remedy the situation according to his satisfaction, his tone added, and stung her to fury.

'In that case, you can consider us unmarried, as from now.' Netta's self-control snapped, and she struggled to pull the ring from her finger with frantic haste. Her hurry, and her own indulgence in wallowing in the warm bathwater, was her undoing. The ring was a perfect fit to start with, and the warm wetness had slightly swollen her fingers. The slender gold band resisted her hasty tugging, and stubbornly refused to budge.

'I told you before,' Joss caught both her hands in a hard grasp, and pulled her to him with fierce impatience, 'while you're with me, you'll wear my ring.' His voice was tense, his face tight with an anger that matched her own, and he glowered down at her with a look that made her catch her breath. A small detached part of her remembered that when he was angry, tiny deep bronze flecks glowed like living coals deep in the gold of his eyes. They glowed now, and her own eyes faltered before them.

'I brought you to Thimbles as my wife,' he gritted, 'and while you're here you'll observe the conventions.'

'You dragged me to Thimbles against my will, and while I'm here there's one convention I've no intention of observing,' she stormed back.

She felt him go still as her meaning penetrated. It was like the dark, brooding stillness before a mighty storm, bottomlessly silent, yet cracklingly alive with electric currents that might at any second erupt in a lightning sheet of flame, to sear and burn.... For a brief, agonising second his grasp on her hands increased to bone-crushing force, and she pulled away, and opened her mouth to cry out at the pain of his grip, and then could have cried at the even greater pain as he released them, and thrust them away from him as if he hated their touch, so that she found herself pulling against nothing, and staggered backwards against the side of the bed, shaken out of balance by her own momentum. She put out her hands and grasped at the quilt to save herself from falling full length across it, and her stunned mind heard him say coldly,

'I don't force my company on any woman.'

He spun away from her then and strode towards the door. The handle rattled under the force of his grip as he wrenched it open, and the sharp noise kindled Netta into a retort.

'Don't wait for me to follow you down,' she threw at his retreating back. 'Mary can bring my meal up here to me.' He paused, his back still turned, and she rushed on recklessly, 'I'm sure you'll enjoy your tête-à-tête with Caroline much better without my presence!'

He turned, then, and the tightly leashed anger in his face dried the words unspoken on her lips. Instinctively she ran the tip of her tongue across them, her mouth suddenly parched, and a tremor ran through her when he spoke. His words seemed to cut across the room like a lance, and she flinched away from their barb.

'Now you mention Mary,' his look pierced her, refusing to allow her to look away, and she felt like a butterfly fluttering helplessly against a pin, 'you will kindly refrain from questioning the house staff on matters that concern the family.' He did not say 'will you', he said, 'you will', and Netta bridled resentfully at his order. 'If you want any information, ask me,' he commanded her harshly.

'Since you didn't volunteer any information, I'd no option but to ask the servants,' she defended herself hotly. 'And in case you want a full account of my conversation,' she ignored his impatient gesture and rushed on, 'I wasn't questioning Mary about your family, we were discussing a newspaper article that it seems appeared after you and I left Lak, and gave the news that the people in the plane landed safely in Italy. I suppose even you must consider I'm entitled to receive news of my friends?' she demanded with spirit.

'That's exactly what I came upstairs to show you.' He stepped away from the door and came back towards her, digging a folded newspaper from his pocket on the way. 'Mrs Berry gave me a copy of the paper, and as you say you intend to remain upstairs you might as well have it for company.' He slung it on to the bed beside her, and she steeled herself not to move away. It hit the counterpane beside her with a sharp slap, and the sheets fluttered apart where it landed, then settled with a sigh, and automatically she glanced down at the front page.

Two large photographs looked up at her. One was of Wendy and Harry, and the other—she blinked to clear her eyes—the other was a bright, laughing photograph of Joss. Her heart gave a painful wrench. If only she could make him look like that!—carefree, happy, so different from the set, stern face of the Joss she knew. Who had he been looking at, when he laughed like that? she wondered wretchedly. Caroline? He spoke in a clipped voice.

'The meal will be served in the dining room in,' he flicked his shirt cuff back from his wrist, 'in exactly a quarter of an hour. Mary will be serving at table, and she won't have time to bring food upstairs. You can either join me at table, or go hungry.'

And he was gone. With the same swift tread that never ceased to astonish her, and left her no time in which to think of a retort, he closed the door behind him and she was alone, except for the image of his likeness on the counterpane beside her. It gazed up at her from the printed page, and she caught her breath on a sob. Was it her fancy, or did the pictured eyes really seek out her own? Laughing at her. Mocking. . . .

CHAPTER ELEVEN

'I WON'T go downstairs and join Joss. I'll starve first!'

It was easier said than done. Netta flicked through the newspaper in a desultory fashion, and tried in vain to subdue the hollow pleading from inside her that cried out for the waiting meal. And all the time, Joss's eyes seemed to follow her every movement from the photograph on the front page.

'Oh, do stop looking at me!'

In desperation she turned the paper face down and flung it back on the bed.

'I'd better move these dresses, it's a shame to crease them.' Restlessly, she began to sort out the clothes Mary had brought her. Movement brought some small relief from the tension, and she paused as she came to the primrose yellow dress. 'I might as well get dressed,' she decided. 'I can't stay in a robe for the rest of the day.' There was not much of the day left now, but she felt better when she slipped the dress over her head, and found it was a perfect fit, as were the white sandals, she discovered, which the young maid had thoughtfully provided to go with it. She smoothed sheer tights over her legs and eyed herself critically in the mirror. 'Mmm, it's good to be in a dress again!' However much she enjoyed wearing slacks when the occasion demanded, after weeks with nothing else to put on each day but her safari suit, it was a treat to wear something feminine again. Netta frankly enjoyed being a girl, and had every lovely woman's delight in pretty things.

Her own reflection returned a solemn, hazel-eyed stare from the full-length mirror. It showed little, she thought thankfully, of the emotional storm through which she had just passed. Perhaps her eyes were a trifle over-bright, but that could have been the glint of renewed confidence that surged through her as she surveyed her own slender, primrose-clad figure. Her still damp curls formed a tight halo round her head, and her flawless skin, that went with her bright colouring, was becomingly tanned. It was about the only bonus she had to remind her of her stay abroad, she thought wryly.

'My, but you do look nice! What a difference a pretty dress makes.' Mrs Berry's ample reflection appeared beside her own in the mirror, and the apple-cheeked face beamed approval. 'I said Miss Rosemary's clothes would be a good fit for you,' she observed with satisfaction.

'They're lovely, and just the right size.' Netta smiled back, suddenly glad of the older woman's company. Perhaps—quick hope rose in her—perhaps she might be able to persuade Mrs Berry to bring her something on a tray.

'I saw Mr Joss go downstairs, so I told him I'd show you the way to the dining room. He said you weren't going to bother to dress for dinner, seeing as it's early anyhow, so what Mary brought you to put on will do nicely,' she surveyed Netta with open approval. 'Mr Joss persuaded his cousin to eat with you at the same time, so as to save me cooking twice. He's considerate that way, is Mr Joss.' Which implied that Caroline was not, Netta thought, unsurprised, then her heart sank.

'I can't ask for a tray upstairs now,' she realised despondently. Unwittingly, Mrs Berry had foiled her intentions, and she turned towards the door with reluctant feet. 'I wasn't going to bother to eat,' she began, 'I'm not really hungry any more.' Her stomach instantly gave a loud wail, and proclaimed her statement to be a lie.

'You've gone past eating, that's why,' Mrs Berry clucked her concern. 'Just come down and try a morsel or two, and you'll find your appetite will come back,' she promised cheerfully.

'I don't know.' Still Netta hesitated. 'Joss will have someone to talk to, if Caroline's eating with him.' The thought of sitting with Caroline at the meal table really did take away her appetite.

'Aye, I don't doubt she'll enjoy the opportunity,' the housekeeper answered slyly, and Netta glanced at her

suspiciously. On the face of it, it was a casual enough comment, but.... She made up her mind swiftly.

'I won't give Caroline the satisfaction of driving me
away,' she told herself firmly. 'I think, after all, I'll take
your advice,' she added aloud, and summoned up a smile,
which broadened of its own accord at Mrs Berry's instant
nod of satisfaction. She regarded the housekeeper in a new
light. Underneath her kindly good humour, she was not
above a little guileful manipulation if she wanted to obtain
her own way, Netta realised amusedly. The faded eyes
twinkled, but Mrs Berry did not say anything until they
were half way down the stairs, where she paused, as
seemed her habit, to regain her breath.

'That's a picture of the first Jocelyn de Courcey,' she
indicated one of the portraits hung at a vantage point
above them. 'He's very like our Mr Joss, isn't he?'

'Our Mr Joss....' Netta's heart gave a painful lurch at
the housekeeper's choice of words, and then another that
made her draw a hard breath as she looked up obediently,
and met the gold, painted stare of the man in the portrait.
The likeness to Joss was startling. Given that the portrait
had been painted nearly six hundred years ago, it could
almost have been Joss himself, in fancy dress. The hair was
longer, in the fashion of the age, but the same pointed
features looked down at her, and the same gold eyes. The
long-ago artist had even captured the tiny amber-coloured
flecks deep within them.

'They called him the Fox,' Mrs Berry observed, and
Netta turned on her a startled look.

'They called Joss that, too, in Lak.'

'They're not the only ones to see the likeness....' Now
she knew what he had meant.

'Well, I never!' Mrs Berry resumed her journey, and in
deference to her age and bulk Netta slowed her own steps.
'It's the eyes, I expect,' the housekeeper went on chattily.
'Now and then they come out, somewhere in the line. The
old Earl had them, but they missed Mr Joss's father, and
came down to Mr Joss. It's odd, how these things happen
in a family, isn't it?' she mused. 'They miss a generation

or two, and then they pop up again, just when you think they've gone for ever.'

'The portrait's in a wonderful state of preservation.' Netta deftly sidetracked the housekeeper. She did not want to let her thoughts dwell on men with gold-coloured eyes. 'The colours are still so bright,' she hurried on, her voice slightly breathless, though not for the same reason as Mrs Berry. 'Even the stones in the ring on his finger look as if they're real.' Her training made her notice them particularly. They glowed richly coloured, one large central ruby, surrounded by diamonds and rubies graded in size, in a richly ornate setting.

'It's a lovely ring,' Mrs Berry agreed amiably. 'The old Earl left it to Miss Caroline. It's the only thing he did leave her,' she added in a dry tone.

And Caroline hoped to remedy what she considered a poor inheritance, by marrying Joss, Netta thought with quick intuition. No wonder the newspaper article had come as such a shock to her!

'Not so loud, girl, not so loud!' Mrs Berry reached the hall and regained breath and voice in shocked protest as Mary sounded the gong with more energy than discretion. 'You're calling folk to eat, not waking the shades,' she scolded.

'Mr Joss is already in the dining room,' Mary volunteered, unabashed. 'Miss Caroline isn't down yet.'

'She won't be able to complain she hasn't heard the gong,' Mrs Berry returned with an asperity that Netta suspected was not entirely directed against the maid, and then she nearly lost her resolution as it dawned on her what Mary had just said.

Joss was already in the dining room. Alone. And although she did not relish the thought of Caroline's company, her courage failed her at the prospect of facing Joss on his own.

'I'll come in with you for a minute,' Mrs Berry prevented her from giving way to cowardice, and running back to her room—their room.... She forced herself to listen to what the housekeeper was saying. Anything, to still the sudden wild beating of her heart as she approached the dining room door.

'I just want to check that Mary's laid the table properly,' Mrs Berry fussed. 'She's a good girl, and coming along nicely, but now and then she forgets.' She opened the door and bustled into the room, and straight away made for the small circular table placed in front of the open french windows. The snowy cloth and gleaming silver looked inviting in the evening sunlight, but Netta hardly noticed them. She paused in the doorway, and her eyes were drawn across the room as if by a magnet, straight to Joss. He leaned easily against the fireplace. He, too, had changed into casual clothes, a cream silk shirt which he had left open at the neck so that it showed the strong, dark column of his throat, and dark chocolate-coloured slacks that made him seem even taller and slimmer than before. He must have showered, too, she noticed with a detached kind of interest that his hair was still damp, like her own.

He looked up, and their glances met and locked across the room. Her heart stopped its wild beating. For a brief, electrifying second, it seemed to stop beating altogether.

'It's only because I'm hungry,' she told herself desperately. But hunger could not be responsible for the strange paralysis that kept her rooted to the spot in the doorway, unable to move, scarcely able to breathe.

'Mary can start serving right away, Mrs Berry.' After what seemed an aeon of time his eyes left her—released her—and she drew a deep, shuddering breath. 'You'll sit here, beside me.' With his silent, lithe tread he crossed the room and stood over her. He reached down and took her elbow, and she quivered at his touch, but she did not, could not, draw away. In spite of the warmth of the evening she felt icily cold, and she shivered. She felt him look down at her, as if the shiver had communicated itself to him, but she did not look up. She could not—dared not—meet his eyes again. Somehow, her legs carried her beside him to the table, though she felt herself walk woodenly, like a doll without joints, and it was with an infinite sense of re-

lief that she collapsed, rather than sat, on the chair he drew
out for her.

'Miss Caroline isn't down yet, Mr Joss.' Mrs Berry
hesitated by the door.

'She won't be long,' Joss answered absently, 'she's just
gone upstairs to change her dress.'

'I had to, after Tara scraped her paws all down the
front of the other one, and spoiled it.' Caroline appeared
and darted a spiteful look in Netta's direction. 'It wouldn't
have happened if the dog had been left where she was
until Joss called her,' she added critically, and Netta gripped her hands together under the cover of the table cloth.

'I won't quarrel with her,' she resolved firmly. 'I'm only
here for a day or two, so it isn't worth it,' only to have her
good intentions nearly fail her as Caroline added,

'You can start serving now, Mrs Berry.'

'I should be giving the instructions, not Caroline.' The
thought caught Netta by surprise. It should not matter to
her, since she did not intend to remain, either at Thimbles,
or as Joss's wife. But she found, unexpectedly, that it did
matter. It angered her unaccountably. Caroline was deliberately usurping her place as Joss's wife. It was she who
was the guest in the house, not Netta. She was not to
know that Joss's marriage was merely one of convenience.
Or had Joss told her, while they talked together in the
drawing room? The possibility gave her pause, and increased her anger against both Joss and Caroline. He had
no right to discuss their marriage with anyone. It was
something that belonged to them alone. To bring a third
person in, particularly if that person was Caroline, seemed
like trampling over sacred ground, and her resentment increased accordingly.

'Come and sit this side of me,' Joss performed the same
courtesy for his cousin, and held her chair until she sat
down.

'Not so far away, darling.' She immediately edged it
closer to his. 'You've been too far away for too long. Do be
careful, Mary!' she broke off and rebuked the young maid
sharply, careless of the fact that it was her own action

which had caught the girl's elbow and hazarded the dishes in her hand. Her move nearer to Joss had made it difficult for the maid to serve properly, and Netta had a moment's irresponsible hope that if anything spilled as a consequence, it might do so over Caroline.

'It's not like me to be catty.' She took a tight hold of her thoughts, and smiled encouragingly at Mary, and was rewarded as the girl's face brightened and she continued to serve with renewed confidence.

'I wish we'd gone to a restaurant for our meal.' Netta concentrated on her soup, and tried to think of something to say. Mrs Berry's cooking certainly lived up to Mary's recommendation, she thought appreciatively, but it was spoiled for her by the currents of tension and antagonism that loaded the sun-filled air across the table. If Caroline felt the atmosphere, she gave no sign, though most of it emanated from her. She kept up a running flow of small talk, mostly directed at Joss about people and places they both knew, and which, Netta did not doubt, was specifically designed to exclude herself, although now and then Caroline seemed to recollect herself, and directed a remark to Netta which she noticed each time did not require a reply. The effect was to give Caroline the appearance of a gracious hostess expertly coping with a difficult and rather gauche guest, and Netta seethed inwardly as the meal progressed.

'She manages to look the part,' she conceded grudgingly. Caroline had changed into a short black dress as severely cut as her green linen, but in a softer, more becoming material. It acted as a perfect foil for her upswept hair, and made Netta's simple summer primrose seem childish by comparison. The inference was obvious, at least to Netta. Caroline was trying to impress upon Joss, without actually saying so in so many words, what a mistake he had made in marrying Netta—and how much better Caroline herself would fulfil the role of chatelaine at Thimbles. It was cleverly done. Netta could even guess at the phrases Caroline would employ to her friends, to explain the situation.

'Some little ingénue Joss picked up abroad. They were both caught up in the uprising in Lak. Men do quixotic things at such times. A moment of madness. . . .' And then the punch line. 'Fortunately, such moments aren't irreparable, these days.'

She became aware of a waiting sort of silence, and looked up. Caroline and Joss were both looking at her, as if they expected her to say something.

'I didn't catch. . . .' she began, guiltily conscious that she had shut her ears to Caroline's chatter, and become totally absorbed in her own thoughts. It rankled that her own inattention had put her at a disadvantage.

'Caroline was suggesting we might hold a ball at Thimbles,' Joss broke the strained silence, and his voice held more than a hint of impatience.

'I suggested a party, darling,' Caroline corrected him prettily, 'but of course if you'll agree to a ball. . . .' Her face brightened. 'It's time Thimbles saw a bit of life again. We could have a ball right away, to celebrate your homecoming.' She did not say, celebrate *their* homecoming, Netta noticed, nor suggest celebrating the fact that she and Joss were married. Perhaps Joss had told her that there was nothing to celebrate in that connection.

'And then we could have the Hunt Ball here, at the end of the season,' the other girl planned ahead enthusiastically, and Netta looked across at her speculatively. Surely Hunt Balls took place after Christmas? She counted up the months, aware of a growing feeling of dismay. How long did Caroline intend to remain at Thimbles? It should not concern her, because she herself would not be here, but. . . . She checked her thoughts hastily and forced herself to pay attention to what Joss was saying. She did not want to give Caroline the satisfaction of attracting his criticism again.

'Not the Hunt Ball. Not at Thimbles.' Surprisingly, he refused his cousin, and Netta looked at him questioningly. There seemed to be an underlying something in his tone which she did not understand. From her reaction it was evident that Caroline did.

'Oh, darling, don't say you're going to carry on all those old prejudices,' she protested. 'I thought all that had died with the Earl.'

'My uncle didn't consider them to be prejudices,' Joss answered her quietly, 'and neither do I.'

'Just because of a silly old family crest?' Caroline scoffed, but Netta noticed that her gracious air was beginning to fray slightly at the unexpected opposition. 'It's only a picture,' she persisted, 'even if it is carved in stone, or whatever.'

'It was more than a picture to my ancestor,' Joss pointed out in a mild tone, and Netta looked at him sharply. That was twice he had said it. 'My uncle', and then, 'my ancestor'. Not 'our uncle—our ancestor', which suggested that his relationship with Caroline was not a particularly close one by blood. He had called her his cousin, but it could be that she was a second or third time removed. Which, and Netta's heart gave a painful twist at the thought, which would make marriage a more acceptable proposition between them, if their blood tie was only a distant one.

'Oh, that!' Caroline began to sound impatient in her turn. 'Just because the first Jocelyn de Courcey happened to be nicknamed the Fox—goodness knows why.' Netta knew, but if Caroline could not see the simile in the pointed face and the strange golden eyes, there was little use in anyone trying to tell her, she thought.

'It was the reason the first Jocelyn included the animal in his crest,' Joss pointed out reasonably, and Netta listened with interest. She had noticed the crest carved in stone over the main doorway when they arrived. There was a small replica of it in the stone of the mantel over the fireplace in the room they now occupied. It consisted of crossed swords supporting an open book, and surrounded by a wreath of wheat ears, symbolising a soldier, a scholar, and a landowner, the whole surmounted by his own particular monogram of a fox's mask. The shield was still peculiarly applicable to the present owner of Thimbles, Netta thought, and became aware that he was still speak-

ing. His voice remained mild, but it had in it an under-
tone of inflexible determination that she had heard herself
on more than one occasion, though for some reason she
felt surprised that he applied it to Caroline.

'The first Jocelyn's nickname, and his crest, were the
reasons why he refused to have the fox hunted on his land.
He knew what it felt like himself, to be hunted,' Joss
added reflectively.

And so did Joss. And, for that matter, so did she, Netta
thought ruefully. A vision of the rebels fanning the flames
among the scrub, in the hope of flushing them both out
of hiding, rose vividly in her mind's eye, and for a brief,
revealing second she turned her head and looked straight at
Joss, and knew that his thoughts were following her own.
It gave her a momentary feeling of closeness with him, the
shared terror, and the shared escape, and all that went between. She must not think of all that went between. She
drew a long breath and sat up straight in her chair, and
with an effort kept her mind from wandering, even though
she did not particularly want to listen to what Caroline was
saying. The latter unwisely continued to protest.

'Surely you can't be serious, Joss? If you carry that kind
of outlook to its conclusion, you'll stop crop shooting next.
And where will you be then? Overrun with rabbits,' she
concluded triumphantly.

'Since I intend to leave the foxes to breed freely on
Thimbles land, they'll keep the rabbit population in check
for me,' Joss returned amusedly, but his eyes held a hint of
steel that his cousin must have caught, because she
shrugged and gave a light laugh, and waved a deprecating
hand.

'Oh well, it's your land,' she conceded. 'Perhaps one day
I can persuade you to change your mind.'

'I wish you luck, if you try to make him change it,'
Netta thought with an inward flash of humour of her own,
and found her eyes caught by the glint of jewels on
Caroline's finger as the girl cupped her hands round her
face and regarded Joss indulgently, as if she was temporarily giving way to what she regarded as a harmless

whim, that she would talk him out of later. Surely—Netta
looked at her hand more keenly—surely it was the same
ring as the one she had seen in the painting on the stairs?

'That belonged to the first Jocelyn de Courcey.' Joss
caught her glance, and firmly directed the conversation
into another channel.

'I noticed it on the painting as I came downstairs,' Netta
followed his lead with relief. Perhaps now she would be
able to join in the conversation, instead of Caroline
monopolising both it and Joss, she thought tartly.

'How very observant of you,' the other girl sneered, but
Joss did not seem to notice her sarcasm, and went on con-
versationally,

'It's not really so very remarkable,' he pointed out.
'Netta's a jeweller by profession. Her father is John
Vaughan, the jeweller and goldsmith.'

Did she imagine it? Netta wondered, or did a wary
look creep into Caroline's eyes as he mentioned the renowned name? She dismissed it as nothing but fancy, and
made another effort to help the conversation along.

'It's a lovely ring,' she tried holding out an olive branch.
Few women could resist having their jewellery praised, and
if it made the atmosphere between them a little easier it
would be worth it, she thought cynically. 'I see you've resorted to the same safety measure as a lot of our clients,'
she gave the ring a professional glance, 'so many people
nowadays are having the real stones replaced by synthetics,
and keeping the originals in the bank.' She tried not to let
her own regret show through. 'It's a sensible idea, and so
much safer than wearing the originals.'

'How dare you suggest the stones are synthetic?'
Caroline's outburst startled her. It could not possibly
have been assumed. The girl's face went white with fury,
and she glared at Netta balefully across the table. With a
swift movement she drew her hands away from her face,
which effectively removed the ring from view. 'You come
here as a complete outsider,' she ignored the fact that Joss
had brought her as his wife, 'and within minutes you're
responsible for spoiling my dress, and now you have the

impertinence to suggest my ring isn't genuine! It's a family heirloom,' she stormed, the last vestiges of her gracious behaviour vanished, and naked hostility burning in her pale blue eyes. 'What right have you got to say such a thing?' she demanded hotly. 'You've scarcely set eyes on the ring.'

'I haven't had a close look at it,' Netta began, completely taken aback by the other girl's verbal attack. She did not need to look at the ring closely. When Caroline had leaned on the table, her finger had been less than a couple of feet away, and Netta possessed excellent eyesight, and a professional judgment equal to that of her father where gemstones were concerned.

'There, you see?' Caroline appealed to Joss. 'She's just saying that, to try to make trouble.'

'Even professionals can be mistaken.' To Netta's amazement, Joss took his cousin's side without hesitation, and the look he directed at herself was both angry and impatient. 'Netta will acknowledge that, and apologise,' he added sternly, his eyes accusing her of deliberately upsetting his first evening back in his own home. Netta gasped at the injustice of his attitude. He was as bad as Caroline, she thought furiously. Worse. As her husband, he should have taken her side, or at least listened to her point of view. She felt as if she was on one side of a high door, hammering for admission, with Joss and Caroline both on the other side, keeping it firmly shut against her.

'I'm sure it can be sorted out amicably.' Joss paused significantly, evidently waiting for Netta to make the desired apology.

'In that case, you must do the sorting yourself,' she declared mutinously, and rose from her chair with a swift angry movement. She felt a moment's irreverent thankfulness that she had managed to eat a good part of the meal before the outbreak of hostilities; it would have been difficult to make a dignified exit if her hunger had remained unsatisfied. As it was,

'I've never had to apologise for a professional judgment yet, and I don't intend to do so now,' she informed Joss with quiet dignity. 'If you doubt my word,' she spoke coldly to Caroline, 'I suggest you have your ring valued. You'll find your insurance premium will be drastically reduced,' she told the other girl confidently, and added in a biting tone, 'that is, if you've got it insured in the first place.'

She did not wait to see the effect of her words on either Caroline or Joss. As she finished speaking, the dining room door opened to admit Mary with the trolley, and the presence of the maid effectively precluded any further conversation while she was in the room. Netta took advantage of the interruption to slip through the door and make good her escape upstairs. Her heart was hammering in agitated protest at the sheer unreasonableness of Joss's attitude, but despite her upset feelings she nevertheless paused in her hasty flight as she reached the oil painting, and gave it a closer scrutiny. She had not been mistaken about the ring. The painting confirmed what she already knew. She recommenced her ascent with slower steps, and shrugged. It was not her business. Caroline owned the piece of jewellery, and what she did with it was her own affair, but Netta's sense of justice smarted under Joss's criticism, as affronted as was her professional pride by his open expression of doubt.

'The sooner I'm back in London, and working again, the happier I'll be,' she told herself, and knew it was not true. To do her work properly, her heart had to be in it—and her heart refused to be parted from Joss. It beat wildly when he finally appeared through the bedroom door over an hour later, that seemed like a million years of waiting to Netta. She picked up the newspaper from where she had thrown it on the counterpane, and looked again at his photograph, then turned it back face downwards again on the bed, because she was unable to bear the knowledge that his smile was not for her. Unable to bear to be without it, so that she turned it back again, then found she could not see it properly, because her eyes were blurred with tears. She wiped them hastily as the door handle rattled and he strode into the room.

'I'll apologise to Caroline, if it's only to keep the peace,' she decided miserably as the door opened, then had her weakening resolution tossed to the winds by Joss's very first words as he came towards her across the room.

'Did you *have* to provoke an argument with Caroline over her ring?' he demanded angrily, and the deep amber flecks glowed like coals in his eyes. 'I've been until now trying to calm her down.' He evidently did not think it important to try and calm Netta, and anger rose in her again at his unfair discrimination, but he went on before she could speak, 'She was trying her utmost to be pleasant to you all during dinner, and you scarcely spoke a word until this upset started. You might at least have met her half way. Just because you've got red hair, you don't need to start a battle with everyone in sight....'

'For heaven's sake!' She jumped to her feet, her temper flaring in her own defence. 'If you think Caroline was trying to be pleasant to me, you know very little about women,' she told him scornfully. 'And my hair isn't red, it's auburn.' She was too angry to notice the slight twitch to his lips as she said it, and it was gone immediately as she stormed on, 'I didn't provoke any argument with Caroline. I made the mistake of trying to join in the conversation, instead of allowing her to monopolise it, that's all. How was I to know she'd flare up like that over her beastly ring?' she demanded passionately.

'It's enough to make any woman flare up, when the authenticity of her jewellery is put into question,' Joss observed drily.

'I wasn't questioning it,' Netta denied flatly. 'I was stating a fact.'

'What possible proof have you got?' Joss began, and she interrupted him impatiently.

'I don't need proof.' She faced him squarely. 'My own knowledge of jewellery is quite sufficient.' Her voice rang with conviction. She was sure of her ground on this score, at least, and wished it gave her some satisfaction. 'But of course, if you'd prefer not to listen to me,' she said coldly.

'Go on—tell me.' The stern look on Joss's face did not

relax, and she spoke defensively. There was no reason why she should shield Caroline, and since it was not Joss's ring, it was not his business either, she decided with a mental shrug.

'Wendy told me your family went back to Agincourt, which would be the first Jocelyn de Courcey—the one in the painting on the stairs?' Joss nodded, but he did not speak, and she took a deep breath and went on, 'The portrait shows him as a young man in soldier's dress, wearing the ring. Presumably that was after Agincourt. The battle was fought in 1415, and I imagine the portrait was painted when he returned, to hang in the house he built here?'

'You're remarkably accurate so far.' Joss's voice was expressionless. 'Go on guessing,' he invited.

'It's deduction, not guesswork,' Netta replied coldly. 'One look at the ring told me enough to know that whoever put the synthetic stones in it,' she saw Joss's face tighten, but she went on uncaring, rubbing in her point with angry emphasis, 'whoever replaced the real stones made the mistake of, putting it crudely, trying to "tart up" the ring.'

'In what way?' Still his face remained tight, but she sensed she had at least gained his attention.

'By cutting the stones with facets,' Netta mustered her patience to explain as simply as she could. 'Until the fifteenth century, stones were not cut with facets. They were used solely for their colour. I imagine the ring worn by your ancestor was fairly old, even when he acquired it?' she raised questioning eyebrows, and Joss nodded.

'It was bestowed as a gift for valour. He returned with it from France.' He confirmed her judgment, and it gave her renewed confidence to continue.

'Synthetic stones have to be cut and polished in exactly the same manner as natural gems, and whoever cut the stones in the present ring did so by using what we call, in the trade, the brilliant cut. That didn't come in until round about 1700, it's got fifty-eight facets, and it's used to reflect and refract light, which gives the stones, particularly diamonds, the brilliant sparkle we're used to now. That sparkle alone told me the gems had been tampered with, even though the setting itself is obviously old, probably the original one.'

'Anything else?' Joss queried, and Netta looked at him, suspicious of sarcasm, but his face revealed nothing, and she went on thoughtfully,

'There's one other thing, though it wouldn't point to the ruby being necessarily synthetic,' she conceded. 'But from where I sat, the principal stone looked to be absolutely flawless. I couldn't be sure without a closer examination, but it isn't often one gets a natural, completely flawless gem of such a size. It could be confirmed by a test,' she went on, 'and if such a large ruby were indeed flawless, it would be virtually priceless as well, so if Caroline's right and I'm wrong, she'd be well advised to make sure her ring's insured,' she added drily, and her tone said she was confident of her own facts, and at the same time doubted if the ring would be insured, adequately or otherwise. 'My father's got a testing kit in our lab at home,' she offered, 'or,' and her voice held a thin edge of sarcasm, 'or if Caroline doesn't trust us, she could always take the ring to the London Chamber of Commerce laboratory, they'd test it for her there. But I've no doubt they'd confirm everything I say,' she said with spirited conviction, 'which is why I've got no intention of apologising to her,' she finished defiantly.

CHAPTER TWELVE

'You could at least come downstairs and attempt to make it up,' Joss said shortly, and Netta stared at him in amazement.

'Make up what?' she demanded angrily. 'I didn't quarrel with Caroline, she quarrelled with me. And if there's any making up, or apologising, to be done, it's her place to do it,' she declared stormily. 'Besides, I'm tired,' she added. 'It's been a long day, and I've got no intention of coming downstairs again tonight.' That at least was true, she thought dispiritedly. A cloud of weariness caught up with her and she suddenly felt limp, although she suspected that most of it was caused by nervous tension rather than by actual tiredness. With an effort she rallied her energies. Now was not the time to give in.

'There's another thing,' she said, before Joss had time to speak. If grievances were going to be aired, she decided, she might as well do her share, instead of sitting back meekly and letting Caroline and Joss toss all the arrows in her direction. 'Your cousin behaves as if I don't exist,' she complained bitterly. 'It's true,' she insisted, as he opened his mouth to speak. 'She's planning parties, right into next year, and she speaks to the servants as if it's she who's mistress here. For that matter, why is she here?' she demanded to know. 'And how long is she going to stay? She's acting as if she intends to make it her permanent home, and she's behaving as if I'm the guest in the house, instead of herself. You married me to solve your own difficulties,' she accused him bitterly, 'but I'm still entitled to be treated....'

'Caroline came here for the same reason as you did yourself, because her house in London is in the throes of redecoration, and she didn't want to stay in an hotel,' Joss interrupted her curtly. 'And as for entitlements,' he went

on harshly, 'you can't have those without the obligations
that go with them. You can't have it both ways, Netta.' He
looked at her squarely, and she flinched away from the
message in his eyes. 'You've got to make the choice,' he
reminded her. 'You seem to have abdicated from your
obligations,' his bitterness of tone matched her own, 'and
regarding entitlements, surely I should be the one to complain about lack of those? Oh, you needn't worry,' as her
eyes widened, 'I won't disturb you. You can sleep in blissful solitude,' he told her cuttingly. 'I'll use my dressing
room.'

'Perhaps you'd prefer to go to Caroline?'

She did not know what made her say it. The moment
they were uttered, she wished the words unsaid, but it was
too late. He had heard them, and his face went white under
his tan, and she drew a sharp breath of fear. He spoke, and
she shivered at the ice in his voice.

'I'm married to you, not to Caroline,' he reminded her
silkily. Did he mean, 'Not to Caroline—yet?' She could not
be sure, and he gave her no time to surmise. He continued
in a tight voice, 'Since you won't come downstairs, I might
as well bid you goodnight now.'

She thought he would turn and go, then, and leave her
alone. She did not expect him to turn towards her. She
tried to back away, but only succeeded in backing into the
bedpost. It was hard, and unyielding—as hard and unyielding as Joss's arm, that went round her and pulled her close
against him in a vice-like grip.

'Goodnight, Netta,' he gritted, and bent his head over
her. She twisted her head to one side, trying to avoid him,
but his other hand came up and caught her under her chin,
and turned her face back towards him, tilting it upwards to
meet his lips. They descended with a hard, angry pressure,
forcing hers apart. They hurt, but the pain was as nothing
compared to the agony of knowing that it was anger and not
love that drove him. There was no gentleness, no desire,
only fury and a fierce urge to retaliate. His kiss went on and
on, it felt as if for ever, denying her breath, draining her
strength, until she began to feel as if he would never re-

lease her. When at last he did, she swayed, half fainting, away from him. She drew in her breath in short, sobbing gasps, and her voice, when she found the strength to use it, came as a thin whimper of sound, scarcely audible as she forced the words through bruised and throbbing lips.

'I hate you. . . .'

She reached back shaking hands and grasped at the bed-post for support.

'Go away . . . go. . . .' she gasped. If he did not leave her soon, she would surely collapse. Her legs would not support her, and she clung to the bedpost with the strength of desperation, feeling her senses begin to slip away. Joss's face wavered and became blurred in front of her eyes, and the room began to grow dim.

'Leave me,' she implored. She must not faint in front of him. She must not let him see her weakness. Through a rapidly darkening haze she heard him speak, and the icy fury in his voice acted as an astringent on her failing senses.

'I'm going—and glad to,' he flung at her cuttingly. 'Goodnight, Netta.' And he was gone. She did not see him go. She heard the door slam behind him, but her eyes were closed, although the delicately veined lids could not hold back the welling tears that would no longer be denied, and poured like rain across her cheeks as her nerveless hands loosed their weak hold on the bedpost and she slid help-lessly to her knees on the soft sheepskin rug on the floor.

She was back on the cargo vessel. She had to be. There could be no other reason why she still felt seasick. A wave of nausea gripped her, and she opened her eyes and strug-gled upright against the pillows—and became aware that she was in a bed, not in a bunk. The big double bed in the master suite at Thimbles, that was made up for two. She reached across for the second pillow. It lay in its em-broidered case of pristine freshness, uncreased and, she winced, obviously unused. With what seemed a mighty effort she managed to drag it on top of her own pillow, and lay back against the pile with a sigh of relief.

Vaguely she remembered getting into bed the previous

night, but she could not recall what time it was when she
finally pulled herself upright off the rug, and with the last
vestige of strength crawled between the sheets. Somehow
she must have managed to get undressed first. A glance
downwards confirmed that she was wearing Rosemary's
nightdress, the daisy-sprigged one that went with the robe.
She wriggled uneasily, and reached behind to pull the
second pillow further down under her shoulders. Her own
pillow felt uncomfortably damp and, she stroked her face
with cautious fingers, her cheeks felt sore as a consequence.
So did her eyes. Listlessly she dropped her hands, and
hoped Rosemary also kept some spare make-up in the
bathroom cabinet. When she went downstairs to face Joss
and Caroline she would need something to disguise the
ravages of her distress of the night before.

'Ah, you're awake.' A light tap on the bedroom door was
followed by Mrs Berry's beaming face above a silver tray,
on which reposed a dainty china morning tea-set and a
plate of biscuits.

'It can't be breakfast time yet?' Netta sat up hastily. 'Oh,
my goodness!' she groaned, and subsided back on to her
pillows, her face as pale as the linen behind her.

'Whatever's the matter?' Mrs Berry's kindly visage was
full of concern, and she put the tray hurriedly on the bedside table and took both Netta's hands in her own.

'I don't seem to have got rid of the seasickness from the
voyage over.' Netta closed her eyes, and waited for the wave
of nausea and giddiness to pass.

'Drink your tea and have a biscuit,' Mrs Berry let go of
her hands, and the clink of china, and an inviting pouring-
out sound, brought Netta's eyes open again.

'I'd love a cup of tea, but I don't want anything to eat,'
she shuddered.

'Just a nibble, you'll find it'll help,' Mrs Berry insisted.
'They're only plain arrowroots, there's nothing to hurt you
in these,' as Netta still hesitated.

'It's only the aftermath of seasickness, that's all.' Amusement stirred in Netta as she took the cup and the plate
with two crisp round wafers on it. 'It's not. . . .' She

stopped, and the amusement died within her. She could not be sure. And seasickness did not normally continue after docking. In fact, she had been free from it for several days before they docked, once the storms subsided. She shivered, suddenly cold, and took a hasty gulp of her tea. It was hot and sweet, and to her surprise it did as Mrs Berry had predicted. She began to feel better immediately.

'There now, that's brought some colour back to your cheeks.' The housekeeper eyed her keenly as she finished the cup. 'You're tired out,' she told Netta. 'You just take your time, and finish your tea and biscuits.'

'I'll get up for breakfast.' Joss had refused to allow her to have her dinner brought up the evening before, and she determined she would not ask again. 'What time?' she began.

'Just whenever you're ready,' Mrs Berry said accommodatingly. 'Mr Joss and Miss Caroline had their breakfast early, and went out riding. Mr Joss said to let you sleep on, so I didn't disturb you.'

He would, Netta thought irascibly, but not for any reasons of consideration, as Mrs Berry supposed. It would be convenient for him, if she slept on. It would give him a watertight excuse to enjoy Caroline's company, without being hampered by her own presence, she thought bitterly.

She slid out of bed cautiously, and tried her legs, then gave a sigh of relief as she stood up without the giddiness and nausea returning. Her legs felt strong enough, she walked a few steps experimentally, her confidence flooding back as they performed with their normal agility.

'It was nothing but hunger,' she told herself robustly. 'I'd been all day without food yesterday, and thanks to Caroline I didn't wait to finish my dinner last night. I've been worrying over nothing.'

In a more cheerful frame of mind she donned a summer skirt and top that Mary produced for her, and ran downstairs to tackle Mrs Berry's substantial breakfast with more zest than she would have believed herself capable of an hour ago.

'I think I'll go for a stroll, it's a lovely morning,' she

decided as the housekeeper came to clear away the table.
'Perhaps I'll take Tara with me, if she'll come,' she smiled
as a russet head appeared round the breakfast room door,
with a wary eye on Mrs Berry. As Joss had seen fit to leave
her to her own devices, she would be glad of the dog's
company.

'Just try and stop her,' Mrs Berry laughed. 'She's been
bothering me to let her in here ever since she heard your
voice when you came downstairs, but I reckoned you were
entitled to eat your meal in peace, so I shut her in the
kitchen until you'd finished.'

'I'm free now, so let's go.' Netta held out her hands to
the dog, which responded with an eagerly waving tail, its
lovely feathering acting like a soft fan and setting up a cool
draught against her legs. 'Which way shall we go?' she
murmured as they reached the steps outside the front door
together, but the setter knew no such indecision. With a
backwards look that clearly invited Netta to follow her, she
trotted off in the direction of the stable block.

'It's easy to see where your favourite haunts lie,' Netta
smiled, but for want of any better direction to follow she
strolled slowly in the wake of the setter. The sun was
pleasantly warm, promising heat as it rose higher. It would
have been nice to go riding while the air was still fresh, she
thought wistfully, and thrust down a wish that Joss might
have roused her to go with him, or even waited for her. But
he had chosen to ride with Caroline instead.

Netta shrugged. There was nothing she could do about
it now, and at least she had Tara for company. Or had she?
She had become so absorbed in her own thoughts that she
had not noticed the setter disappear. She looked round.
The dog was nowhere in sight, but an open door in the
middle of the stable block gave her a clue, and as she
turned towards it, a broad country voice raised in good-
humoured protest confirmed her guess as to her quarry's
whereabouts.

'Leave my brushes alone, will you, you young limb!
They're to groom the horses with, not to play with. Hey,
come back!'

Sounds of a scuffle preceded the setter's reappearance through the stable door. She hurtled into the yard in full flight, swinging a big oval brush in her teeth by its webbing hand strap, then frisked across the gravel and dropped her trophy at Netta's feet with a gruff invitation to play.

'I'll skin you, that I will!' From Tara's reaction, it was evidently a morning ritual which she thoroughly enjoyed. She danced expectantly round the owner of the voice as he thrust the door wide open, and she noticed he carried a ball in one gnarled hand. 'Have this instead,' he invited the setter, 'and let me have my brush back.'

With a strength and accuracy that made Netta exclaim, 'You must be a cricketer!' the newcomer lobbed the ball half way across the paddock that backed on to the stable block, and the dog took off after it like a russet streak.

'The gate. . . .' Netta held her breath. A high five-barred gate guarded the paddock, and it did not seem possible that the dog could stop in time.

'She'll climb that, never fear, ma'am.' The setter did not hesitate. She made straight for it, and went up and over the barrier with the agility of a cat, and Netta let out her breath with relief.

'You'd better have your brush, before she comes back,' she handed it over with a smile.

'She'll not touch it again,' the man said confidently, 'she only grabs it first thing in the morning, just to start the day off, so to speak. Just to let me know she's around.'

'You must be . . .?'

'Will Dyer, ma'am.' He smiled back, and his face creased in a thousand tiny wrinkles, like a friendly prune. He must at one time have been fairly tall, Netta judged, but a life on horseback had bandied his legs, and reduced him much nearer to Netta's own height, but his clear, young-looking eyes belied his bald head, and he obviously took her observation as a compliment.

'You're right about the cricket, Mrs de Courcey.' Netta caught her breath and wished, not for the first time, that her heart would not behave so unsteadily each time someone called her by her married name. But at least the effect did not show, she consoled herself, because Will went on cheerfully, 'I play for the Long Minton team. So does Mr Joss, he's the captain, though we've had to do without him up to now, this summer. I reckon he'll be around a bit more from now on, though?' with a quizzical look at Netta.

'Perhaps.' It was not a question she was in a position to answer. She could only speak for herself, and she did not intend to be around for very long. And afterwards, if Joss married Caroline.... Her heart contracted in a sharp thrust of agony at the thought, and this time it must have shown, because the groom glanced at her keenly.

'You look a bit peaky,' he began, and Netta gave a rather shaky laugh.

'We had a bad journey across on the boat, and I still haven't quite found my land legs yet,' she explained hurriedly. 'It was a cargo ship, and a bit unsteady, and I'm not a very good sailor at the best of times,' she excused herself.

'Come and sit in the stable with me for a minute, the sun's a bit warm out here,' the groom suggested considerately. 'Don't worry about Tara,' he added, as Netta hesitated, glancing towards the paddock, 'she'll hunt rabbits in the hedges for a while before she brings her ball back. She always does.'

He led the way into the stable. It was blessedly cool, and smelt sweetly of hay, and the pleasant, musty aroma of fresh straw. Will pulled up a clean straw bale and motioned to Netta to sit down. 'Rest in the cool for a while,' he suggested kindly.

'Do you mind if I watch?' Netta sat down and eyed the palomino mare on which he had evidently been working when Tara interrupted him.

'Watch away,' Will answered goodhumouredly. 'I can see you like horses,' he discovered the link between them with evident pleasure.

'She's beautiful. It's a long time since I've been able to go riding.' She realised now how much she missed it. Her eyes roamed admiringly over the pale golden mare, her cream mane and tail like silk, evidence of the groom's patient care.

'Aye, she's Mr Joss's favourite, is Fleet.' The proud head turned at the mention of her name, and Netta fondled the soft muzzle that was thrust enquiringly into her outstretched hands.

'Yet Joss isn't riding her?' It seemed strange, if the mare was his favourite.

'She's in foal, ma'am.' Will stopped his tuneless whistle to answer her, and his hands stilled for a moment from his rhythmic brushing. 'She'll need peace and quiet, and a bit of coddling for a while, won't you, old girl? We've got the other two mares to cope with any riding Mr Joss wants to do, while Fleet's out of action.' He resumed grooming, and Netta relaxed as she watched him. She found the timeless occupation peculiarly soothing to watch. Men had been performing the same task from the time they first gentled horses to do their bidding, and hands would still be so occupied as long as men and horses remained. There was no doubt that under Will's hands the palomino would be carefully tended. 'Coddled,' he had said. She smiled as she watched him, and knew a quick stab of envy for the mare. The palomino would have her foal, calm in the security of familiar surroundings lavished with care that only love can give....

'Stop it!' she begged her mind, aghast at the trend of her own thoughts, and turned with relief as Tara bundled through the door and headed straight for her, to drop the ball in her lap.

'She's taken to you,' Will commented with a smile, and Netta rubbed the setter's soft ears.

'It's mutual,' she answered, and stood up. 'I'll take her ball into the paddock, out of your way.' She paused as the crisp clop of hooves sounded on the gravel outside.

'Sounds like Mr Joss is back,' Will commented, but Netta did not stop to listen.

'Come on, Tara!' She snapped her fingers to the setter, and started hurriedly towards the door. If she was quick, she might be able to slip away without Joss seeing her.

'I'm a coward,' she told herself scornfully, but her heart failed her at the prospect of meeting him. She reached the door with the setter at her heels, and stopped irresolutely. Another minute and she would have made her escape undetected. But the minute was gone beyond recall, and the two riders were already approaching the stables. Tara gruffed a welcome, and destroyed any hope she might have had of slipping away without Joss seeing her. His eyes levelled with her own across the stable yard, and she felt her throat go dry. It flashed across her mind that the two cousins made a handsome couple. Joss's horse was a dark chestnut. The animal was tall, and Netta surveyed it with knowledgeable eyes; it was a full sixteen hands, if not more, and man and beast made a superb study in bronze against the clear morning light.

'I'll take over the horses for you, Mr Joss.' Will appeared in the stable doorway leading the palomino, and perforce Netta had to step right outside in order to allow him past.

'Thanks, Will.' Joss swung lightly out of the saddle, and turned immediately to help his cousin to dismount. Instead of reaching ground in the orthodox manner, Caroline kicked her feet free from the stirrups and swung her legs across the horse's back, then slid down straight into Joss's arms, where she remained for an unnecessarily long time, Netta thought sourly, laughing up into Joss's face. Watching the two together, a strange feeling took possession of Netta, a primitive feeling, that took no account of civilisation and good behaviour. Her heart gave an agonising throb of outraged anger and pain.

'That was a gorgeous ride, darling. Now you're home, we'll be able to go out together every morning.'

'Joss should be taking me out, not Caroline.'

In a violent upsurge of rebellion that took her completely unaware, her heart finally took control. In a few brief, devastating seconds that left her mind shaken and defeated, it put all her predetermined resolutions to flight, and came at last into its own.

'Joss is my husband, and I love him. . . .'

Although outwardly she uttered no sound, the words

echoed like a clarion call, and Netta responded as if hypnotised. Capitulation was remarkably easy, she discovered with a numb lack of surprise. It would have been easier still if only Joss loved her.

'My horse needs rubbing down immediately, she's sweating.' Caroline spoke to the groom imperiously, and tapped her riding crop against the top of her boot with a sharp, impatient sound that sent a surge of irritation through Netta.

'I was just about to take Fleet to the paddock, Mr Joss. I'll only be a couple of minutes.' The groom spoke directly to his employer, and Caroline's lips thinned in temper.

'I said immediately,' she began, and Joss broke in quietly.

'Carry on with what you were doing, Will. I'll throw a rug over the mare, she's still a bit blown,' he observed. 'I warned you not to gallop her in this temperature,' he added to Caroline, but his voice was uncritical, and he slipped the girths with quick fingers, and pulled the saddle from the mare's back. The animal was dark with sweat, though Netta noticed Joss's horse was virtually unmarked.

'Don't stand right in front of the saddle rack,' he spoke curtly to Netta, 'you can see I want to put this down.'

She could see nothing of the sort, she thought shortly, but nevertheless she stepped out of his path to allow him access to the rack. The saddle was heavy and awkward to hold, but she had not even noticed the saddle rack was there, until he mentioned it, and resentment rose like gall in her at the sharpness of his tone.

'We'll have to get you mounted, Mrs de Courcey.' Will freed the palomino into the paddock, and rejoined them at the stable, and saved her from having to make any reply. 'I'll see to the mare now, sir,' he took charge of Caroline's mount, and turned to Netta as he was about to lead it into the stable. 'In a week or two's time, the mornings will be nice and crisp, ideal for hacking. It's grand country for riding hereabouts.'

'I'd love it,' Netta responded with equal enthusiasm. 'It's ages since I've had time to ride.'

She needed time now, not so much to ride as to think. Until a few brief moments ago, her overwhelming priority had been to escape from Thimbles, and Joss. Escape from her marriage. Now, life had turned upside down again, and she felt bewildered and lost. Her fingers sought her ring, twisting it round and round on her finger. Twisting it downwards, as if she was trying to screw it on, so that it would never come off again. The jewels were all that had kept her at Thimbles until now, and the necessity to honour her promise to Ranjit to see them securely locked away in his bank in London. Now, except that she still must keep her promise, the jewels seemed unimportant—valueless. Joss had locked away her heart even more securely than the jewels, she thought bitterly, and in its turn it had erected barriers of its own which imprisoned her far more effectively than the lock on any safe could hope to do.

'You won't be able to ride,' Caroline turned on her waspishly. 'There isn't a spare horse. Fleet's in foal, and that only leaves the other two mares—Joss's and mine.'

Perhaps it was the other girl's arrogant attitude that tipped the balance, or it could have been the strange new feeling that possessed her, and seemed to dictate her actions without any conscious effort on her part. Netta did not stop to dissect her emotions, she simply acted on them without question, guided by instinct as women have been since the days of Eve. She swung round and faced Caroline, and snapped,

'Joss's mare, and *mine*,' and had the satisfaction of seeing the fair-haired girl pause, nonplussed. Now I've gone this far, I might as well carry on, she told herself stoutly, and added before Caroline could reply, 'For the short while you're a guest here,' she emphasised the other girl's position at Thimbles determinedly, 'we can hire a mount for you. I'm sure there must be a livery stables somewhere locally.' She ignored Caroline's gasp. Curiously, she felt some sympathy towards her. She knew exactly how it felt to be an unwanted outsider. Caroline looked like an alsatian that had been suddenly bitten hard by a pekinese, she thought with a detached sort of amusement, and turned to the groom.

'Will seven o'clock tomorrow morning suit you, Will?'
She tried not to notice Joss's frown, and the dawning grin
of approval which showed on the groom's face as he replied
with alacrity,

'That'll be fine, Mrs de Courcey. I'll have the mare
ready saddled up for you.'

'I'll be here by seven, then,' she nodded her thanks. 'In
the meantime,' she turned back to Joss, and her courage
very nearly failed her at the sight of the bright, glowing
flecks in his eyes. She had made him angry, but it could not
be helped. Her chin rose in a defiant tilt. She was fighting
now for her very existence, she realised bleakly. Life without Joss could hold no meaning for her, and having stirred
up her own rebellion, she thought with a grim lack of
humour, she might as well fight on, whatever the consequences—or the cost. She met his eyes without flinching. 'In the meantime, I'll start making arrangements for
the ball,' she decided in a firm voice. 'When had you in
mind to hold it?' she queried politely, knowing full well,
because she had heard Caroline discuss it with him.

'I've already made plans for next week,' the other girl
began angrily, and Netta threw her a look of glacial indifference.

Curiously, Caroline did not seem to pose so much of a
threat any longer. The real threat, Netta acknowledged unhappily, came from Joss himself. From the reason why he
had married her in the first place. From his indifference
since. She could deal with hate, she told herself forlornly.
Hate at least was a tangible emotion, something she could
have fought against. Indifference was like trying to scale a
high wall, the further up it one climbed, the higher it grew.

'In that case, the quicker I start climbing, the better,'
she told herself robustly.

'Next week is too soon for the ball,' she said aloud. 'The
week after will suit me better. I'll see Mrs Berry about it,
as soon as I go indoors. Then I'll get you to help me with
the guest list,' she added to Joss sweetly.

'Can't you and Caroline manage that between you, without dragging me into it?' Joss evinced every man's reluctance to get involved with the nitty-gritty of arrange-

ments. 'I've got months of estate work to catch up on.'

'In that case you'll be in your study,' Netta deduced, 'so I'll know where to find you.'

With a calm smile that belied the inner torment which threatened to tear her in two, she snapped her fingers to the setter and walked off towards the house with her head held high. And had to hold on tight to Tara's collar to prevent her legs from taking flight, and carrying her to the blessed privacy of some quiet corner where she could let flow the torrent of tears that, without warning, suddenly threatened to overwhelm her.

CHAPTER THIRTEEN

LONG before seven o'clock came the next morning, Netta knew she could not go riding as she planned. She also knew, with an unshakable certainty that needed no confirmation, that she would not be able to ride for several months to come.

'I've *got* to stay with Joss now. It's his child as well as mine. When I tell him....'

She paused, and her brief moment of joyous excitement vanished like morning mist.

'I won't use my baby as sticking plaster to hold our marriage together,' she told herself stubbornly. 'Joss has got to want me for myself, because he loves me—not because of our child. If he doesn't....'

If Joss became aware of her condition, she knew there would be no possibility of them parting. Clearly she remembered Wendy's words at the Embassy, minutes before the marriage ceremony.

'Joss is an honourable man....'

'But I don't want it to be that way.' Rebellion rose within her. 'I won't force myself on any man.' She gave a wry smile as she realised she had twisted Joss's own words to suit herself. She accepted her morning tray of tea and biscuits from Mary, and blessed whatever circumstance had prevented Mrs Berry from bringing it upstairs herself. The housekeeper had disconcertingly sharp eyes, whereas Mary would not question her desire to take her early morning refreshment in recumbent comfort. She would doubtless put it down to Mrs Berry's insistence that Netta must rest after her recent ordeals, and her own meek obedience in this respect would go unremarked by the young maid. For the moment at least her secret was hers alone. And must remain so for as long as possible, she determined. At least until she was sure where her future lay, either with Joss—or without. If he wanted her to remain, it must be on her own terms. Otherwise....

The bright morning outside the windows looked suddenly bleak, and she sipped gratefully at the warmth of her cup of tea to combat the icy chill that took possession of her. Her heart had started the rebellion, but it was she who would have to fight its battles, she realised ruefully. Undoubtedly, the first clash would be with Joss himself, when he discovered she had not turned up at the stables that morning. He had heard her ask Will to prepare the horse in readiness. Cravenly, she hoped he would be occupied by estate work. That he might not appear at breakfast time. That he might have eaten his meal early, and gone out. She moved slowly down the stairs, her eyes apprehensively on the breakfast room door, but it was closed, and told her nothing. She passed beneath the portrait of the first Jocelyn de Courcey, and something made her glance upwards. The painted gold stare seemed to attract her, hold her.

'You'd have battled for what you wanted, wouldn't you?' she exclaimed softly. 'You wouldn't turn and run.' A sudden sense of oneness with Joss's long-ago ancestor flooded over her, and she nodded to him companionably. 'Neither will I,' she promised, and continued on her way with renewed courage. There was no sound from the breakfast room, and no sign of Mrs Berry or Mary serving. Perhaps Joss was not there, after all? She pushed open the door and went in.

Joss was there, and one glance at his set face told her that he already knew of her defection. He must have been waiting for her, because he turned the second she walked through the door, and she knew a moment's swift thankfulness that her early morning weakness was gone. To her relief, the tea and biscuits had worked as effectively this morning as they had done the day before, and as she turned to face Joss, all traces of her early malaise had vanished. He spoke curtly, the moment she appeared.

'You said you were coming riding. Will prepared the mare ready for you.'

He was in riding kit himself. He had obviously been for a canter, and just as obviously he was very angry that she had opted out of doing the same. If she had felt well enough, she could have gone with him. Her heart wept at the loss, and she had difficulty in keeping her voice steady as she replied,

'I changed my mind.'

'You changed your mind? After you'd given Will definite instructions to get the mare ready for you by seven o'clock, you changed your mind? Just like that?' His voice flicked her like a whiplash, and she flinched away as if he had struck her a physical blow.

'I didn't. . . .' She stopped. She could not tell him she did not feel well when she woke. It would mean questions—and explanations. Joss paused for neither.

'You didn't intend to come in the first place,' he accused her angrily. 'You only ordered the horse for yourself, so that Caroline shouldn't be able to ride.'

'Nothing was further from my mind,' she denied hotly.

'Don't make excuses,' he cut her short impatiently. 'It was nothing but childish spite, on your part, to prevent Caroline from enjoying her ride. There could be no other reason for you not to turn up at the stables.'

There was an excellent reason, but it was not one she dared to divulge to Joss.

'I heard you come down, Mrs de Courcey, so I thought I'd bring in breakfast while it was nice and hot.' Mrs Berry's appearance put an end to any further conversation between them as she wheeled the trolley into the room and began loading the sideboard. 'Miss Caroline asked for her breakfast in her room as she's not riding this morning,' she explained, and anger stirred in Netta. Caroline could have her breakfast in bed, but Joss refused to let Netta have her dinner brought up on a tray the evening before.

'That's all right, if you can cope?' Joss answered the housekeeper mildly, and the latter nodded, although her expression seemed to Netta to be the reverse of enthusiastic over the extra work entailed.

'I'll manage,' she said, and turned to Netta. 'Will you

help yourself, Mrs de Courcey, or would you like me to serve for you?' she offered helpfully.

'Netta will cope for us both,' Joss answered for her, and his tone was hard.

'Then I'll leave you in peace to enjoy your meal.'

Netta could have laughed at the irony of her choice of expression. Peace was the last thing Mrs Berry had left behind her when she walked out of the room. She turned towards the sideboard, resenting what amounted to an order from Joss, but thankful for the excuse to present her back to his angry countenance.

'Porridge?'

They might have been strangers, conversing politely to one another in some hotel.

'Coffee?'

She handed Joss his bowl. He handed her a filled cup.

'Aren't you eating?'

She did not think he would notice.

'I don't want....' She stopped. She would have to eat properly, now. She had not got only her own health to consider. Besides, food would give her the strength to face the day ahead, she was under no illusion that it would be anything but difficult.

'I'll just have porridge.' It was smooth and creamy, and slipped down easily without needing much help from her aching throat. Like the early morning tea, it was warm and comforting, and by the time she had finished her helping she did indeed feel stronger, and more able to summon up the courage to bridge the tight silence which stretched between them like an invisible barrier. She asked, in what she hoped was a reasonably calm voice,

'Will you be in your study this morning?' She did not even know where his study was, she realised with a pang. 'I need to know who to invite to the ball.'

'If you still insist on taking the arrangements out of Caroline's hands,' Joss frowned impatiently. 'She could have sent out the invitations without reference to me. She knows all the people who're likely to come.'

'I shan't need to take up much of your time,' she in-

sisted. She needed his time for the rest of their lives, she
thought mournfully, but she could not tell him so.

'Oh well, if you must,' he capitulated ungraciously. 'It's
your privilege.'

As his wife, it was her right, but she forbore to tell him
that, also. It would only provoke another quarrel.

'We might as well get it over now, if you've finished
eating.' Joss put down his coffee cup with a sharp click that
made her wince for the safety of the fine china. 'I can't give
you long, I've got to go out with Will on estate business.'
His tone left her in no doubt that he considered the estate
business more important than her own, and she bit her lip,
but she rose with him,

'I'll come right away.' She would not need to ask the
way to the study if she went along with Joss, she thought
wistfully, and preceded him into a square panelled room
on the other side of the hall. It overlooked the gardens and
the river in the distance, and she viewed her surroundings
interestedly. This room, more than any of the others in the
house, would reveal Joss to her. It was opposite the breakfast room, and larger in size, but the panelling was similar,
each separate plank being craftsman carved in the char-
acteristic linenfold pattern of the period.

There the similarity with the other rooms ended. The
elegant furnishings and sumptuous comfort that char-
acterised the rest of the house were conspicuous by their
absence. The study furnishings were strictly functional,
serving the needs of a busy office on an extensive and well
run estate. A solid oak desk dominated the room, its
antiquity doing nothing to detract from its workmanlike
appearance. A large wheelback chair, cushioned to match
the curtains, stood behind the desk. It was pushed aside,
Netta noticed, as if Joss had already been working there
that morning after he returned from his ride, and only
broke off because of the necessity of eating breakfast. The
rest of the room reflected the appearance of the desk. Enclosed bookcases, filled with what looked like bound
ledgers, lined the whole of one wall, and Netta's eyes were
attracted to the dates, boldly embossed on the leather

spines. The set of books nearest to her encompassed the 1840s, one for each year. The sheer number of the volumes on the tightly packed shelves told her that the wall held a fascinating history of careful husbandry spanning the centuries. It was something she longed to delve into. Would she ever have the opportunity? she wondered.

She gave a sharp sigh and turned her back on the books, then her eyes caught the gleam of a safe in the far corner of the room. It was square, and solid, and looked about as impregnable as Fort Knox.

'Yes, that's where your suit is.' Joss caught the direction of her glance, and his voice was as hard as the steel the safe was made of. 'And if that's the reason you were so insistent on coming into my study yourself for the address book,' the look he turned on her was one of flint, and the tiny amber specks in his eyes burned like fire, 'I might as well make it clear to you now that the safe's got a combination lock—and only I know the combination. And your safari suit, and the jewels, will remain in the safe until I personally hand them over to your father on his return to England.' Grimly he reiterated his earlier intention.

'Nothing was....' Angry crimson rose in a tide across Netta's throat and cheeks, and her eyes sparked at this further unjust assumption. The possibility had not occurred to her. She had not even thought about the jewels.

'Nothing was further from your mind,' he finished the sentence for her with harsh mockery. 'You told me that before. I didn't believe you then, and I don't believe you now. Yes, come in?' He broke off as a confident rap sounded on the study door.

'You said to come in after breakfast, Mr Joss.' Will appeared round the door and threw Netta an apologetic glance. 'I didn't mean to disturb you, Mrs de Courcey. I'll come back a bit later.'

'There's no need, Will, I've finished.' With a supreme effort Netta managed to summon up a smile. 'We're planning to hold a ball, and I just came in for the address book,' she explained as the groom still hesitated. 'I want to make out the invitations.'

'It seems a shame to stay indoors writing, on such a lovely morning,' Will said sympathetically, and turned to Joss. 'The one mare wasn't exercised earlier on, sir, so I harnessed her to the trap to give her a run. I thought as we were going down as far as the ten acre, it would be quicker than walking. Why not come along for the ride, before the sun gets too hot?' he suggested to Netta kindly. 'You looked a bit peaky yesterday morning,' he remembered, 'maybe a bit of fresh air, sitting in the trap, would help. It'll take less energy than riding.'

Will had guessed why she had not turned up at the stables, even if Joss did not. Netta saw his head come up at the groom's mention that she had been 'a bit peaky', and his look seemed to sear her across the room.

Let him make what he pleased of it, she thought defiantly. He had not waited for her to explain. She ignored the reality that she dared not offer him the true explanation. She did not feel like being just, she still smarted too much under his infamous assumption of her reason for wanting to visit his study. He had actually implied that she might try to break into his safe. Her blood boiled at the suggestion. He had accused her of being a jewel thief, once. Her lips set. She would rather waste the sunshine than ride in the trap with Joss. If Will had been going on his own she would have delighted at the opportunity for the ride. But not with Joss. She opened her mouth to refuse.

'That's an excellent suggestion.' Once again Joss spoke for her, and she bridled resentfully. She was quite capable of answering any questions addressed to her, for herself, she fumed inwardly, prevented by the presence of the groom from saying so out loud to Joss himself. 'Fresh air blows away a lot of cobwebs,' he added obliquely, and directed a look at Netta that made her grit her teeth to prevent the words on the tip of her tongue from flooding out.

'Leave the address book until we come back. You can collect it on your way indoors.' He effectively prevented her from having any excuse to refuse, since she did not know where he kept the address book in any case, and would have to wait for him to give it to her.

'The trap's outside the door, Mr Joss.'

The jet mare which Caroline had ridden the previous morning was harnessed between the shafts. Will walked to her head and held her rock-steady while Joss opened the door at the rear of the high vehicle and helped Netta to mount the step. His fingers closed over her hand with a firm grip. Assisting her? Or making sure she came with him? His hold felt warm and strong, and for an agonised second she stood still on the step and closed her eyes, fighting down a fierce longing to clasp his fingers to her, cling to them, and turn into his arms, ignore the presence of the groom and let the words fall from her lips that were so different from those that lay there just a moment ago.

'Joss! Oh Joss, I love you!'

Surely—surely he must feel her unspoken cry? But all he said was,

'Walk on, right to the front, it's quite safe.'

He misunderstood her hesitation, assumed it to be nervousness as the trap rocked slightly under her weight. She opened her eyes again and stepped in obediently and walked to the front of the trap. And the sun shone, and the birds sang, and Will's homely face smiled encouragingly at her from beside the horse's head, and with a numb sense of disbelief she saw that the world went on behaving quite normally, no matter that her heart broke in two inside her.

The trap was the bucket type, with high wheels and room for four passengers, and Joss mounted after her. He continued to hold her hand until she sat down, when he sat beside her, leaving the opposite seat for Will to take the reins, and for a wild moment of hope Netta thought he might forget to release her fingers. Perhaps not even want to let go of them.

'Let's go that way, Will, down the drive and alongside the river, then come back across the park from the ten acre. It'll take us by all the growing fields, then.' Joss dropped her hand to point out the route to Will, and the sun seemed to go in. Netta shivered, and went very still.

'Are you cold?' He must have felt her shiver, the confined space forced them to sit close together, and her slight movement must have transmitted itself to him.

'No, it's....' She stammered to a halt.

'It's cool here, we're standing in the shadow of the house.' Will found her excuse for her as he joined them in the trap and unhooked the reins from the metal upright on the front. 'The sun's hot enough out of the shadow,' he consoled. 'Giddup!' He clicked his tongue to the mare and they moved smoothly across the gravel into the warm brightness away from the house, that in spite of its strength still could not melt the ice that closed about her heart with an iron grip. She winced as they passed by the clump of hollyhocks. She could not shut her eyes as she would have liked to, in case Joss noticed, so she turned her face away and pretended to admire the view, because she found the ice could not freeze away the pain.

'They keep love in the house, do hollyhocks....'

'Tara's waiting for us.' Will broke the silence and drew their attention to the setter, quietly sitting at the bend of the drive, cleverly anticipating their arrival and their route.

'Shall we stop to pick her up?' Netta begged. It would be a comfort to feel the dog with her. She needed something to hold, now Joss had released her hand.

'Tara won't sit in the trap with us,' Will laughed the idea out of court. 'She's much too energetic for that. She prefers to run alongside until she hears a rustle in the hedge, then she'll go off on her own, to investigate. She'll catch up with us again, along the way,' he predicted, as the trap bowled along at a smart pace, and the setter veered off after a couple of hundred yards and disappeared into the fields.

If only she had felt happier, she would have enjoyed every minute of the drive, Netta thought, looking around her. The casual clip-clop of the mare's hooves made a lazy accompaniment to the screaming swifts which wheeled and dived above them. Silver-green barley, and the pale ash blonde of oats, lay on either side as they turned across parkland, moving deeper into the estate. Ideal riding country,

as Will told her. The groom slowed the horse to a walk,
and smiled across at Netta.

'It's smooth enough when you're in the saddle, but it
gives you a shaking up if you go too fast over the sward
in the trap.'

'It's comfortable enough,' she responded. His considerate
action ensured the jolting was kept to a minimum, and the
high wheels cushioned any bumps so that she hardly
noticed them. 'It's so peaceful, after Lak,' she responded to
the groom's desire to talk. Anything was better than listening to her own thoughts. If only her heart could soak in
some of the quiet that surrounded them, she thought wistfully. Instead, it seemed to have drawn to itself the turmoil
of that unhappy country. 'It seemed to be all destruction
and hate, out there,' her eyes darkened at the memory.
'They even burned a hillside of growing bushes, in a land
where there was hardly any greenery. It seemed such a
waste.' She did not tell him why the rebels fired it. It did
not seem important now.

'Aye,' Will digested the information with a serious face.
'Them as makes war reaps a wild harvest,' he said
sentiently, and reined the horse to a halt beside a gateway
leading into a field of wheat, dark gold, and ripe for gathering.

'I reckoned we'd start to cut next week, if the weather
holds,' he suggested to Joss. 'I've booked the combines,
but I've got to confirm by tomorrow morning, and I
thought I'd see what you said first.'

'It looks about right. Let's go and see.' Joss unlatched
the door at the back of the trap and started to dismount.

'I'd better not come, because of leaving Mrs de Courcey
in the trap on her own,' Will began.

'You needn't worry about me,' Netta told him confidently, 'I'll take over the reins for you, if you like.'

'If you're sure?' Will still looked doubtful, and Netta
laughed his fears to rest.

'I'm positive,' she told him firmly. 'I've done quite a lot
of driving in the States, with trotting horses, and they
were a good deal faster than your mare's likely to be.'

'In that case. . . .' Reassured, the groom handed her the reins and joined Joss, and left to herself, Netta relaxed. The two men walked across to the field gate, swung it open, and went inside. She saw first Joss and then Will reach out and pluck an ear of corn each and rub it between their fingers, judging its ripeness and quality. She heard Joss speak and Will answer him, discussing the coming harvest, but it was a background noise along with the rustle of the grain that bowed in shifting waves to the light wind. Her mind dismissed it, and instead turned inwards, wrestling with her own problem. Her thoughts went round and round like caged mice on an exercise wheel, seeking a solution, and finding none, and with a weary sigh she slumped back in her seat and let the reins go slack in her fingers, and the mare dropped her head to browse among the herbage of the hedge bank for green delicacies to while away the waiting.

It happened without warning.

Out of the corner of her eye Netta vaguely registered a sinuous russet body coursing the hedge, but she took little notice. Will said the setter would rejoin them, and she watched idly as Tara headed in the direction of the horse and trap, threading her way through the growth in the hedge bottom, the waving fronds of wild parsley marking her track, and her nose eagerly dropped to seek out hidden signs of life. She was almost on top of the crouching pheasant when it exploded upwards with a harsh croak of alarm, and blundered in panic flight straight into the face of the browsing mare.

The horse gave a whinny of fright and shied violently. It reared backwards, the trap tilted at a terrifying angle, and Netta grabbed at the side to save herself from sliding out through the rear doorway, which swung outwards because Will had not bothered to latch it properly when he joined Joss. With quick presence of mind she tightened her hold on the reins with her other hand and pulled in the slack as the mare's front hooves slipped wildly on the sloping bank. Gently she applied pressure on the leathers, and the mare scrabbled backwards on to terra firma again, and

Netta let out a breath of relief—but it changed to a cry of dismay as the trap rocked back on to an even keel and the rear door swung inwards again and slammed to with a sharp, resounding bang.

It was too much for the mare. Beset by unprovoked, feathered assault, and what must have sounded like a gunshot from the rear, she tossed valour to the winds and bolted across the open parkland. Behind her, Netta heard Joss shout,

'Netta, hang on! Hang on. . . .'

And simultaneously, Will's bawled injunction, 'Pull her in, ma'am. Pull her in!'

'I can't do both at once!' A surge of sudden anger gave her strength—anger at being shouted at. She did not stop to rationalise the reason. Fright touched the limit of her overcharged emotions, and fury boiled over inside her. With a quick movement that in her saner moments she would never have dared to attempt, she swung to her feet in the wildly swaying trap. The seemingly smooth sward of the parkland hid hitherto unsuspected hillocks, and the high wheels of the vehicle bounced across their curves like rubber balls. It was physically impossible to hold on, as Joss told her, and apply pressure on the reins at the same time, and some instinct made her choose the reins. One hand did not have the necessary power, she needed two, and all her strength. Joss or Will might have managed it, but Netta did not possess the iron-hard muscles of the men, or the necessary height, and in self-defence, to save herself from being rattled about like a single pea left in a pod, she braced herself on her feet so that her knees took the jolts like the springs of a car.

Horror descended on her as the ride of trees loomed in front of her, racing towards her at dreadful speed. And just beyond lay the wide gleam of the river. Netta knew a moment of sheer panic as they headed straight towards an enormous horse-chestnut.

'I'll never see Joss again!' She closed her eyes, and her mind went blank. For some reason she did not stop to dissect, she still clung to the reins. They were the only things she had, to cling to. She could not cling to Joss. She would never be able to cling to Joss again. Looking back afterwards, she wondered perhaps if it was the uneven pressure she applied on the reins, not caring how she pulled on the leathers, so long as she pulled.

She felt the trap veer to one side, and her eyes flew open again in added alarm. Was it going to tip over? She stared with a dreadful fascination as the mare started to turn away from the row of trees, that seemed to present a solid wall of living wood against them. Slowly, agonisingly slowly, the horse began to veer in a wide arc, and despair touched Netta.

'She'll never turn in time!'

The twigs from one of the lower branches of the horse-chestnut actually touched her hair, and then, seconds before the trap must surely have splintered to pieces against the trunk of the tree, the mare straightened out and raced parallel with the ride of trees, running uphill, and away from the river, instinctively heading for home and the known safety of her stable. The ground rose steeply away from the water, and it was this, and the heat of the sun, combined with the steady pull of the reins, that finally slowed the wild undisciplined gallop, first to a canter, then a trot, and then,

'Thank goodness!'

Abruptly Netta's anger deserted her, and with it her courage. She groped for the seat behind her, and dropped into it as the mare slowed to a trembling walk. She was in no better state than the horse, she realised ruefully. She shook all over.

'I'll never make a Boadicea!'

An hysterical desire to laugh and cry at the same time took possession of her, almost overwhelmed her, and it was only the sound of running feet, and Will breathlessly exclaiming in broad country parlance, fright and haste making him forget his more careful English, 'Bye, but tha' did well to pull her in like that! Tha' did real well,' that prevented her from succumbing. She took a deep, steadying breath as the groom ran to the mare's head, while Joss came

over the back of the trap in an agile vault that ignored the
easier, slower way through the door. He landed lightly beside her, and impulsively Netta turned towards him, her
hands reaching out to him, seeking the reassurance of his
hold. But instead of grasping them, and uttering the words
of comfort she ached to hear, he remained apart, rebuffing
her advance. She looked up into his face and checked,
appalled. His eyes bored down into hers, and they glowed
like coals in a face that was white under his tan.

'Surely he can't be angry with me, because of this? It
wasn't my fault that the mare bolted.' Her throat closed
into silence, choking back the words, and her hands
dropped back on to her lap, and numb despair gripped her
as he shouted,

'Why on earth did you let the mare browse like that?
Will and I would only have been gone for about five
minutes. Was it too much to ask, that you kept the horse
standing quiet for that short time? Look at the lather she's
in!' He gestured furiously towards the mare.

'How was I to know Tara would put up a pheasant right
in her face?' Her anger returned, stung back into life by
his tone. He had not criticised Caroline for deliberately
galloping the mare the day before, and getting her into
the same state, yet he blamed her—Netta—for something
she could neither foresee nor prevent.

'If you'd bothered to hold her in check properly, instead
of letting the reins go slack, she wouldn't have had her nose
to the bank, and the bird would have flown over her.'

'And she'd have bolted, just the same,' she retorted
hotly.

'She'd have been less likely to bolt if you'd kept a tight
rein on her,' he thrust back angrily. 'You might have been
killed!'

They might both have been killed. Herself, and her
baby. A cold chill descended on Netta, and she started to
tremble again. Joss would be even angrier if he knew about
the baby.

'I'm surprised you even bother to think about what
might have happened to me,' she flared back bitterly. 'Go

and look after your mare, she seems more important to you than I am.' She turned her shoulder on him abruptly. She heard his sharp hiss of breath, but she kept her head averted. She could not continue to face him for much longer, and still remain calm. Tears rode on the back of her anger as reaction set in, and she dared not allow herself to break down in front of him. If she did, she would not be able to find the strength to hold back the longing of her heart. She would have to let it pour out its love, and then he would know. . . .

'He'd have been concerned if it had been Caroline, instead of me.' Deliberately she whipped her anger into life again, desperately drawing round her the only armour she had left, to prevent her from blurting out her feelings, begging him to love her in return—and risking his rejection, that would turn the rest of her life into an empty waste of time. The silence seemed to stretch for ever. Her neck ached with the effort of keeping her head turned away from him. And then the trap rocked sharply as he made a swift, impatient movement.

'I'll do just that,' he ground out, and left the vehicle by the same method he used to get in. He leapt lightly over the side, she hardly heard any sound as he landed on soft-soled shoes, and he did not look at her as he passed the front of the trap on his way to the mare.

'Heel, Tara!' He checked the setter's tendency to roam with a curt command, and took the mare's head leather from Will, a move which effectively kept his back turned towards her. With soft words of encouragement to the horse, such as Netta would have sacrificed the earth to have heard addressed to herself, and which nearly succeeded in destroying her hard-won self-control because they were not, he coaxed the mare at a gentle pace towards the distant house.

'Now I know how the prisoners in the tumbrils must have felt,' she thought bleakly, riding alone and ignored in the trap behind. Accused—found wanting—and condemned, with not even the opportunity to speak in her own defence.

'It's hopeless. I might as well stop trying.'

The combined effects of misery and shock made the shadow cast across the gravel by the approaching house seem even darker than when they started out, and colder, too, symptomatic of the bleakness that touched her spirit. She shivered uncontrollably as Joss halted the trap by the front door. With a quiet word he gave the horse to Will to hold, and turned back towards the trap, and Netta galvanised into action. Dread gave her renewed strength. He must not touch her. If he did, all her resolve would vanish. She pushed herself to her feet and somehow managed to remain there, fumbling at the catch of the trap door. With shaking fingers, she forced it open and gained the gravel without help, but she was not in time to escape into the house, as she intended. Joss rounded the end of the trap, and took hold of her arm.

'You're still trembling.' The shudders that shook her were intensified by the feel of his fingers round her arm. She felt a wild urge to pull away from him, and controlled it with difficulty because of the presence of the groom. To relieve her tension, she snapped,

'It's hardly surprising if I am trembling, after what happened!' He might show some sign of concern for her, she thought angrily.

'If you must go chariot riding across the park....' he shrugged.

'It was hardly a joy-ride. And it wasn't through any fault of mine,' she blazed back.

'That's a matter of opinion,' he replied cryptically, and opened his study door. 'You said you wanted the address book.' He dismissed her ordeal, and followed her into the room, and her overwrought nerves gave way.

'You could at least say you're glad I wasn't hurt!' she cried furiously, and he straightened up from the desk and threw her a level glance. His hand closed the drawer with a dull slap, and the address book echoed it with a much louder one that made her jump as he dropped it with slow deliberation on to the desk top. She drew in a quick, apprehensive breath. His eyes were like flint, and his voice about as hard, and suddenly she longed to turn and run, only she found her legs would not obey her, because they trembled even more at the expression on his face than they had at the end of what he casually termed her chariot ride.

'I'm glad you weren't hurt,' he repeated her words after her with brittle emphasis, and went on silkily, 'but if you don't believe me—if you want proof—you can have it.'

She could not escape him this time, either. Her legs refused to carry her away, and she stood rooted to the spot as he reached her with one quick stride. She stared at him as if mesmerised, helpless to dodge away from him.

'I'm *very* glad you weren't hurt,' he mocked, and bent his head above her. Netta tried to push him away, but when her hands touched his arms they clung there instead and refused to let go. She longed to cry out, 'Stop!' but because of the relentless pressure of his lips the only sound she could utter was a low moan, and treacherously her heart did not want him to stop. With a wild beating it begged him to go on until her puny rebellion should cease, and she acknowledge that if it was anger that made him put his arms round her, it was better that than he should not hold her at all.

'Is that the proof you wanted?' He let her go at last, and she swayed against the side of the desk for support, and shook in every limb.

'Joss ... I....' She swallowed hard and tried again, her lips too numb to form the words at her first attempt.

'Go up to your room and lie down.' He spoke first, curtly. He said 'your room' not 'our room', and it was her own fault he called it that. Her pride had denied her his closeness, and now she had no pride left, and her opportunity was gone. 'I'll send Mrs Berry up to you with a hot drink.'

She longed to cry out, 'I don't want Mrs Berry, I want you.' But perversely, her dry throat and aching lips prevented her utterance, and she listened in numb silence as he went on,

'You can take the address book with you, if you still want it.' He slid it across the desk towards her. 'Unless

you'd rather I gave it to Caroline to finish?' His tone said
he would prefer she gave it to Caroline, and sudden hot
rage flooded strength back into her limbs and gave her
back the use of her voice.

'It's not Caroline's place to do the invitations. It's mine,'
she spat at him furiously. 'I'll be the hostess at your celebra-
tion ball.' The words held a bitter mockery. There was
nothing for her to celebrate, and she rushed on recklessly,
ignoring the grim set of his jaw, 'I'll observe the conventions in front of your guests. That's what you wanted,
isn't it? That's what you told me you wanted. And afterwards....'

Tears choked her voice, and she bent swiftly and
snatched the address book from off the desk, holding it in
front of her like a shield, to ward off what she scarcely
knew.

'And afterwards ... what?' Joss enquired icily, and his
eyes were twin fires that she could not meet, because she
dared not contemplate life afterwards. Life without Joss.

She gave a strangled sob and spun away from him, pulling at the handle of the study door with frantic fingers. It
swung open and she ran through, and without waiting for
it to shut she fled for the stairs. She was half way up them
when the door banged to behind her, and the echo of it resounded through the quiet hall, slamming shut on her
most precious dreams.

CHAPTER FOURTEEN

SHE did not go down to the stables again. She knew Joss went riding, because she heard him moving about in his dressing room very early each morning. On occasions, the hands of her bedside alarm stood at exactly six o'clock when her door closed behind him, but he did not ask her to go with him, which was a relief and a pain at the same time. Caroline accompanied him once, Netta watched them from her window as they cantered side by side across the park, but when Joss persisted in his early start it proved too much for his cousin, who desisted with a very bad grace.

'Can't you do your work first, and then come riding at a more reasonable time?' she pouted illhumouredly at breakfast one morning. 'Surely you needn't go out at such an unearthly hour?'

'Once I start on estate work in the morning, I don't want to have to break off for anything except meals,' Joss answered her firmly. 'It's either an early ride, or none at all, at least for the moment until I've caught up with the backlog of paper work that's piled up since I've had to spend so much time abroad,' he grimaced. He evidently took the management of his estate seriously, and Netta could sympathise with his need to clear away the outstanding debris, even if Caroline could not. It was not an enviable chore, and the longer it was delayed the worse it would become as other tasks superimposed their own demands on his attention. He treated her own modest request for his time with unconcealed impatience.

'I've done the invitations, ready for posting.' She handed him a neatly scripted list. 'I'd like you to look down the names, in case there are any you disagree with.' She did not know his friends or his relations. One or two of the names in the address book she recognised as her father's clients, but the rest were just names, and the lack

171

of recognition hurt her intolerably. 'I've clipped some blank cards to the list, in case you want to add any.' She had left a dozen blank cards, and he picked up her list with a gesture of irritation.

'Is it absolutely necessary to bother me with these?' he frowned. 'Surely you and Caroline between you could attend to the arrangements?'

'I could have done it easily, if I'd been asked,' Caroline put in sweetly, and Joss's frown grew deeper as her meaning penetrated.

'In that case, I'll ask you, now.' He tossed Netta's carefully written list across the breakfast table to his cousin, and drained the last of his cup of coffee preparatory to returning to his study. 'I haven't the time to attend to it myself this morning.'

Netta drew in a quivering breath, then slowly she began to count. One . . . two . . . three. . . .

'I won't retaliate,' she vowed. 'I won't. . . .' She could not afford too many emotional upsets now, the precious life she bore was worthy of better treatment, and was infinitely more valuable to her than any temporary satisfaction she might derive from giving Caroline or Joss a verbal thrashing, and she battled to subdue her natural inclinations. She longed to scream—to hit out at Joss and Caroline—to throw things. To break her second cup of coffee, still piping hot, over Joss's insensitive head. With an effort that was to cost her a raging headache half an hour later, she did none of these things. 'I mustn't give way. Some time, I've got to learn not to let it matter.' It would be easier when she was no longer at Thimbles, no longer in reach of the sound of Joss's voice, of the accidental touch of his hand against her own as they passed the salt, the marmalade. . . .

'I'll use the spare invitation cards myself, to bring in one or two of my own friends,' Caroline decided, and Netta gritted her teeth. Caroline should have asked, not stated. Joss did not seem to notice the omission, he merely nodded indulgently.

'Yes, do that. You'll find envelopes and stamps in my

study.' He had not offered these facilities to Netta, and
Caroline did not afterwards seem to think it was necessary
to mention who it was she had invited, or even how many.

'I won't give her the satisfaction of asking,' Netta told
herself determinedly, and racked her brains to circumvent
the inconvenience of not knowing. Her lack of precise
knowledge of numbers was the biggest hurdle.

'A buffet supper, that's the answer,' she hit on the ideal
solution triumphantly. 'Numbers won't matter then.'

In fact, among the sixty or so guests who turned the long
ballroom at Thimbles into a kaleidoscope of vividly
coloured evening gowns, complemented by the magpie
black and white of the men's evening dress, the half dozen
or so of Caroline's friends who turned up did not make
much difference, although they were instantly recognisable,
Netta noticed. The women's hair and dress and make-up
were just a shade too bright, and the men too obviously
prosperous, and their laughter a note too loud, to mix easily
with the other guests, and they remained as they came, in
a clique apart.

Joss's face was impassive as he stood with Netta at the
entrance to the ballroom to greet them. She had contemplated buying a dress of her own for the occasion, but it
meant asking Joss for money, and for transport to go into
the nearest town, and rather than do either she once again
resorted to raiding Rosemary's emergency wardrobe, and
blessed her absent sister-in-law for providing her with
just the right dress for the occasion.

It was in pure silk, of a delicate silvery green, with a high
neckline and tiny cape sleeves. The cool shade showed off
her tan to perfection, and the soft, flowing lines of the
skirt whispered as she walked. The style did not call for
much jewellery, and she reversed her watch so that the
gold band made a bracelet. That, and her wedding ring,
would be sufficient, she decided. She would not ask Joss for
adornments, either.

She felt him glance down at her as she joined him at
the entrance to the ballroom. She did not join him until
the last minute. The less time they spent together, the less

likely they were to quarrel, she acknowledged drearily, and she wanted tonight to go as smoothly as possible. She had spared herself no effort to make the evening perfect. The ball was the only thing she had been able to do for Joss—except marry him, she thought wryly—and if the latter had turned out to be a disaster, at least she intended to see that the former was a success. Caroline criticised the arrangements, but she had not expected anything less.

'Do we *have* to have a string orchestra?' she complained. 'Can't we have something a bit livelier?' The intrumentalists Netta chose were a small, exclusive band known to her through various functions she herself had attended in London, and their music set the seal on any gathering.

'It's the one I've chosen.' She refused to budge from her initial decision.

'It isn't only the music, it's the supper as well,' Caroline appealed to Joss. 'I'd have thought a proper dinner would have been more in keeping with the occasion.'

'Since you didn't think fit to tell me how many guests you'd invited, a buffet meal was the only possible choice,' Netta silenced her effectively, and looking round the assembled gathering, from her position at Joss's side, she was glad she had stood firm. The musicians, the flowers, the whole elegant gathering, with the possible exception of Caroline's guests, fitted at Thimbles. Her choice had been instinctively right, and on that, at least, she could feel satisfied. She joined Joss only seconds before the first guests arrived, and her heart sank as she noticed the specks in his eyes glow as he looked at her.

'You're. . . .' he began, and his voice sounded tight.

'I'm not late,' she denied angrily, before he could go any further. 'You said eight o'clock, and it's exactly that now.' She reversed her wrist so that he could see her watch face, and at the same time gave away her strategy as regarded jewellery, or its lack.

'You haven't a proper bracelet.' He noticed immediately.

'I've got all I need.' Proudly she scorned to borrow more, and turned away from the fire in his eyes to force a smile she did not feel for the benefit of the first arrivals. For the

next half hour there was no time for any private conversation as their guests flowed through the door in a constant
stream. Her right hand was shaken until it ached. She knew
just how celebrities must feel, she thought ruefully, flexing
her tingling fingers behind her back as yet another party of
people she had invited, and yet did not recognise, came
through the big double doors to greet them.

In swift succession she found herself kissed, congratulated and questioned in the friendliest manner, and when
there were no more guests left to arrive she realised, with
a heart that broke at the sheer irony of it all, that Joss's
relations and closest friends accepted her, even if Joss did
not.

'Shall we open the ball?'

He swept her into his arms. He looked incredibly handsome in evening dress. The stark black and white enhanced
his already distinguished appearance and those looking on
must have thought she was the luckiest woman in the
world. How wrong they were! she thought bitterly. But her
heart did not listen to her denial, it quickened in a way that
had nothing to do with the beat of the music as Joss
guided her expertly along the gleaming expanse of floor
that opened up in front of them as their guests followed
the time-honoured tradition, and parted on either side to
allow them the opening dance.

'You dance well,' he said.

'So do you,' she responded politely.

Banalities, even if they were true. Stiffly formal, keeping them apart. But she discovered that even unhappiness
could not hold the music at bay. Netta was a natural
dancer, and Joss's performance was a polished equal of
her own, and the music drew them both like Pan pipes,
beckoning, insistent. He held her firmly, but not too tightly,
and her heart cried out to him to tighten his hold, crush
her if he wanted to, as loving him had crushed her heart
until it was like a withered sponge, fit only to be thrown
away. Without conscious thought she adjusted herself to
his hold, and allowed the tempo of the music to carry her
along, drugging her into an oblivion that obliterated her

surroundings, her guests, everything but the fact that she
was in Joss's arms.

They reached the end of the room and he turned her
once, twice, making the skirt of her dress billow in a soft,
whispering cloud of silver-green about her feet. The notes
of a violin rose high and sweet, throbbing a message she
did not want to hear—dared not listen to. . . .

'Some enchanted evening, you may see a stranger. . . .'
She had seen a stranger, and——

'Joss, oh, Joss, I love you!'

She rested her cheek against his lapel, and closed her
eyes, but she could not shut out the tune. It haunted her,
like the sound of the official's voice in the Embassy drawing room haunted her still.

'To love and to cherish. . . .'

Like the sound of Joss's firm rejoinder,

'I do.'

It was so real, she could even smell the heady, overpowering perfume of the tua lilies. It flowed about her in
cloying sweetness, and her feet missed the rhythm, and she
stumbled and would have fallen but for Joss's arms, which
instantly tightened round her.

'Has your sandal come undone?'

'No.' Her eyes were open now, and wide with memory,
and pain. 'I thought . . . just for a moment . . . I thought I
smelled lilies.' It was ridiculous, of course. She had not
ordered lilies in the floral decorations for the ballroom.
Her voice trembled into silence.

'They're a bit overpowering, so close.' To her astonishment he did not contradict her. 'I had them put in the
corner, because of their height.' He twirled her round
again, so that she could see for herself the tub of lilies,
their great golden heads spotted with brown velvet blobs
near the centres. Netta caught her breath.

'How could you?' He must have thought the floral
decorations she ordered were inadequate, but did he *have*
to supplement them with lilies, of all flowers?

The music swelled to a crescendo, and Joss did not
hear. He twirled her round again to face the return journey

the length of the room, and the tub of lilies was lost to her sight.

'I had them brought in from the gardens this evening. They're a bit like the tua lilies, don't you think? Or don't you remember what they looked like?'

It seemed to her an odd question to ask. How could she ever forget? Their perfume had followed her across two oceans, all the way from Lak. It tormented her dreams by night, so that she woke crying out as if from fever, and tantalised her by day like a silent wraith to which she would be chained for the rest of her life. The perfume of them followed her now, even across the length of the great ballroom, choking her, denying her air. Through a mist she saw Joss turn with a smile to acknowledge the friendly applause that followed their performance, saw the dancers close the gap as the orchestra broke into a quickstep. She swayed, and from a long way off heard someone say, in a voice she ought to recognise,

'Give Netta a drink, she's feeling dizzy.'

And Caroline's voice reply, spitefully,

'Maybe that's why she's feeling dizzy.'

'Sit down for a moment or two, and drink this.' Joss pressed her into a chair, and someone put a glass into her hand. She sipped obediently, too bemused to do anything else. She had never particularly liked wine. She did not realise until now just how much she *dis*liked it. The sharp, dry sherry stung her throat and made her cough, but it gave her an excuse for the tears that sprang to her eyes, and it revived her enough to allow her to turn and thank the woman who had given it to her, and who still stood beside her.

'Wendy!' She looked up into her friend's laughing face. 'And Harry!' She jumped to her feet, her daze vanishing. 'When did you get here?' She had not sent them an invitation, did not know they were due to arrive. 'I didn't know you were even back in this country yet.'

'We had to report to Paris first,' Harry gave her a laughing hug—a different Harry, rested and cheerful, with the troubles of Lak left far behind him.

'Joss traced us,' Wendy gurgled at the amazement on Netta's face. 'He rang us in Paris and told us about the ball, and begged us to come over. We didn't need much coaxing,' she chuckled. 'But we couldn't write and let you know, because Joss said he wanted it to be a surprise for you.'

'It's wonderful!' Netta supposed she ought to thank Joss. It was considerate of him to give her a pleasant surprise, for once, she thought cynically. And then she remembered that the Frasers were his friends as well as her own. Had he invited them in order to discuss their marriage? she wondered dully. Perhaps to ask Harry's advice on how best to get it annulled? The Frasers had been witnesses, and knew the circumstances, and the ex-Ambassador might be prepared to pull strings to obtain an annulment quickly and quietly. Perhaps Caroline had been pressing Joss.... Through the coldness that gripped her she could feel Joss standing close behind her, feel the electric currents of question and answer pass unspoken between them.

'Ranjit sent a message for you,' Harry broke across the tight silence, and Netta turned to him with quick relief.

'Is he safe? When did you hear from him?'

'Only an hour before we left Paris to come here,' her informant told her with a smile. 'And he's quite safe, and unharmed. He asked me to tell you that he intended to come to England in about three months' time, when he's had an opportunity to sort his business into some kind of order again. Oh, and he said something about having recovered most of the settings from your hotel. He said you'd understand?'

'I understand.' So did Joss. She could feel him tense, his thoughts reach out to her, meeting her own in a mental telepathy that had no need of words. Now he must know her story of how she came by the jewels. It had mattered to her that he knew, once. Now, she felt vindicated, and uncaring. Empty, except for an ache that grew with every hour, but it was for Joss, and not for the jewels.

'Was his business damaged much?' She found she did

not care about that either, any more, but politeness demanded that she should ask.

'Some,' Harry answered her laconically, 'but nothing that can't be mended, given time. The Government has regained control in Lak, and there's a measure of order been restored, but I'm afraid it'll be a long time before things get back to normal again. The insurgents had a field day when they ran riot, and there was a great deal of damage done, not least to the economy of the country. It seems such a pity, when they'd made such strides during the last few years in extending education and up-to-date medical treatment even into their remote mountain regions. And now the culmination of years of effort has been virtually destroyed overnight by a handful of hotheads.' The expression on his face was compounded of anger and regret. 'It'll take a decade to recoup the damage they've done.'

'Them as makes war, reaps a wild harvest. . . .'

It was as if Will's words had just been spoken aloud between them. Joss's look pierced her, silent, compelling, so that she was forced at last to turn and meet his eyes. She raised her face to his, and was lost. In one fleeting second, plucked from an ocean of time, a frail link of understanding reached out between them. She hesitated, half raised her hand in a tentative, pleading gesture. For a brief, heart-stopping minute she thought Joss might respond, might reach across and take it.

'My dance, I think.'

Harry grasped her hand. The ex-Ambassador to Lak swung her on to the floor in a well executed foxtrot, and in that moment Netta felt her life had ended. She twisted her head to look back at Joss, her heart mirrored in her eyes, but he was following Harry's example and drawing Wendy on to the dance floor, his head bent, listening as his partner chatted, and he did not see Netta look back. And then other couples danced between them, and Joss was lost to her sight. And there was only desolation, and the sickly sweet perfume of the lilies as they neared the end

of the ballroom. And her own heart's wild harvest, of longing, and bitter regret.

'You dance like a dream,' Harry grinned when the music
stopped. 'Be sure to save me another twirl later,' he demanded.

'I will,' Netta promised, 'but just now I need a cool
drink and a sit down. It's hot in here. Why don't ladies
carry fans any more?' she complained.

'Come and sit over by the french windows, and I'll bring
you a lemonade,' Harry offered, and led her towards where
the big double windows lay open to the wide flagged terrace leading on to the gardens.

'That's better!' She subsided thankfully on to the chair
he found for her, and leaned back, breathing in the warm
scented air from the garden outside. It was a fresh,
essentially English sweetness, redolent of moist earth and
new-mown lawns, and the free second blooming of well
tended roses, refreshing to her nostrils after the heavy,
cloying scent of the lilies. Harry left her in search of the
lemonade, and her mind wandered. Someone had already
sought the sanctuary of the terrace, she became aware of
movement outside in the dusk, and half rose from her
chair. She had no desire to eavesdrop, however unwittingly,
on a courting couple, then she sat back again. 'There's
more than one couple outside,' she realised, as her eyes became more accustomed to the dusk, and she picked out a
group of people, four or five figures on the outer edge of
the terrace. The glow of a cigarette, and the snowy gleam
of a man's shirt front sprang into being against the wide
stone pillars. Another man spoke, and a woman's voice
answered him: Caroline's voice. The man said,

'It's a pity about the Hunt Ball. Thimbles would be an
ideal place to hold it. Ideal hunting country, too, it should
be well stocked with foxes if the packs have never been
run across it.'

'Oh, Joss's family have got this bee in their bonnets
about hunting,' Caroline replied scornfully, and Netta rose
swiftly to her feet. She had no desire to listen in to other
people's conversations, either. She took a couple of steps
away from the windows, and Joss said,

'Sit down again.' He appeared at her side and handed her the glass of lemonade he bore in his hand. 'Our guests are enjoying the buffet, so we might as well relax for a while.' He said 'our guests' and 'we might as well relax'. Her fingers trembled as she took the glass, hazarding the liquid inside, and she sat down abruptly lest it should spill.

'I thought ... Harry said....' She foundered to a stop and stared mutely up at Joss.

'I met Harry coming back with your lemonade, so I took the glass from him and brought it instead,' he explained. 'Sit back and enjoy it,' he insisted, a superfluous injunction as it turned out, since the chair suddenly became necessary to aid the alarming weakness in her legs, that refused to allow her to stand up unsupported. She lowered her eyes to the glass, and sipped at its contents that might have been plain water for all she knew, but she was thankful to slake a throat that had suddenly gone as dry as sand. She could not look at Joss any longer, at the deep burning fire in his gold eyes that had the power to scorch her until she could have cried aloud with the pain. Surely he could not still be angry with her because she had not asked him for jewellery to wear with her dress? she thought wretchedly. And she had not been late in joining him to greet their guests, she had told him she was not late. Did he not believe her about that, either? Perhaps his wrist watch was fast, or hers might be slow.... The thoughts raced round and round in jumbled confusion through her mind, and in desperation she at last raised her head. 'I can't keep my nose buried in a lemonade glass for the rest of the evening,' she thought half hysterically, and risked an upward glance at him. He did not *look* angry, his expression was mild as he stood over her, watching her, and yet his eyes still smouldered with that inward light she had come to know so well.

'Leave the rest of your drink if you don't want it,' he suggested as she toyed nervously with the glass, unable to bring herself to drink again. 'Come and walk in the garden with me, it'll cool you off better than lemonade.'

'I'll put the glass down first.' An unaccountable, heady

excitement took possession of her, far more potent than any wine.

'Put it on the windowsill.'

'It's still half full, it might get spilled. There's a waiter coming towards us, I'll give it to him.'

She grasped for time to compose herself, to make her legs obey her will and walk beside him in the garden. She turned to put her glass on the waiter's tray, shook her head at the offer of another drink, and then turned back again in time to hear Caroline say,

'When Joss and I are married, I'll make him change his mind about letting the local hunt come across Thimbles land.'

The excitement died within her, and she felt sick. Was that why Joss wanted her to walk with him in the privacy of the garden? To tell her he intended to marry Caroline? To tell her in the dusk, because he could not face her in the light with such news? She spun round to speak to him, to tell him she would not come with him, but he had already stepped through the french windows ahead of her while she was attending to her glass, his silent tread making no sound on the smooth flags of the terrace.

'I thought Joss was married to that redhaired girl who stood with him when we came in? Who was she?' one of the men with Caroline asked, curiously.

'Oh, they're married—at the moment,' Caroline replied significantly. 'She's some little ingénue he picked up in Lak. They were caught up together in the civil uprising there. Men do quixotic things at such times. Fortunately these days they're not irreparable.'

Netta drew a hard, painful breath. It was uncanny. Caroline was explaining her marriage to Joss almost word for word as she, Netta, had predicted she would. She felt as if she was taking part in the scene of some weird play, the lines of which she had already learned by heart.

'Are you using this chair, Mrs de Courcey?' A black and white figure appeared beside her, coveting her recent seat for his partner, and she shook her head numbly. The chair found another occupant, and a burst of chatter and laughter broke out round her as men plied their partners with spoils from the buffet table, and sought a quiet corner in which to enjoy them. Tears pricked the back of her eyes, and she turned on to the dusk of the terrace to hide them.

'I might as well get it over, and have done with it,' she told herself wretchedly. And have done with Joss, too.... With a valiant effort she held her head high and walked out to join him, then paused irresolutely. He was strolling towards Caroline and her guests, was nearly upon them, and it was obvious the group had not heard him coming. His peculiar lightness of tread denied them any warning of his presence.

'We'll hold the Hunt Ball at Thimbles next year, never fear,' Caroline continued her conversation confidently.

'You're neglecting your guests, Caroline,' Joss spoke from just behind her, and there was ice in his voice. She spun round with a gasp, and a look of startled dismay spread across her face.

'I ... I ...'

'I can recommend the buffet,' he cut smoothly across what she was about to say, and instantly turned back to Netta. 'Mind the steps,' he cautioned, 'the rest is level walking, once we're on the lawns.'

He gave the group on the terrace a cool nod, and guided Netta down the shallow stone flight. She needed guidance, for the tears would no longer be denied, and they treacherously aided the deeper darkness of the garden, so that she trod blindly where he led, conscious only that the lights of the house grew dim behind them, and the noise of the ballroom faint as the garden received them into its blessed quiet, that for Netta held no peace. She shivered.

'You haven't got a wrap,' Joss realised. 'Take my jacket instead.' Without waiting for her to answer, he slipped his jacket off his own shoulders and draped it round her, then spoke softly down at her through the darkness.

'You're such a tiny thing, it's nearly an overcoat on you.' It was warm, from the warmth of his own body, but clothing could not combat the chill that gripped her, which came from inside her, and not from the gentle air of the end-of-summer night.

'It won't stay on.' She put up her hands to grasp at the jacket as it slipped on her too slender shoulders, in danger of falling to the ground, but Joss caught it and held it round her, pressing his hands across her shoulders and back. Holding the jacket against her. Holding her against him. She spoke hurriedly, grasping at the first subject that entered her mind, because she could not bear his closeness, knowing they were a million miles apart.

'It was kind of you to ask Wendy and Harry to come.'

'It's a relief to know they're safe. And your client, too,' he remembered their message from Ranjit.

'At least you know now, I'm not a jewel thief.' She could not disguise the bitterness in her voice, and she felt him go still.

'You *were* a thief. You are still,' he said deliberately, and she stiffened as if he had struck her. Fury seethed in her. She longed to throw off his jacket, risk the chill of the evening air, throw his words back in his face, and refute his infamous suggestion. And then he spoke again, very softly, drawing her close against him with a strength that even her anger was powerless to resist.

'You stole my heart,' he told her, so low that she had to strain to hear him. And even then her ears did not believe what they heard, so he repeated it slowly, to convince them. 'You stole my heart, the first moment I saw you, in Lak. You still possess it, and you always will, because I don't want it back.' He had given it to her to keep, freely, unreservedly.

Was she dreaming? Could it be her overwrought imagination, that made her hear words that her wildly palpitating heart had longed to hear, and so far had waited for in vain? But the music of the string orchestra played softly in the background, the lights of the house glowed distantly across the lawns, and from far away she could hear the call of a hunting owl, real, tangible things, none of them the stuff of dreams.

'Netta—darling—I love you.' His voice vibrated with urgent passion, and he strained her to him as if he feared to let her go. 'I love you—I love you. Say you love me, too?' he demanded, and now, incredibly, she knew she was not dreaming. Knew the words were real, that she had never thought to hear from his lips. 'I love you, I love you....' He thought her silence meant she did not hear him, but it only meant she wanted to hear him say it again, with ears that would never tire of hearing it repeated, never so long as she lived.

'I shouldn't have forced you into marriage,' he groaned, when she still did not speak. 'It was wrong, but I was afraid of losing you. I brought the lilies into the ballroom tonight, in the hope they might remind you—speak for me....'

'You told me you married me to get me on the plane, with the rest of the Embassy staff.' She raised her face to his, a pale flower in the darkness of the garden.

'I lied,' he confessed. 'You could have come on the plane without marrying me. But if I'd let you do that, once we reached England you might have disappeared, out of reach, and I'd have lost you. I thought if I bound you to me, at least I should be able to hope ... I wouldn't want to live, if I lost you,' he declared, and his face worked suddenly, unmanned by the thought of losing her, and with a muffled sound he lowered his head and buried his face in her curls.

'Don't!' She could not bear to see him suffer. She had suffered herself in the same way, and knew how it felt. 'I love you,' she crooned, 'I'll always love you. We'll never lose each other,' she comforted him from her newfound position of strength and confidence. 'Marriage is for ever, and so is our love.' She reached up tender hands, and drew his face down to her own, responding with a tremulous joy to the passionate pressure of his lips as they lingered on her hair, her eyes, and the soft, throbbing hollow of her throat, leaving rapture in their train, and a deep, contented joy such as she thought she would never know. With a tiny sigh she surrendered to his arms, and the quiet of the garden folded round them. Neither noticed the setter trot towards them and stop, front paw up-raised, to give them a long, wise look, then turn away again, leaving them alone.

'The moment I saw you with Wendy and Harry at the Embassy, I was lost,' Joss confessed at last with a smile, and Netta raised eyes that shone, but not with tears, and knew happily that the fire that glowed deep in his gold orbs burned not only with anger, but when his heart was deeply stirred.

'I didn't give you a proper wedding ring,' he recalled remorsefully. 'And you a goldsmith's daughter, too!'

'I don't want any other ring but yours.' She nestled in the safe, warm circle of his arms like a bird that has come to rest.

'After tomorrow we'll be on our own at last,' he said contentedly. 'All our guests will have gone home, and we can be alone.' A thrill of pure happiness ran through her, at the way he said 'alone'.

'Won't Caroline ...?'

'Caroline will leave first thing in the morning,' his tone hardened. 'I've tolerated her outrageous behaviour before, for the sake of her parents, but this time she's gone too far. She won't return to Thimbles.'

'I didn't opt out of riding that morning, just to spite Caroline. I didn't feel well when I woke....' Suddenly it was important that he should believe her.

'I didn't think you did.' He kissed her tiny worry away.

'You were angry.'

'Only because I was disappointed. I'd set such store, by having that ride with you, having the chance to talk with you alone. Do you realise, since we've been married, we've hardly ever been alone?' he asked her incredulously. 'There's always been something to come between us. The jewels....'

'My father can have those, he'll look after Ranjit now. You can give them to him when he comes home.' The jewels no longer mattered.

'The civil uprising....'

'That's behind us now.' She had almost forgotten it, except that it gave her to Joss.

'There's always been something,' he insisted.

'Except in the cave,' she reminded him in a small, breathless voice. Would he remember, too? Desperately, she wanted him to remember.

'Ah, the cave.' His voice, his look, showed that he remembered, and they turned those few brief hours into a thing of unutterable beauty. He lowered his head and his lips reverently sealed the memory deep in her heart, so that it was a while before he recalled,

'We can ride together now, whenever you like,' he said happily. 'But if you're uneasy about riding the jet mare after she bolted on you, I'll find you another mount. You needn't feel obliged to ride her, after that. Dear heart!' he hugged her even closer to him, and his voice shook as he remembered, 'I thought for sure I'd lost you then. I was so afraid.'

'I shan't be able to ride, for a while,' she told him.

'You can have the palomino, for your own,' he laid his most precious possession at her feet, misunderstanding her hesitation, putting it down to nervousness after her ordeal in the trap. 'Fleet's as gentle as a lamb,' he reassured her, 'but she won't be ready to carry you yet.'

'When she's ready will be time enough for me.' She could give him her own news now, safe in the warm security of his love. 'Fleet's foal will be ready for riding at about the same time that our son will need his first mount.' Shyly she nestled her head against his heart, her face downturned, even though the dusk laid gentle fingers on the soft rosy tide that warmed her cheeks and throat.

'Our ... son?'

Joss's voice died into silence, and a quick fear stabbed through Netta like a knife. Did he mind? Did he not want their child? Perhaps.... She raised her head, and the incredulous joy on his face told her that her fears were unfounded. That, and the deep, enduring tenderness that shone out from his eyes, spoke from the strength of his arms as he clasped her close to his heart in a strong, safe embrace, holding her, and their child, and their future. . . .

'You didn't let me tell you how lovely you look,' he murmured after a long, sweet time had passed between them. 'I tried to tell you, when you joined me in the ballroom tonight, but you thought I was going to say you were late coming down.'

He laughed softly at the memory, and she joined in gaily. She had been wonderfully, blissfully, on time. She started to tell him so, but his lips claimed her own, masterfully silencing the words that no longer needed to be spoken.

Harlequin Romances

The books that let you escape
into the wonderful world of romance!
Trips to exotic places...interesting
plots...meeting memorable people...
the excitement of love....These are
integral parts of Harlequin Romances –
the heartwarrning novels read by
women everywhere.

Many early issues are now available.
Choose from this great selection!

Choose from this list of Harlequin Romance editions.*

*Some of these book were originally published under different titles.

For Jonathan, Elizabeth, and Katherine

The right of the people to be secure in their persons, houses, papers, and effects, against unreasonable searches and seizures, shall not be violated, and no Warrants shall issue, but upon probable cause, supported by Oath or affirmation, and particularly describing the place to be searched, and the persons or things to be seized.
—*United States Constitution, Amendment IV, 1791*

Whatever privacy remains for the American citizen, it remains because the federal government is presently too inefficient to pull all its personal information files together.
—*Senator Edward V. Long (D-Mo.), 1968*

As for our common defense, we reject as false the choice between our safety and our ideals. Our founding fathers, faced with perils we can scarcely imagine, drafted a charter to assure the rule of law and the rights of man, a charter expanded by the blood of generations. Those ideals still light the world, and we will not give them up for expedience's sake.
—*President Barack Obama, Inaugural Address, January 20, 2009*

CONTENTS

INTRODUCTION

The headline for the lead story in the *New York Times* on December 16, 2005, was stunning in its starkness and simplicity: "Bush Lets U.S. Spy on Callers without Courts."

Underneath the column-spanning banner was a massive 3,300-word story, written by veteran reporters James Risen and Eric Lichtblau, describing in detail a decision by President George W. Bush to authorize the National Security Agency (NSA) to listen to the conversations of American citizens and others inside the United States without first seeking court permission to do so. According to the *Times* story, "under a presidential order signed in 2002, the intelligence agency has monitored the international telephone calls and international e-mail messages of hundreds, perhaps thousands, of people inside the United States without warrants over the past three years in an effort to track possible 'dirty numbers' linked to Al Qaeda."

Following the 9/11 attacks, the NSA intensified its tracking of calls and e-mails to and from known Al Qaeda figures, aided in large part by Central Intelligence Agency seizure of terrorists' cell phones and computers in the Middle East. With President Bush's executive order in hand, the NSA for the first time began also tracking domestic phone calls and e-mails of people, including U.S. citizens, suspected of having links to Al Qaeda, regardless of how remote those links might be.

Based on interviews with unnamed former and current members of the administration, the *Times* reported that at any given moment, the NSA was monitoring the communications of up to five hundred Americans. Since the names on the NSA surveillance list shifted over time, however, the *Times* said that the total number of Americans targeted since the domestic eavesdropping program was launched "may have reached into the thousands."

Ten days later, after the Bush administration admitted that the NSA had conducted warrantless surveillance of "several hundred" Americans, the *Los Angeles Times* published a story, under the headline "U.S. Spying Is Much Wider, Some Suspect," in which various security experts suggested that the NSA was actually conducting wholesale, "look-at-everything" surveillance. As the *Los Angeles Times* itself conceded, the article and its conclusions were largely speculative, since none of the surveillance experts interviewed had any specific evidence regarding the full extent of the NSA's domestic spying program.

But the quintessential "black" agency was about to get a little bit grayer. It turned out that the NSA was in fact "looking at everything," or at least had the opportunity to do so.

THE ROOM THAT WASN'T THERE

Information about the secretive National Security Agency has been notoriously difficult to obtain since the agency was quietly established by President Truman in 1952. The existence of the agency itself didn't actually remain a secret for all that long: the following summer, the *New York Times* reported that the Defense Department was launching a $30 million construction project to build a new home for the agency at Fort Meade in Maryland. But little information was available about what the agency would do in its new home.

"The National Security Agency," the *Times* said, "which functions under the Defense Department, runs a super-communications network, monitoring and translating broadcasts from all parts of the world. Its services are used not only by the Defense Department, but also by the State Department, the C.I.A., the White House and other Government units."

The specific nature of the services provided by the NSA to other branches of the government was classified at the time and remains so today. Nonetheless, the veil that has long shrouded the agency has thinned somewhat, particularly during the last couple of decades. The NSA received its largest (unwelcome) publicity boost in 2000, when a committee of the European Parliament issued a report outlining a global program of signals intelligence, code-named ECHELON, that is reportedly operated by the NSA on behalf of the United States, the United Kingdom, Australia, Canada, and New Zealand. Using a combination of satellite, telephone, and microwave intercepts, the ECHELON program enables the NSA to review the contents of millions of phone calls, faxes, e-mails, and text messages sent to and from devices around the world. The European Parliament cautioned, however, that "the analysis carried out in the report has revealed that the technical capabilities of the system are probably not nearly as extensive as some sections of the media had assumed."

When President Bush freed the NSA from its warrant requirements under federal law, the NSA decided to take a more straightforward approach: directly intercepting the data transmissions flowing through the nation's largest and busiest telecommunications companies. In January 2003, an AT&T communications technician named Marty Klein noticed that a new room was being built next to AT&T's 4ESS switching equipment in the San Francisco office in which he worked. The switching equipment, Klein later told *Wired* magazine's Ryan Singel, handles all long-distance and international calls. Klein subsequently learned that the person setting up the equipment in the new room had been recruited the previous fall by the NSA.

Not long after the NSA's arrival at AT&T, Klein was assigned to connect the company's massive Internet circuits to a so-called "splitting cabinet," which contained a beam splitter that divided the Internet traffic into two identical streams, one of which flowed into the NSA's secret room. The diverted data stream was not limited to just AT&T's customers; thanks to peer sharing agreements among the various companies operating Internet backbones, NSA's secret room captured data carried on AT&T's network from other telecommunications companies. Klein said that similar setups were installed in other AT&T switching offices, "including Seattle, San Jose, Los Angeles and San Diego."

Among other things, Klein reported, the secret room was equipped with a Narus STA 6400, a supercomputer that is part of the NarusInsight Intercept Suite (NIS). In a product description on the Narus Web site, the company says that the NIS "provides service providers and government organizations unmatched flexibility to intercept IP [Internet protocol] communications content and/or identifying information, enabling law enforcement and government organizations around the world to effectively gather evidence of illegal activity in the multi-faceted world of IP communications." In simpler terms, the

NIS is designed to collect huge amounts of data from various types of data networks and apply so-called "semantic traffic analysis" to determine whether any of the traffic contains information of interest to the organization collecting the data. Since 2004, the Narus board of directors has included William P. Crowell, an "independent security consultant" whose prior positions include deputy director of operations and deputy director of the National Security Agency.

While the Narus Web page for the NIS stresses the importance of capturing "*all* targeted data but *nothing* else," it leaves unanswered the thornier question of what constraints exist, if any, for determining whose data should be targeted. It was no accident that the European Parliament opened its report on the NSA ECHELON program by quoting the first-century Roman poet Juvenal: "Sed quis custodiet ipsos custodies?" (But who will guard the guardians?)

SHADES OF WATERGATE

In theory, at least, Congress has primary responsibility for establishing limits on the domestic surveillance that can be conducted by federal agencies, and has done so on two particularly notable occasions in the past forty years. In 1968, Congress adopted Title III of the Omnibus Crime Control and Safe Streets Act (known colloquially as the Wiretap Statute). The law was passed in reaction to the U.S. Supreme Court's decision in *Katz v. United States* (1967), in which the Court threw out a conviction based on evidence collected by the Federal Bureau of Investigation (FBI) through warrantless electronic surveillance of a public phone booth. Writing for the Court's majority, associate justice Potter Stewart identified a zone of privacy that surrounds each individual: "Wherever a man may be," he said, "he is entitled to know that he will remain free from unreasonable searches and seizures."

But the late 1960s were a period marred by political assassinations, a rising national crime rate, and increasingly violent antiwar protests, and legislators feared that the *Katz* ruling would effectively ban the use of electronic surveillance in federal criminal investigations and prosecutions. Over the objections of President Lyndon B. Johnson, who reluctantly signed the bill, Congress for the first time explicitly authorized law enforcement to gather evidence using electronic surveillance. The authorization was not unlimited: a prosecuting attorney was required to get court approval by showing probable cause that a crime had been committed or was about to be committed, and to detail the kind of electronic surveillance that would be conducted. The surveillance order also had to be renewed every thirty days. Nonetheless, it was the first congressional endorsement of eavesdropping.

As he signed the Omnibus Crime Control bill on June 20, 1968, President Johnson urged Congress to reconsider its authorization of electronic snooping and warned that the new provisions "could result in producing a nation of snoopers bending through the keyholes of the homes and offices in America, spying on our neighbors."

It didn't take long for President Johnson's words to prove prophetic. During the administration of his successor, Richard M. Nixon, federal agencies ranging from the Department of Defense to the Department of Justice conducted extensive warrantless surveillance of American citizens under the guise of "national security." The program—known as the Mitchell Doctrine, after U.S. attorney general John Mitchell—targeted those whom the Nixon administration suspected of "subversive" activities.

The revelations of the Nixon wiretapping in turn led to, among other things, the passage in 1978 of the Foreign Intelligence Surveillance Act (FISA). Under this act, a president may authorize warrantless electronic surveillance for up to one year if the goal is the collection of information about a foreign power or its agents, whether located in the United States or beyond its borders.

If the proposed target of the surveillance is an American citizen located in the United States, however, the president is required to file an application for a court order allowing electronic surveillance and must show probable cause both that the surveillance target is an "agent of a foreign power" and that the location of the surveillance will be used by a foreign power or its agent. The president must also demonstrate that if the target of the surveillance is a United States citizen, the amount of unnecessary information collected during the surveillance will be kept to a minimum.

Given the sensitive nature of the surveillance in question, Congress established a secret court, the Foreign Intelligence Surveillance Court, to evaluate government requests for domestic surveillance warrants. Meeting behind closed doors at the Justice Department, this court considers the government's grounds for a domestic surveillance warrant, which it can grant, modify, or reject.

As some have observed, President Bush's 2001 executive order on domestic surveillance was not needed to circumvent an obstructionist tribunal. From 1978 through 2004, the U.S. government filed 18,761 warrant requests for domestic surveillance of American citizens allegedly working as agents for a foreign power; just five of those requests were rejected outright, and fewer than two hundred were modified by the court before being granted. Nonetheless, President Bush argued strenuously at the time of the *Times* story (and continued to do so through the end of his presidency) that the FISA warrant requirements made it more difficult, if not impossible, for the government to respond quickly and effectively to terrorist threats.

Bush's arguments echoed those of the Nixon administration, which vigorously defended its wiretapping program before the Supreme Court in the spring of 1972. The government's arguments were presented by Robert C. Mardian, an assistant U.S. attorney general under John Mitchell who also headed up the Justice Department's aggressive campaign against the radical left. He told the justices that requiring "judicial warrants for electronic surveillance could frustrate the President's power to protect the nation from domestic and foreign security threats."

The Supreme Court unanimously disagreed, ruling 8–0 in *United States v. United States District Court* (1972) that domestic surveillance to combat a domestic threat is covered by the protections of the Fourth Amendment. (William Rehnquist, then an associate justice who had joined the Court in January 1972, did not participate in the decision, since he had helped draft the Nixon administration's wiretap policy while serving as an assistant attorney general.) Associate justice Lewis Powell, a recent Nixon appointee, made it clear that the Court had little patience for the administration's claims:

Although some added burden will be imposed upon the Attorney General, this inconvenience is justified in a free society to protect constitutional values. Nor do we think the Government's domestic surveillance powers will be impaired to any significant degree. A prior warrant establishes presumptive validity of the surveillance and will minimize the burden of justification in post-surveillance judicial review. By no means of least importance will be the reassurance of the public generally that indiscriminate wiretapping and bugging of law-abiding citizens cannot occur.

In an impassioned concurrence, associate justice William O. Douglas put the threat posed by the government's position in even starker terms: "We have as much or more to fear from the erosion of our sense of privacy and independence by the omnipresent electronic ear of the Government as we do from the likelihood that fomenters of domestic upheaval will modify our form of governing." Douglas's outrage was fueled by the disclosure that Attorney General Mitchell had authorized roughly eight thousand warrantless wiretaps of suspected dissidents in 1969 and 1970. It is hard to imagine his reaction to the news that the president of the United States allowed the NSA to eavesdrop on tens of millions of Americans.

NOT A GOOD DAY FOR THE CONSTITUTION

Many Americans were appalled by the revelation that the Bush administration had been listening to the domestic conversations of U.S. citizens for more than four years without court supervision. On January 6, 2006, the Electronic Frontier Foundation (EFF), a nonprofit organization devoted to protecting the First Amendment in the digital age, filed a class action lawsuit against AT&T for its alleged "participation in a secret and illegal government program to intercept and analyze vast quantities of Americans' telephone and Internet communications, surveillance done without the authorization of a court and in violation of federal electronic surveillance and telecommunications statutes, as well as the First and Fourth Amendments to the United States Constitution." The plaintiffs were three individual subscribers to AT&T's long-distance and Internet services.

"On information and belief," the EFF stated in its complaint, "AT&T Corp. has opened its key telecommunications facilities and databases to direct access by the NSA and/or other government agencies, intercepting and disclosing to the government the contents of its customers' communications as well as detailed communications records about millions of its customers, including Plaintiffs and class members." The EFF claimed that AT&T's actions, among other things, violated the First and Fourth Amendment rights of the plaintiffs, as well as the provisions of the various federal surveillance statutes.

Eleven days later, the American Civil Liberties Union (ACLU) filed a similar lawsuit directly against the NSA in the U.S. district court in Michigan. The ACLU raised similar objections to the program, arguing that the NSA's warrantless surveillance of American citizens within the United States constituted a violation of their rights under the First and Fourth Amendments. The organization also argued that President Bush had violated the constitutional principle of the separation of powers and exceeded his executive authority by unilaterally disregarding the limits imposed by Congress on domestic surveillance in the Wiretap Statute and FISA.

"Because of the nature of plaintiffs' communications and the identities and locations of those with whom they communicate," the ACLU alleged, "plaintiffs have a well-founded belief that their domestic and international communications are being intercepted by the NSA under the [surveillance program]." Among other things, the ACLU said, the NSA's eavesdropping was inhibiting the ability of U.S. citizens to "obtain information from sources abroad, to locate witnesses, to represent their clients, to conduct scholarship, and to engage in advocacy," all of which is constitutionally protected speech.

In the weeks and months that followed, more than forty additional lawsuits challenging the domestic spying program were filed against various telecommunications firms and the government in U.S. district courts around the country. In response, the White House launched an aggressive public relations campaign to defend the eavesdropping program. At a speech delivered at Kansas State University on January 24, 2006, President Bush said that Congress had given him "additional authority" to track down the individuals responsible for the September 11, 2001, attacks.

"I'm not a lawyer, but I can tell you what [the phrase 'additional authority'] means," President Bush told the audience. "It means Congress gave me the authority to use necessary force to protect the American people, but it didn't prescribe the tactics. It said, 'Mr. President, you've got the power to protect us, but we're not going to tell you how.'"

It didn't take long for one federal court to conclude that whatever

Congress may have meant by the phrase "additional authority," it didn't include massive levels of warrantless surveillance of American citizens within the nation's borders. On August 17, 2006, U.S. district court judge Anna Diggs Taylor granted the ACLU a permanent injunction against the NSA surveillance program. In a lengthy and detailed opinion, she concluded that the surveillance program violated both the terms of FISA and the protections granted by the Fourth Amendment. The government immediately appealed the decision, and Judge Taylor granted a stay of her injunction until the appeals court could issue its decision.

Administration officials were harshly critical of Judge Taylor's decision and her reasoning, but she was not the only judge with reservations about the legality of the Bush administration's actions. One month earlier, in the EFF case, U.S. district court judge Vaughn R. Walker (who was nominated to serve on the federal bench by President George H. W. Bush) had rejected AT&T's motion to dismiss, and he also denied a motion by the U.S. government to dismiss the case or grant summary judgment on the basis of state secrets.

Rather than wait for a formal determination by the courts (and perhaps fearing an outcome similar to the 1972 Supreme Court ruling against domestic surveillance), President Bush began aggressively lobbying Congress for legislation that would both update the thirty-year-old FISA statute and grant legal immunity to the telecommunications firms (like AT&T) that cooperated with his administration's eavesdropping program. With the 2008 federal elections looming, the debate over the proposed changes to FISA and, in particular, the granting of legal immunity to telecommunications companies grew deeply contentious. Democrats, goaded by increasingly large numbers of liberal bloggers, fought the idea of letting the telecommunications companies off scot-free. In response, the Bush administration and its Republican allies did their best to characterize the opposition as another example of the Democrats being "soft on terrorism."

Despite having majorities in both the House of Representatives and the Senate (a by-product of the 2006 midterm elections), it was the Democrats who blinked first. In the summer of 2008, Congress adopted legislation that granted telecommunications companies nearly complete immunity for their role in the Bush administration's warrantless surveillance program. The legislation reaffirmed the principle that the government should not spy on Americans without a warrant, but gave future administrations the right to do so for up to a week before filing a warrant request.

Left unanswered at this juncture is what effect the historic 2008 election will have on the debate over FISA. President Barack Obama's attorney general, Eric Holder, made it clear during his confirmation hearings in 2009 that he does not believe that the president has the intrinsic right to disregard FISA, which is a refreshing change from his predecessors.

But FISA is merely one relatively narrow aspect of the much broader issue of domestic surveillance and widespread data profiling. The more fundamental question is what President Obama and future administrations will do to preserve and protect the right to privacy at the heart of American freedom. This is the story of that right and the grave threats to its continued existence.

THE DECLARATION OF PRIVACY

At its core, the history of America *is* the history of the right to privacy. The myriad immigrants who have come to these shores, from the Pilgrims forward, have been motivated by many factors in their decision to come to the New World, but above all by that quintessential manifestation of privacy: the freedom to make up one's own mind about fundamental human issues, including religion, marriage, politics, employment, and education.

Admittedly, what we usually think of as "privacy" today—space for ourselves, out of the sight of others—was at best a sometime thing in seventeenth- and eighteenth-century America: the typical home was small, and few families had enough space for each child, or even the parents, to have a separate bedroom. Towns and villages were similarly compact, and neighbors were known to keep a close eye on each other. Anyone who has spent any time in a small, close-knit community (home, work, or school) knows full well how quickly news and information can spread and how difficult it can be to escape the (mostly) benign surveillance. Nonetheless, American colonists not only were aware of the concept of personal privacy, but from the start recognized it as a necessary quality of both communal living and a broader sense of personal freedom.

Few aspects of personal privacy are more important than the confidentiality of one's thoughts and communications. In an ideal world, it would not matter if our most intimate personal or professional communications were open to everyone; but in reality, significant harm can result when confidential messages go astray. Human nature being what it is, there are countless reasons why we value the power to choose who, if anyone, hears what we have to say on a particular subject.

"I am under no moral or other Obligation," future president John Adams once wrote in his diary,

> to publish to the World how much my Expences or my Incomes amount to yearly. There are Times when and Persons to whom, I am not obliged to tell what are my Principles and Opinions in Politics or Religion. This kind of Dissimulation, which is no more than Concealment, Secrecy, and Reserve, or in other Words, Prudence and Discretion, is a necessary Branch of Wisdom, and so far from being immoral and unlawful, . . . [it] is a Duty and a Virtue.

The only truly secure communications (so far) are the conversations we have within the confines of our own heads. Once those thoughts are expressed externally in any fashion—speech, diary, letter, telephone conversation, e-mail, instant message—our ability to control the spread of information is diminished by varying degrees. And as a general rule, the farther away the recipient is from us, the more difficult it is to control the privacy of the communication.

It comes as no surprise, then, that the history of communicating over any distance is tightly woven with the history of efforts to keep such communications private. Nearly four thousand years ago, for instance, during the reign of the Babylonian king Hammurabi, messages were written on small clay tablets that were then covered with a second layer of thin clay and baked again. Once the message was delivered, the outer envelope of clay was broken off so that the interior message could be read. Similar clay envelope-wrapped letters have been recovered from the burial sites of Egyptian kings.

The techniques for sealing correspondence in Western Europe developed somewhat more slowly (as did the practice of writing itself). Parchment scrolls or folded sheets of paper might be left loose, or at most tied shut with a leather thong, ribbon, or scrap of string, none of which offered any means of showing whether the message had been opened and read en route. By the middle of the seventeenth century, the use of sealing wax had grown more common, and the familiar red circles offered some assurance of privacy if they arrived undamaged.

However, a cracked or broken seal might just as plausibly indicate rough handling as espionage. The introduction of mass-produced envelopes in the middle of the nineteenth century offered a somewhat greater assurance of privacy; but as most people quickly realized, the contents of even the most tightly sealed envelope could fall prey to a naked light bulb or a steaming teakettle.

Concern over the privacy of personal communication was hardly the only issue that drove the American colonists to rebellion against the British Empire. But privacy in general, as a critical component of human freedom, was reflected in virtually every complaint levied by the colonists against King George III in their Declaration of Independence. As will be illustrated later on, those same concerns for personal privacy were woven into the U.S. Constitution eleven years later and unequivocally affirmed by the adoption of the Bill of Rights in 1791. In ways both large and small, the formation of this country was a ringing declaration of the importance of personal privacy.

PRIVACY'S PROGRESS

Ironically, the privacy of personal communications in America got off to a rocky start in Plymouth, the landing place of the Pilgrims in 1620. The Pilgrims had a visceral interest in the issue of privacy: the British monarch, Elizabeth I, was hostile to their Puritan beliefs, and the Pilgrims (originally known as Separatists) were forced to meet in secret in order to avoid the baneful gaze of the Crown and its agents. In 1607, the Pilgrims fled to Holland and eventually to the New World.

Just four years after the Pilgrims landed, the fledgling colony was already facing its first political crisis. On January 24, 1624, William Bradford, the governor of the small colony, received word that the English merchants underwriting the Massachusetts Bay Colony expedition had decided to send the Reverend John Lyford to Plymouth. Although nominally a Puritan, Lyford also was a member of the Church of England, which had effectively driven the Pilgrims out of England. Bradford was aware that the colony's financial underwriters viewed the Pilgrim's strict religious control of the colony as a significant barrier to its economic success, and he suspected that Lyford's arrival was intended to weaken or overthrow Pilgrim authority.

In his history *Of Plimoth Plantation*, Bradford wrote that upon landing, Lyford went to great lengths to ingratiate himself with the colony and its leaders, even offering to join the Pilgrim church. But at the same time, he fell in with John Oldham, one of the colony's malcontents, whom Bradford described as an "intelligencer to those in England." Suspicion quickly grew that the two were plotting to overthrow Bradford and establish the Church of England as the colony's religion. Bradford's response to Lyford's seditious activities illustrates just how little privacy there was within the stockaded confines of Plymouth:

> Both Oldam and he [Lyford] grew very perverse, and shewed a spirite of great malignancie, drawing as many into faction as they could; were they never so vile or profane, they did nourish & back them in all their doings; so they would but cleave to them and speak against ye church hear; so as ther was nothing but private meetings and whisperings amongst them; they feeding themselves & others with what they should bring to pass in England by the faction of their friends their, which brought others as well as them selves into a fools paradise. Yet they could not cary so closly but much of both their doings & sayings were discovered, yet outwardly they still set a faire face of things.
>
> At lenght [*sic*] when ye ship was ready to goe, it was observed Liford was long in writing, & sente many letters, and could not forbear to comunicate to his intimats such things as made them laugh in their sleeves, and thought he had done ther errand sufficiently.

As the ship that had carried Lyford to Plymouth set sail for the return voyage to England, Bradford and other leaders of the colony rowed out into the harbor, boarded the departing ship, and asked to see the letters that Lyford had written to his friends back home. Bradford said that he was handed more than twenty letters, "many of them larg, and full of slanders, & false accusations, tending not only to their [the Colony's] prejudice, but to their ruine & utter subversion."

According to Bradford's account, when confronted with the written evidence of their plot, Lyford did not protest the seizure of his letters, but Oldham complained bitterly about the invasion of his privacy. Bradford was apparently somewhat embarrassed by his actions, because he offered two different arguments in his defense: First, the governor "shewed the people," Bradford said, "he did it as a magistrate, and was bound to it by his place, to prevent the micheefe & ruine that this conspiracie and plots of theirs would bring on this poor colony." And second, Bradford argued that Lyford himself had opened letters from other colonists, added "disgracefull anotations," and sent copies to his confederates in England. Both arguments— exigency and combating an enemy through its own methods—have popped up at various times in our nation's history to justify a wide range of privacy intrusions.

The privacy of postal communications in colonial America did not improve significantly for nearly a century. For the first seven decades of European inhabitation, the delivery of letters was entrusted to private messengers and often serendipitous delivery at boardinghouses and taverns. The first official postmaster in the American colonies was Richard Fairbanks, the owner and operator of a waterfront tavern in Boston. He was appointed by the General Court of Massachusetts in 1639 to receive "all letters which brought from beyond the seas, or are to be sent thither." The state legislature also decreed that Fairbanks "must answer for all miscarriages through his own neglect." But the General Court itself neglected to provide any specific protection for the confidentiality of the letters themselves, despite the fact that it was well known that letters left for delivery or collection were a frequent source of amusement and entertainment for bored or inebriated tavern patrons.

The origins of a functioning North American postal system can be traced most directly to the letters patent issued on February 17, 1691, by England's King William and Queen Mary to Thomas Neale, Esq., appointing him postmaster general of America. Neale was given authority for a period of twenty-one years to establish post offices in the King's colonies and to "receive, send, and deliver" letters at rates consistent with English postal rates. A longtime member of Parliament and master of the British mint, Neale had no interest in traveling to America to personally supervise the creation of a postal service and appointed Andrew Hamilton to serve as deputy postmaster general for America.

A good argument can be made that the postal system Hamilton subsequently created was responsible for first sparking a nascent sense of unity among the disparate and often mutually suspicious British colonies. Under the terms of the letters patent issued to Neale, the various colonies were not required to participate in the new postal system. Despite the fact that he was also serving at the time as governor of the East Jersey and West Jersey colonies, Hamilton personally traveled to each of the other colonies and persuaded them (with the exception of Virginia) to pass legislation creating a unified system of post roads and postal rates up and down the Atlantic seaboard. Not only was this legislation the first cooperative action taken by a majority of the American colonies, but it put in place a system that over time would allow the relatively rapid sharing of news and information from one end of the colonies to the other. The unintended consequences of Hamilton's initiative would prove profound.

Actual mail delivery on Hamilton's Intercolonial Postal Union began on May 1, 1693, with a weekly delivery between Virginia and Portsmouth, New Hampshire. Neale reportedly had been counting on sufficient revenues from the American postal system to help pay off some outstanding debts (including large sums owed to Hamilton himself), but the mail service was perpetually unprofitable. Unwilling or unable to wait for the American post to start generating a profit, he assigned his rights in the system to Hamilton and his business partner, Robert West. It proved to be a smart move. Hamilton and West continued to lose money, and a few years later, they sold the North American postal system back to the British government, which folded it into the existing postal system for England and Ireland.

BENJAMIN FRANKLIN, POSTMASTER

The takeover of the colonial postal system brought immediate improvements to the delivery of mail, including a formal recognition of the importance of postal privacy. During the reign of Queen Anne, the Parliament adopted the Post Office Act of 1710, which included a provision that "No Person or Persons shall presume wittingly, willingly, or knowingly, to open, detain, or delay, or cause, procure, permit, or suffer to be opened, detained, or delayed, any Letter or Letters, Packet, or Packets." Violators faced a fine of up to twenty-five pounds. In addition, each postal employee was required to take the "Oath required by the Act of the Ninth of Queen Anne":

> I, A.B., do swear, That I will not wittingly, willingly, or knowingly open . . . or cause, procure, permit, or suffer to be opened . . . any Letter or Letters . . . which shall come into my Hands, Power, or Custody, by Reason of my Employment in or relating to the Post Office; except . . . by an express Warrant in Writing under the Hand of one of the principal Secretaries of State for that purpose.

The imposition of a warrant requirement for the seizure of mail is a clear indication of just how seriously British subjects valued the privacy of their correspondence.

Since running governmental institutions entirely from England was obviously impractical, it was standard practice to hire or appoint colonists to handle various ministerial occupations. On October 27, 1737, an announcement appeared in the *Pennsylvania Gazette*, a newspaper published by a struggling printer named Benjamin Franklin, declaring that he was now the operator of "the Post-Office of Philadelphia."

The appointment, as Franklin himself later conceded in his *Autobiography*, gave a significant boost to his publishing business: "Though the salary was small, it facilitated the correspondence that improved my newspaper, increased the number demanded, as well as the advertisements to be inserted, so that it came to afford me a considerable income." In 1753, Franklin and William Hunter of Alexandria, Virginia, were appointed by the British government to run the Parliamentary Post as deputy postmasters general of the colonies.

Over the next twenty-one years, the energetic Franklin revolutionized the delivery of mail in the American colonies. Shortly after taking office, he went on a sixteen-hundred-mile horseback tour of post offices and postal roads from New England to southern Virginia. Based on his observations, Franklin recommended surveys for new post roads, the installation of mile markers, and the rerouting of some postal routes to shorten delivery times. For the first time, mail carriers began using lanterns to ride through the night, vastly increasing the speed of mail deliveries. Although the postal system continued to lose money for the first few years under Franklin and Hunter, the improvements eventually proved so attractive to the colonists that the two deputy postmasters were able to pay themselves a salary from the postage profits.

Franklin and Hunter not only enforced the privacy provisions of the 1710 Post Office Act, but went even further. They issued regulations instructing local postmasters to keep their post offices separate and apart from their homes and to make sure that no unauthorized individuals handled the mail. They also ordered postmasters to seal the mail for each town in a bag and instruct postal route riders to unseal the mail bag only when they reached the destination town. Perhaps most foresightedly, postmasters were required to request proof of identification before allowing someone to retrieve a posted letter, although in the absence of state driver's licenses, Social Security cards, or other indicia, it is unclear what people actually offered as proof of their identity.

In any case, despite the best efforts of Franklin and his fellow deputy postmasters, security of the mails remained tenuous in colonial America. The diaries and correspondence of early Americans are filled with veiled (or not so veiled) references to the insecurity of the postal system, and the use of codes and ciphers was commonplace. In 1742, for instance, Dr. Oliver Noyes, a Boston physician, self-censored a letter to his friend David Jeffries: "I'll say no more on this head, but When I have the Pleasure to See you again, shall Inform you of many Things too tedious for a Letter and which perhaps may fall into Ill hands, for I know there are many at Boston who dont Scruple to Open any Persons letters, but they are well known here."

As relations between England and its colonies steadily worsened, concerns about the security and secrecy of the colonial post grew more acute. When various political crises arose, the American colonists formed "Committees of Correspondence" to exchange information more rapidly and more securely than could be done using the regular postal routes. By the early 1770s, every colony had formed a correspondence committee, which colonists used to rally support for beleaguered cities like Boston, organize opposition to acts of Parliament, and ultimately, coordinate plans to hold the First Continental Congress in September 1774. Although Benjamin Franklin did not attend that first Congress, he was so openly sympathetic and supportive of the growing rebellion that he was fired from his position as deputy postmaster for the British government at the end of that year.

THE WORST INSTRUMENT OF ARBITRARY POWER

The battles at Lexington and Concord on the morning of April 19, 1774, were the spark that lit a conflagration that had been smoldering for decades. Even as early as the middle of the eighteenth century, North America was causing Britain no end of trouble. The Seven Years' War between Britain and France (which ran from 1756 to 1763) had spilled over to the American continent from Europe. In the New World, it became better known as the French and Indian War, due to the fact that Britain was fighting a fierce coalition of French soldiers and American Indian tribes, including the Algonquin, the Ojibwa, and the Shawnee, for control of North America.

In general, colonial support for Britain's military efforts was strong, in part because the mostly Protestant colonists feared the imposition of religious restrictions by the Catholic Church following a French victory, and in part because the colonists were eager for the economic opportunities offered by a British takeover of the French territories in the New World.

At the same time, however, the economic aggressiveness of the American colonies was one of England's own biggest problems during the Seven Years' War. In the early part of the eighteenth century, the northern and middle American colonies had developed a thriving trade with the molasses-producing islands in the West Indies. For various reasons, the trade opportunities for the American colonies were better on islands controlled by the French, Dutch, and Spanish than those held by the colonists' fellow Englishmen. In an effort to protect the molasses industry on British islands, the British Parliament had passed the Sugar and Molasses Act in 1733, which imposed a high import tax on goods from non-British islands. In response, the colonists developed a widespread and effective smuggling network to avoid British customs officials.

Colonial smuggling was always a thorn in the paw of the British lion, but during the French and Indian War, it rose to the level of a national security issue. Part of the problem was strategic: colonial trade with the French islands provided the French with supplies and funds that were used to prolong the conflict both in Europe and in North America. But of more immediate concern to the British was the loss of vitally needed tax revenues for its own war efforts; as many governments have discovered since, the costs of fighting an overseas war can rise quickly. According to a contemporary estimate by Boston attorney John Adams, the British government collected somewhere between £1,000 and £2,000 in importation revenues each year; but had the full amount of revenue been collected, the total would have been closer to £25,000 per year for molasses alone. Many an old American fortune can trace its roots to untaxed profits from the Caribbean trade.

In an effort to recapture some of the lost revenues needed for its military campaigns and for other colonial expenses, the British Parliament announced a crackdown on the collection of import duties. In doing so, however, the British authorities unintentionally set in motion a train of events that, in less than a generation, cost them a continent.

A century earlier, under the reign of Charles II, legislation was passed by Parliament authorizing the issuance of "writs of assistance" to revenue officers to help promote more successful tax collections. A writ of assistance was a remarkably powerful investigative tool: it was a general, open-ended search warrant that authorized the person holding it to search any location and any person at his or her discretion. The only practical limitation on the writ was the life-span of the monarch in whose name the writ was issued; under the terms of the statute adopted by Parliament, all writs of assistance automatically expired six months after the death of the British king or queen.

Adding to the profound power of the writs was a virtually complete lack of oversight by an independent judiciary. Although each writ of assistance was initially issued by a judge, an applicant for such a writ was not required to swear out an affidavit specifying the object of the search, nor even state the reasons for requesting the writ in the first place. As long as the writ was still in effect, it could be transferred from one person to another without judicial approval, and there was no requirement that the writs be returned to a court or magistrate with a report of the results of the search.

In 1755, as hostilities with the French in the colonies intensified and the need for revenue increased, the British began issuing writs of assistance in Massachusetts, giving customs house officers essentially unlimited authority to randomly search sailing ships, dockside warehouses, and even private homes for untaxed property. Customs officials began raiding homes and conducting vigorous searches for contraband, often breaking open chests, drawers, and boxes in the process. As one might expect, both the writs of assistance and the Crown's increasingly aggressive efforts to collect import duties met with growing opposition among colonial merchants and sailors.

Matters came to a head in the weeks and months following the death of King George II on October 25, 1760. With the outstanding writs of assistance scheduled to expire, Charles Paxton, the surveyor and searcher for the port of Boston, applied to the Massachusetts Superior Court for the issuance of new writs under the authority of the new king, George III. Paxton's petition was opposed by a large group of Boston merchants, and the case was set for hearing in February 1761.

When the hearing on Paxton's case was held at the State House in Boston (the fully restored building still stands at the intersection of Washington and State streets), it attracted a large crowd of lawyers and citizens from Boston and the surrounding communities. One of the people in attendance was twenty-five-year-old John Adams, who had recently been admitted to the Massachusetts bar. Adams was clearly captivated by the argument of James Otis, who delivered a five-hour oration against the writs of assistance, a speech that Adams later described as a "flame of fire." When the case had originally been filed, Otis was serving as advocate general for the colony's British governor, but he refused to defend the issuance of the writs. Otis denounced his office and volunteered to argue the merchants' case for free. "And I argue it with the greater pleasure," Otis told the court, "as it is in favor of British liberty, at a time when we hear the greatest monarch upon earth declaring from his throne that he glories in the name of Britain, and that the privileges of his people are dearer to him than the most valuable prerogatives of his crown."

According to Adams's account, Otis began his oration with a strong condemnation of the writs of assistance as "instruments of slavery on the one hand, and villainy on the other." Otis conceded that a court could issue a special writ of assistance, authorizing the search of a particular place, provided that the application for the special writ was supported by the oath of the person seeking the writ. But general writs of assistance, Otis argued, were contrary to the most basic principles of British law:

> Now, one of the most essential branches of English liberty is the freedom of one's house. A man's house is his castle; and whilst he is quiet, he is as well guarded as a prince in his castle. This writ, if it should be declared legal, would totally annihilate this privilege. Custom-house officers may enter our houses when they please; we are commanded to permit their entry. Their menial servants may enter, may break locks, bars, and everything in their way; and whether they break through malice or revenge, no man, no court, can inquire. Bare suspicion without oath is sufficient.

But Otis was not content to argue merely that the potential for abuse rendered the writs of assistance invalid; he went much further, and argued that the act of Parliament establishing the writs was void because such writs are contrary to the common law—that is, the accumulated judicial decisions—of the English people. "No Acts of Parliament can establish such a writ," Otis thundered, "though it should be made in the very words of the petition, it would be void. An act against the constitution is void."

The idea that even acts of Parliament are subject to the overarching authority of an English constitution was a concept that would find fertile soil among the colonists, but it fell on deaf ears in the State House. Sensitive to the political tensions surrounding the case, Lieutenant Governor Hutchinson and the other members of the court conferred at length with authorities in England about the legality of the writs and, two and a half years after Otis's stirring speech, ruled against him.

For the time being, the court's decision muted opposition to the writs of assistance, although it is not clear that the writs made much of a dent in the colonial enthusiasm for smuggling. But Otis's speech did make a significant contribution to the ideology that fueled the rhetoric of the American Revolution. Nearly fifteen years before the first shots were fired at Concord and Lexington, Otis compellingly argued that every Englishman enjoyed certain core rights accrued to him over the centuries through custom and practice, a principle best expressed by the "fundamental maxim that every subject had the same right to his life, liberty, property, and the law that the King had to his crown." Those rights, Otis argued, could not legally be infringed on or eliminated by Parliament. His stirring enunciation of the basic rights of English citizens helped bind a collection of fractious colonies into a new nation.

THE INTOLERABLE ACTS OF PARLIAMENT

If Otis's speech, as Adams said, was a "flame of fire," then the incredibly unpopular actions of Parliament over the following decade were the dried kindling that fueled the rise of American nationalism. In the wake of the Seven Years' War, which formally ended with the signing of the Treaty of Paris on February 10, 1763, the British government found itself deeply in debt and struggling to cover the continued costs of housing and feeding soldiers in the colonies. According to George Grenville, first lord of the treasury and chancellor of the exchequer, the British national debt had doubled during the course of the Seven Years' War to £140 million. Grenville was of the opinion that the colonies should bear part of the burden of paying down the debt and supporting troops stationed within their borders. In order to increase tax revenues from the colonies, Grenville proposed an increase in customs dues, tighter policing of smugglers from the West Indies, and most famously, the extension of the Stamp Act to the colonies.

Under the terms of the Stamp Act, which was applied to the colonies by an act of Parliament on March 22, 1765 (eventually taking effect on November 1), a wide variety of printed materials were required to carry a tax stamp, including all legal documents, permits, wills, pamphlets, and newspapers. The new law represented the first effort by Parliament to tax activity that took place entirely within the colonies, and opposition to the act rose swiftly and heatedly. In Massachusetts, John Adams introduced a resolution in the town meeting of Braintree opposing the use of the stamps; the resolution was later adopted by more than forty other towns across the state.

The Stamp Act was merely the first in a series of actions taken by Parliament that the colonists viewed as punitive and unreasonably intrusive. Just a couple of months after the passage of the Stamp Act,

Parliament passed the Quartering Act of 1765. Contrary to popular belief, the law did not require American colonists to provide lodging for British troops in private homes. However, the law did provide that if insufficient space was available in barracks or public houses, the troops were to be quartered in whatever other nonprivate buildings were available, including stables, victualing and spirit houses, abandoned homes, and even outhouses. In addition, colonists could be compelled to provide the troops with various necessities, including "food, alcohol, fire, candles, vinegar, salt, and bedding" without compensation. Resistance to the law was widespread throughout the colonies, so much so that the New York Assembly was disbanded by the British government until such time as the colony was prepared to comply with the law.

Just two years later, the British Parliament adopted legislation proposed by a new chancellor of the exchequer, Charles Townshend, that imposed import duties on a wide range of items commonly used in the colonies (including paper, glass, and tea) and reaffirmed the use of writs of assistance by customs agents bent on collecting the duties. The Townshend Acts, as they came to be known, further infuriated the American colonists and led to a highly successful boycott of the taxed items. The acts also encouraged the growth of increasingly popular secret organizations like the Sons of Liberty and the Daughters of Liberty.

In response to the "Boston Tea Party," a Sons of Liberty–led raid on three East India Company ships trying to land boycotted tea in Boston, the outraged British Parliament wasted no time in punishing its increasingly rebellious and defiant colony. On March 31, 1774, the Boston Port Act was passed, shutting Boston Harbor until the value of the destroyed tea (roughly $2 million in today's dollars) was paid to the East India Company. Several other punitive laws followed in swift succession: the Massachusetts Government Act, which essentially abolished Massachusetts colonial and local government; the Administration of Justice Act, which authorized Governor Hutchinson to transfer the trial of any British official accused of a crime to a venue outside of Massachusetts (including as far away as Britain), thus making it much more expensive and difficult for colonists to appear as plaintiffs or witnesses; and a second Quartering Act, which gave any colonial governor the authority to appropriate unoccupied buildings to house British troops.

If British hard-liners thought the punitive bills would bring the rebels to heel, they were sadly mistaken. The laws, widely described throughout the colonies as the "Intolerable Acts," intensified colonial opposition to British rule and made it more difficult for moderates in both England and the American colonies to defend the Crown's behavior. A Continental Congress was convened in Philadelphia on September 5, 1774, to protest the Intolerable Acts and to petition for their revocation. When that plea fell on deaf ears in London, the delegates returned to Philadelphia in the spring of 1775 and opened the Second Continental Congress on May 10. But the time for petitioning Parliament had passed: just three weeks earlier, British troops had exchanged gunfire with American farmers at Lexington and Concord.

PRIVACY IN ALL BUT WORD

In the contemporary debate over the right to privacy, conservative legal theorists who advocate a strict construction of the nation's founding documents make much of the fact that the Framers never specifically defined a "right to privacy" and indeed, never used the word at all. Strictly speaking, that is true: the word "privacy" does not appear in the Declaration of Independence, the Constitution, or the Bill of Rights, nor in any of the seventeen amendments added to the Constitution since.

But each of those texts must be read and understood in the context of the times that produced it. Consider, for instance, the preamble to the Declaration of Independence: "We hold these truths to be self-evident, that all men are created equal, that they are endowed by their Creator with certain unalienable Rights, that among these are Life, Liberty and the pursuit of Happiness." Thomas Jefferson, the primary author of the Declaration, was clearly referring to the arguments raised by James Otis, among others, against the British writs of assistance. And certainly each of the rights listed by Jefferson—life, liberty, and the pursuit of happiness—are objectives that are both personal and private to each individual.

Included among the Declaration's list of grievances were a number of infringements by the British government on American privacy and autonomy, many stemming directly from the much-despised Intolerable Acts. Independence and autonomy are central components of the concept of privacy, and although Jefferson and his fellow delegates may have eschewed the word itself, there is little question that they were motivated in large part by the belief that the British Crown was illegally infringing on their private affairs.

A similarly profound concern for private autonomy was evident during the debate over the U.S. Constitution a dozen years later. Many Americans, known collectively as Anti-Federalists, worried that the newly formed federal government would infringe on personal liberty as much as the British Crown, or even more so, given that an ocean would no longer separate the states from the national capital. In many states, ratification of the U.S. Constitution was made expressly contingent on the adoption of a series of amendments that would explicitly protect individual freedoms. As with the Declaration of Independence, the evident concern for preserving autonomy and freedom was the functional equivalent of protecting personal privacy.

The text of several of the amendments in the Bill of Rights makes this patently clear. The Third Amendment, for instance, specifically prohibits legislation like the Quartering Act:

> No Soldier shall, in time of peace be quartered in any house, without the consent of the Owner, nor in time of war, but in a manner to be prescribed by law.

Similarly, the language of the First Amendment is designed to protect the autonomy of American citizens in making some of their most private decisions about their beliefs, their thoughts, and their associations:

> Congress shall make no law respecting an establishment of religion, or prohibiting the free exercise thereof; or abridging the freedom of speech, or of the press; or the right of the people peaceably to assemble, and to petition the Government for a redress of grievances.

But of all the amendments, it is the Fourth that most directly confronts the intrusions of the British government that so angered the American colonists:

> The right of the people to be secure in their persons, houses, papers, and effects, against unreasonable searches and seizures, shall not be violated, and no Warrants shall issue, but upon probable cause, supported by Oath or affirmation, and particularly describing the place to be searched, and the persons or things to be seized.

The official birth date of the "right to privacy" in the United States, then, is December 15, 1791, the day on which the eleventh of thirteen states—Virginia—ratified the Bill of Rights. But its conception was decades earlier, when the British government began ignoring the basic rights and privileges of its citizens. The founding of the American republic gave the former British colonists an opportunity to reaffirm basic human rights, including privacy. The question, to paraphrase Franklin's memorable line, was whether they could keep it.

2

POSTAL POLITICS, PURITY, AND PRIVACY

From the start of Franklin's colonial postal system, the privacy of the mails was a central tenet. But while the colonists clearly valued and relied upon a confidential postal system, it did not take long for some in the new nation to question the advisability of allowing unfettered distribution of materials through the mails. A particularly good example of how political concerns could trump privacy involved the long-running efforts to abolish slavery.

In an effort to smooth the passage of the Constitution, particularly in the southern states, the Framers notoriously deferred any action on the issue of slavery until 1808 at the earliest. Although the Framers succeeded in preventing the volatile issue from derailing the formation of the new nation, the political compromise in Philadelphia did little to stem a rising tide of opposition to the institution. Even before the ratification of the Constitution, the Society for the Relief of Free Negroes Unlawfully Held in Bondage, under the leadership of Benjamin Franklin, was working to abolish slavery in Pennsylvania, and similar societies eventually were organized in virtually every state. By 1804, slavery had been abolished throughout the northern United States, and the importation of new slaves was banned altogether as soon as legally possible on January 1, 1808. But the ban did nothing to free the men and women already enslaved in this country or the children born into bondage.

As the abolitionist movement intensified in the early years of the nineteenth century, proponents published an enormous number of books, pamphlets, newspapers, and other materials intended to illustrate the abusive conditions of slavery in the South and to agitate for an end to the institution. It was common practice to mail such materials to sympathizers in the South or, in some cases, directly to the more notorious slave owners and slave traders. But the abolitionist tracts angered many Southerners and contributed to the increasingly strained relations among the states. In Charleston, South Carolina, for instance, public outrage toward the abolitionist tracts ran so hot during the summer of 1835 that the local postmaster was warned to stop their delivery. The clearly frightened postmaster wrote to Washington for instructions on how to handle the matter.

The postmaster general at the time was Amos Kendall, perhaps the most influential member of Andrew Jackson's famed "Kitchen Cabinet." The postal crisis posed a tricky political quandary for Kendall and Jackson, both of whom wanted vice president Martin Van Buren to succeed Jackson in the upcoming 1836 presidential election. Recognizing that an uncompromising defense of the abolitionist tracts could weaken Van Buren's chances in the South, Kendall sent a decidedly equivocal reply to Charleston:

> Upon careful examination of the law, I am satisfied that the Postmaster-General has no legal authority to exclude newspapers from the mail, nor prohibit their carriage or delivery on account of their character or tendency, real or supposed.
>
> But I am not prepared to direct you to forward or deliver the papers of which you speak. None of the papers detained have been forwarded to me, and I cannot judge for myself of their character and tendency; but you inform me that they are, in character, "the most inflammatory and incendiary, and insurrectionary in the highest degree."
>
> By no act or direction of mine, official or private, could I be induced to aid, knowingly, in giving circulation to papers of this description, directly or indirectly. We owe an obligation to the laws, but a higher one to the communities in which we live, and if the *former* be perverted to destroy the *latter*, it is patriotism to disregard them. Entertaining these views, I can not sanction, and will not condemn the step you have taken.

Later that year, in his next-to-last message to Congress on December 7, President Jackson indirectly referenced the Charleston controversy (and others) by calling on Congress to pass "a law as will prohibit, under severe penalties, the circulation in the Southern States, through the mail, of incendiary publications intended to instigate the slaves to insurrection." The idea was taken up with vigor by South Carolina senator (and former vice president) John C. Calhoun, an ardent defender of states' rights and slavery. He introduced legislation, quickly labeled the "Gag Bill," that would have made it unlawful for any U.S. postmaster, "in any State, Territory, or District, knowingly to deliver to any person whatever, any pamphlets, newspaper, handbill, or other printed paper or pictorial representation touching the subject of slavery, where, by the laws of said State, Territory, or District, their circulation is prohibited; and any deputy postmaster who shall be guilty thereof, shall be forthwith removed from office."

Through various parliamentary maneuvers, Calhoun contrived to have the vote on approving the bill for a third reading end in an 18–18 tie, which meant that as president of the Senate, Vice President Van Buren would cast the deciding vote. Van Buren did his best to avoid the dilemma, wanting neither to disappoint the North nor anger the South. But after Calhoun mockingly shouted "Where's the vice president?" Van Buren reluctantly cast his vote with the Southerners.

Through the efforts of the New England senators, most notably Daniel Webster of Massachusetts, the Gag Bill was rejected by the Senate upon third reading. The primary concern was for the law's impact on the First Amendment, but Webster also warned of its impact on personal privacy. An individual's right to private papers, Webster said, including those delivered through the mail, was protected by every nation in the free world and should not be abridged in this one.

Webster's arguments against the Gag Bill helped defeat the first effort to authorize the U.S. Post Office to exclude officially disfavored materials from delivery through the mails, but his victory was more symbolic than substantive. In the absence of a specific prohibition by Congress, local postal authorities continued the practice of blocking the delivery of newspapers and other materials with which they disagreed or which they believed posed a threat to the safety and security of the United States (or themselves). The practice would set a dangerous precedent in the years to come.

A TALE OF TWO INVENTIONS

Just a few years after the heated debate over the Gag Bill, two remarkable technological innovations were introduced that would in time utterly reshape the boundaries of personal privacy. In early March 1839, a meeting took place in Paris between two men who were on the verge, albeit unwittingly, of earning a permanent place in the history of communication. One was American Samuel F. B. Morse, the inventor of the telegraph, who was visiting the French capital in an effort to secure a patent for his new communications device. The other was Louis-Jacques-Mandé Daguerre, a French artist and chemist who just two months earlier had announced the perfection of his method for creating photographs (which quickly became known as "daguerreotypes").

During Morse's visit to his studio, Daguerre showed him numerous examples of the images he had captured, including scenes from the Louvre and outdoor shots of Notre Dame Cathedral. Morse was reportedly amazed by the clarity of the images, and as an artist and inventor himself, was undoubtedly eager to learn more about Daguerre's remarkable invention. However, due to the delicate nature of his negotiations with the French government over the purchase of the patent for his invention, Daguerre was reluctant to disclose to Morse many of the actual details of his photographic process.

Daguerre's invention was announced to the world at a well-attended session of the French Academy of Sciences by François Arago on August 19, 1839. Translations of the daguerreotype process spread rapidly from Paris to London to New York. Although complicated and painstaking, the process of making daguerreotypes was not beyond the competence of most amateur hobbyists, and the necessary materials quickly vanished from store shelves. Within weeks, Daguerre's method had been translated into a dozen different languages, and "daguerreotype mania" was well on its way to becoming a worldwide phenomenon.

In the century and a half since its invention, photography has had a profound impact on personal privacy and continues to evolve in ways unimaginable to Daguerre. In particular, the recent development of digital photography is challenging and reshaping our understanding of personal privacy on a daily basis. It would be some years, however, before the impact of photography on personal privacy would be fully felt in Daguerre's time. Thanks to awkward equipment and long exposure times, it was virtually impossible in the early days of photography to capture an image of someone without the subject's knowledge or consent. When Morse first viewed Daguerre's images in his workshop, for instance, he was surprised that there were no people depicted in scenes of even the busiest places in Paris. As Daguerre explained, however, the exposure times for the images were so long (fifteen to twenty minutes, even in bright sunshine) that people and even carriages moving through the scene could not be captured.

Despite the primitive and awkward nature of the technology, many people quickly saw entrepreneurial possibilities in the new medium. By the time of the World's Fair in London in 1851, there were thousands of professional daguerreotypers in America alone. Thanks to extensive experimentation and innovation on both sides of the Atlantic, the process of taking daguerreotypes grew steadily easier and quicker, with exposure times dropping from fifteen minutes down to just a few seconds. In the decade following Daguerre's invention, literally millions of images were created by avid photographers.

As the large number of surviving daguerreotypes clearly demonstrates, the idea of a relatively quick and comparatively inexpensive personal portrait was extremely compelling, and despite the initially long exposure times, plenty of people were willing to sit or stand still long enough to be photographed (often using painful-looking devices to hold their heads perfectly motionless). Predictably, some people wasted little time in using Daguerre's equipment to push other boundaries of personal privacy: historians debate whether the first nude daguerreotypes were taken weeks or mere days after the technology was introduced. Since daguerreotypes are one-of-a-kind images, however, the first nude photos were simply more realistic depictions of activities already captured on canvas or in prints and etchings. Photography's real impact on personal privacy would be deferred until three separate innovations came together: exposure times measured in fractions of a second (making surreptitious photos possible), widespread use of negatives (allowing for the creation of multiple copies of a given image), and the invention of the halftone process (allowing photographs to be printed in newspapers and distributed around the world).

SACRIFICING PERSONAL PRIVACY FOR SPEED

Of the two inventions that Daguerre and Morse discussed in Paris, it was actually the humble telegram—notwithstanding its truncated syntax and flimsy feel—that had the most immediate impact on personal privacy. More than anything else, Morse's telegraph convincingly illustrated that the average person was willing to trade the widely assumed and legally guaranteed privacy of personal communication by mail for speed and convenience.

Morse's years of effort to obtain federal funding to develop his invention finally paid off in 1843, when Congress appropriated $30,000 to fund the construction of a forty-mile long telegraph line along the railroad tracks from Washington, D.C., to Baltimore. The line was completed in the spring of 1844, and on May 24, Morse formally opened the era of electronic communications by transmitting the now-famous message "What hath God wrought?" to his assistant Alfred Vail in Baltimore, who returned the same message to Morse in Washington just a minute later. The legislators watching the demonstration were reportedly awestruck at the speed with which the message was sent and received, and news of the telegraph's remarkable capabilities spread rapidly. As *The Adams Sentinel and General Advertiser* in Gettysburg grandly proclaimed a few days later, "It is a total annihilation of time and space." The *Milwaukee Sentinel* was even more enthusiastic: "It is in truth, the most wonderful application of science of our age, and with the invention of the Daguerreotype, will make the present century forever memorable in the lifestory of scientific achievements."

But despite its remarkable ability to transmit messages over long distances in mere seconds, the telegraph never quite experienced the worldwide frenzy that marked the introduction of the daguerreotype. While the telegraph's eventual importance in military, political, and commercial affairs cannot be overstated, it was not a technology that was particularly well suited to amateurs or home use. And as Morse himself was painfully aware, substantial financial investments were required in order to build the networks necessary to make it practical to send messages over any significant distance. The combination of cost and complexity meant that there was never any serious discussion of extending telegraph service to individual homes.

Even after telegraph lines were installed between major population centers, the initially high cost of using the new technology to send messages slowed its adoption by the general public. Thanks to passage of postal reforms in 1845 (known colloquially as the "Cheap Postage Act"), as well as the nation's rapidly growing railway system, three or four pages of correspondence could be sent hundreds of miles for just a few cents. By contrast, the earliest telegrams cost several cents *per letter*, which helps explain the development of the telegram's abbreviated syntax: "Home Wednesday STOP Good trip STOP Love Charles STOP." Few people had the financial resources to be more verbose.

But its high costs notwithstanding, the telegram offered so many advantages to business and government that the telegraph network, which would later be dubbed "the Victorian Internet" by historian Tom Standage, grew with surprising speed. In January 1848, three and a half years after Morse's dramatic demonstration, there were roughly two thousand miles of telegraph lines in use, mostly in the northeastern United States. Just two years later, that total had increased sixfold, and by the start of the Civil War in 1861, telegraph wires covered an estimated sixty thousand miles. During the course of the war, telegraph signals would cross both a continent (having already reached California on lines subsidized by the U.S. Post Office in 1861) and the Atlantic Ocean (after several interrupted attempts, a permanent connection was established with Great Britain in 1866). By 1902, it was finally possible to send a telegram around the world.

But the tremendous benefits offered by the telegraph system carried a cost: the confidentiality and privacy of the messages themselves. By the time Morse finally persuaded Congress to invest in his invention, an organized postal system had been operating in North America for more than a century and a half, and the concept of postal privacy was well established, both by custom and by law. Once a letter was sealed with wax or in one of the newfangled prefolded, gummed envelopes, a sender could reasonably assume that it would arrive at its destination unopened. But unlike the postal service, the use of the telegraph to transmit messages necessarily required the disclosure of the contents of the message to a third party; the telegraph company and its employees. Moreover, telegraph companies themselves quickly developed the practice, largely for accounting purposes, of keeping copies (at least temporarily) of the messages sent from one office to another.

Much like e-mail today, at any given time, a copy of a particular telegram might exist in at least three or four separate locations.

A half century earlier, when the memories of British invasions of postal privacy were still green, Congress had acted quickly to pass legislation that guaranteed the privacy of letters carried by government postal carriers. But despite repeated suggestions that it do so, Congress refused to adopt legislation giving telegrams the same federal privacy protections (an omission that was not remedied until ninety years after Morse's telegram to Baltimore).

The situation might well have been different had Congress decided, like its European counterparts, to develop and operate a national telegraph system under the aegis of the U.S. Post Office. Shortly after the successful demonstration of the Washington-to-Baltimore line, the well-known Kentucky politician Henry Clay, who was running for president in 1844 as the nominee of the Whig party, urged Congress to take ownership of the telegraph system. "It is quite manifest it is destined to exert great influence on the business affairs of society," he said. "In the hands of private individuals they will be able to monopolize intelligence and perform the greatest operations in commerce and other departments of business. I think such an engine should be exclusively under the control of government."

But Congress was leery of investing in an expensive new technology that offered no clear sign that it could ever compete on economic terms with the nation's efficient and inexpensive postal system. When Morse offered to sell the rights to his invention to the United States for $100,000, the idea was referred to postmaster general Cave Johnson, who recommended against the purchase on the grounds that the system would never be profitable. Congress rejected Morse's offer and left it to the private sector to prove the telegraph's commercial viability.

In the absence of any federal statutory protections, the privacy and confidentiality of telegrams was dependent on the contractual relationship between the telegraph company and the sender. (A few states did pass laws imposing a duty of confidentiality on telegraph companies and their employees, but they were more the exception than the rule.) Over time, however, a substantial body of case law developed making it clear that despite knowing the contents of every unciphered message presented for transmission, telegraph companies had a duty of confidentiality toward their customers. In his 1916 *Treatise on the Law of Telegraph and Telephone Companies*, S. Walter Jones, dean of the University of Memphis Law School, noted that telegraph companies could be held liable for breaching that duty, except in circumstances where they were required to produce copies of messages pursuant to court order.

The exception at the end of Jones's summary was an acknowledgment that the right of privacy has never been absolute. The Framers underscored the sanctity of private papers in the Fourth Amendment's opening clause: "The right of the people to be secure in their persons, houses, papers, and effects, against unreasonable searches and seizures, shall not be violated." Even so, they left open the possibility of government searches of private papers, provided that adequate safeguards were observed: "No Warrants shall issue, but upon probable cause, supported by Oath or affirmation, and particularly describing the place to be searched, and the persons or things to be seized."

In theory, at least, the legal status of a telegram should have been no worse than the most tightly sealed letter, notwithstanding the absence of congressional protection. But as a practical matter, telegrams were dramatically less secure than letters. This point was driven home repeatedly during the Civil War, when both sides engaged in extensive wiretapping of telegraph lines and routinely sent false messages to disrupt troop movements and sow confusion. The American military even set up a parallel telegraph system in an effort to secure its communications, and telegrams became such an integral part of the conduct of the war that President Lincoln often spent hours or even days in the Army Telegraph Office in Washington. Lincoln's visits and complete fascination with the telegraph were later chronicled by the office's manager, David Homer Bates, in a lengthy book, *Lincoln in the Telegraph Office* (1907).

But notwithstanding his interest in the technology, Lincoln apparently had few qualms about breaching the privacy of telegram senders. In his highly regarded biography *Abraham Lincoln: The Prairie Years and the War Years*, historian Carl Sandburg wrote that less than one month after taking office, Lincoln ordered federal marshals to visit every major Northern telegraph office and seize whatever copies of telegrams they could lay their hands on. The reasoning behind Lincoln's order was understandable: in early 1861, Washington lay completely exposed, with rail and telegraph lines cut or in the hands of Maryland secessionists, and Lincoln was desperate for information about Southern activity and Northern troop-recruiting efforts.

Sandburg's history contains no suggestion that the telegraph office raid sparked much in the way of public outcry, and there is no mention of the seizures in the major newspapers of the time. It is one more illustration, however, of the willingness of even the most enlightened administration to bend or break constitutional principles for what are perceived to be exigent circumstances.

POSTAL PRUDERY AND PERSONAL PRIVACY

Telegrams were not the only form of communication that came under closer scrutiny as the relationship between the North and the South grew steadily more antagonistic. Just as it had during the Jackson administration, the U.S. Post Office came under strong pressure to censor the materials submitted to it for delivery. Nor was the practice restricted to communities in the South: in 1861, after the start of hostilities, postmaster general Montgomery Blair ordered his department to refuse delivery of newspapers sympathetic to the rebellion.

Blair was later called to account by the House Judiciary Committee, which demanded to know "by what authority of Constitution and law, if any, the Postmaster General undertakes to decide what newspapers may and what shall not be transmitted through the mails of the United States." In a lengthy reply, Blair staunchly defended his decision and said that the Post Office "could not and would not interfere with the freedom secured by law" (specifically, the freedoms of speech and press). At the same time, however, Blair argued to Congress that he had both the authority and the duty to block the delivery of seditious printed materials, and that twenty-five years of uncontroverted Post Office practices supported his position:

> It would settle the right of this department and its various officers to resist all efforts to make them *particeps criminis* of treason and rebellion, by compelling them to circulate and distribute with their own hands the moral weapons which are to bring civil war to their firesides, with its horrible train of barbarities in the destruction of life and property.

Upon like considerations I have, at different times, excluded from the mails obscene and scandalous printed matter on exhibition of its criminal morality. If an unsealed printed publication were offered to the mails, instigating murder, arson, destruction of railroads, or other crimes, and advocating an organization for such purposes, I should, upon the same principles, without hesitation, exclude it from the mails as unlawful matter, in the absence of a contravening act of Congress.

It is not clear under what authority Postmaster Blair felt that he could exclude any material from the U.S. mails, given the fact that up to that time, Congress had never passed any law restricting what could or could not be mailed. But concerns over morality, even more than the possibility of aiding rebellion, would soon change that.

Few things are more disruptive to standards of moral behavior and human decency than armed conflict, and the American Civil War was no different. During the course of the conflict, dozens of social and religious volunteer organizations formed, not only to help alleviate the suffering of soldiers and civilians but also to combat the social breakdown caused by the war. One of the leading groups, the United States Christian Commission, was established by the Young Men's Christian Association (YMCA) in the fall of 1861. Over the course of the Civil War, more than five thousand people volunteered to help the commission carry out the YMCA's resolution to "take active measure to promote the spiritual and temporal welfare of the soldiers."

The leaders of the Christian Commission were particularly worried about the amount of licentious material that soldiers were receiving through the U.S. mails. On January 31, 1865, Morris K. Jesup, a wealthy merchant serving as treasurer of the New York Christian Commission, proposed a resolution to the national commission's executive committee "against selling secular Reading matter in the army." Less than a week later, Senator Jacob Collamer of Vermont, a former postmaster general under Zachary Taylor, proposed an amendment to a pending postal bill to address the commission's concerns. "It is said," Collamer told his colleagues, "that our mails are made the vehicle for the conveyance of great numbers and quantities of obscene books and pictures, which are sent to the Army, and sent here and there everywhere, and that is getting to be a great evil."

Collamer's proposal had two parts: a section authorizing postmasters to remove obscene materials from the mails, and a section laying out the penalties for people who deposited them there. The first section immediately raised privacy concerns, as the following exchange between Collamer and Senator Reverdy Johnson of Maryland (President Taylor's attorney general) illustrates:

> Mr. JOHNSON. If they are sent in envelopes, how does the postmaster know what they are?
> Mr. COLLAMER. Printed publications are always sent open at one end. It will not require the breaking of seals.
> Mr. JOHNSON. You do not propose to let the postmaster break seals?
> Mr. COLLAMER. There is not a word about "seals" in the section. If gentlemen are not satisfied with that part of it which authorizes the postmaster to throw them out, that part of the section can be stricken out; and I take it the objection would be mainly that it might be made a precedent for undertaking to give him a censorship over the mails and allow him to discard matter which was not satisfactory, politically, to some party— like throwing out the abolition papers that used to be talked about.

The Senate agreed with Senator Johnson's concern that, as written, the proposed language might give postmasters unfettered authority to root through the U.S. mails looking for obscenity, and that section of the bill was deleted. Nonetheless, after March 3, 1865, when President Lincoln signed the postal law, "no obscene book, pamphlet, picture, or print, or other publication of a vulgar and indecent character" could legally be mailed.

Seven years later, Congress undertook a massive revision of the U.S. postal statutes. While the postal legislation was pending, Rep. Clinton L. Merriam (R-N.Y.) introduced a separate bill intended to prohibit the sale or mailing of "obscene" items in the District of Columbia, including "any article or medicine for the prevention of conception, or for causing abortion." Although Congress had been trying to block the spread of indecent or obscene material for thirty years, Merriam apparently was the first federal legislator to propose a restriction on information about birth control or abortifacients, as well as on contraceptive devices and medicines themselves. His bill did not pass, nor was his proposed language included in the 1872 Post Office Act, but his efforts caught the attention of the YMCA of New York, which had been actively concerned about the rise of obscene materials both during and after the Civil War.

The obscenity law revisions that Congress did approve as part of the Post Office Act on June 8, 1872, addressed some novel legal issues. Namely, the mailing prohibition was expanded to include "any letter, *upon the envelope of which*, or *postal card* upon which, scurrilous epithets may have been written or printed, or *disloyal devices* printed, or engraved" (emphasis added).

The italicized text of this short-lived law—Congress rewrote the obscenity provision of the postal code just one year later—illustrates three different developments affecting the privacy of personal communications. First, the language of the law was an implicit endorsement by Congress of the long-standing prohibition against the opening of sealed letters to see whether "vulgar or indecent" matter might be inside. Instead, postmasters were limited to what they could actually read on the outside of a piece of mail.

Second, the phrase "disloyal devices" was one of Congress's periodic attempts to criminalize written dissent. Since most people recognized that the provision was patently unconstitutional, it was soon dropped.

Third, the law marked the first official recognition by Congress of an increasingly popular type of communication, the "postal card." In 1861, Philadelphian John P. Charlton obtained a copyright for his design for a simple mailing card. He later transferred the copyright to H. L. Lipman, who manufactured and sold a line of "Lipman's postal cards." In his annual report of 1870, postmaster general John A. J. Creswell noted the popularity of postcards in Germany and Great Britain and strongly recommended that the postal laws of the United States be amended to permit their use.

"The want has long been felt," Creswell said, "of some such prompt and easy mode of communication by mail, adapted to the convenience and habits of business men, as well as of that large class of persons who have not the time or the inclination to write formal letters, and therefore seldom make use of the mails." He predicted that the postcard would become a welcome alternative to the much more expensive telegram, and would "create a new postal business." Congress eventually agreed, and the U.S. Post Office entered the postcard business in 1873.

Creswell, who resigned in 1874, obviously had some idea of just how popular postcards would be: based on preorders, he had 100 million cards printed for the first year alone. When the cards were first offered for sale in New York City on May 15, 1873, more than 200,000 cards were purchased in the first two hours. But despite the warm and enthusiastic reception that postcards received, there were those who criticized the public's fondness for such an open form of communication.

In October 1890, for instance, a sharply worded essay titled "Post-Cards" was published in *All the Year Round*, a weekly literary magazine founded by author Charles Dickens. "We do not wish to have our affairs discussed publicly," the editors wrote sternly, "nor do we care for servants and landladies to have full benefit of our private matters." A quarter of a century later, a writer in *The Atlantic Monthly* reported that matters had not changed:

> There is a lady who conducts her entire correspondence through this channel. She reveals secrets supposed to be the most profound, relates misdemeanors and indiscretions with a reckless disregard of the consequences. Her confidence is unbounded in the integrity of postmen and bell-boys, while the latter may be seen any morning, sitting on the doorsteps of apartment houses, making merry over the post-card correspondence.

The criticisms of epistolary curmudgeons notwithstanding, Americans demonstrated remarkable enthusiasm for the postcard. In its annual report for 1909, the U.S. Post Office offered concrete evidence of just how popular postcards had become: for the fiscal year ending June 30, 1908, its postal carriers delivered 677,777,798 postcards—at a time when the entire population of the United States was less than 90 million.

The postcard phenomenon convincingly demonstrated that from the start, Americans were willing to give up a certain amount of privacy in exchange for the fun and convenience of using the cards. But postcards also demonstrated one other critical element of the ongoing privacy debate in this country: the fact that the definition of "privacy" is a highly individual concept. As any postcard collector will tell you, every stack of cards is a fascinating cultural and social record, containing revelations ranging from the briefest travel diaries to heart-rending health updates, from banal restaurant reviews and weather reports to the most endearing expressions of love.

The sheer variety of personal disclosures makes it clear that it is next to impossible to create a "right to privacy" that encompasses every type of personal disclosure; what one person might consider a trivial disclosure, another might find mortifying. Taken together, the common types of nineteenth-century communication—the letter, the telegram, the photograph, and the postcard—illustrate that a "right to privacy" encompasses the *choice* to disclose private information, rather than what is actually revealed. It is the individual decision to seal one's thoughts in a letter or scrawl those same thoughts on the back of a card for the world to see that is the essence of the right to privacy.

ANTHONY COMSTOCK RAIDS THE MAILS

Despite President Lincoln's rather cavalier attitude toward telegram privacy and the explosive growth of the postcard industry, no organized public discussion of privacy occurred during the Civil War or its immediate aftermath. There is no evidence, for instance, that many people were concerned about Lincoln's 1861 raid on the telegraph offices, in large part because it was not widely reported. Similarly, there was no visible public outcry over the peremptory seizure and silencing of two New York newspapers and a major telegraph company in May 1864 for their role in the publication of a proclamation falsely attributed to President Lincoln.

The seeming public indifference to the invasions of telegram privacy was due largely to the deference typically given to the government in time of war. There is a general consensus that when an armed conflict is occurring, the niceties of constitutional law are not necessarily observed. But equally important was the fact that at the time, the concept of privacy had not expanded to encompass much beyond one's home and postal correspondence, and virtually no attempts had been made by the judiciary to rein in the search and seizure activities of federal agents. The Fourth Amendment, guaranteeing freedom from unreasonable searches and seizures, except upon the issuance of a warrant, lay largely dormant: in nearly a century of federal court decisions between 1787 and 1865, the amendment was directly cited just twice.

But in the latter part of the nineteenth century, the attention paid to the Fourth Amendment, and to the practice of governmental search and seizure in general, grew rapidly. Much, if not most, of the credit for that development can be given to one man: Anthony Comstock, perhaps the period's most-feared public official.

Beginning in 1873, Comstock served forty-two years as secretary for the New York Society for the Suppression of Vice and Special Agent of the U.S. Post Office. Over the course of his long career, Comstock reshaped the postal laws, played fast and loose with warrant requirements, and allegedly tampered with the mails to obtain evidence for obscenity prosecutions. He was, in short, the very embodiment of the type of governmental abuse that the Framers intended to prevent through the adoption of the Bill of Rights in general and the Fourth Amendment in particular.

Comstock's rapid rise from self-appointed arbiter of public morals to federal postal agent resulted from the confluence of individual zealotry and a unique period of corporate Christianity. In early 1872, Comstock wrote a letter to the New York Young Men's Christian Association asking for financial donations for his campaign against the sellers of obscene books. He correctly expected a favorable response, since the YMCA had already successfully lobbied for an 1868 state law banning "obscene literature."

Comstock's letter came to the attention of Morris K. Jesup, the former Christian Commission treasurer who was now president of the New York YMCA. Recognizing a potentially powerful ally in the association's efforts to remove temptation from the young working-class men of the city, Jesup promptly wrote a check to Comstock that enabled him to purchase and destroy a large quantity of indecent bookplates. Later that year, the YMCA formed a Committee for the Suppression of Vice (later incorporated as the New York Society for the Suppression of Vice) and hired Comstock at an annual salary of $3,000 (the princely equivalent of just over $82,000 in today's dollars) to wage their battle for them.

One of Comstock's first tasks was to travel to Washington, D.C., in early 1873 to lobby for a more stringent federal antiobscenity law. Both he and the YMCA committee believed that the 1872 Post Office Act was badly flawed, in part because the law contained no prohibition of birth control and other sex aids, and in part because no provision was made for the search and seizure of obscene materials. By contrast, the 1868 New York state law addressed both issues, and Comstock used it as a model for his proposal to Congress.

When Comstock arrived in Washington, he discovered that his influential backers in New York had arranged some powerful allies for him. The language of what eventually became the Comstock Act was drafted by William Strong, an associate justice of the U.S. Supreme Court and the president of the National Reform Association, a group that had just fallen short in its efforts to persuade Congress to pass a "Christian amendment" to acknowledge God in the U.S. Constitution. The legislative maneuvering was led in the Senate by William Windom, an influential legislator from Minnesota, and in the House by Clinton L. Merriam, the representative from New York, who saw in Comstock an ally in his effort to ban the mailing of birth control materials.

Comstock's timing was fortuitous, since Congress was in an uproar over the Crédit Mobilier of America affair, a railroad influence-peddling scandal that eventually implicated more than thirty federal legislators and vice president Schuyler Colfax (whose involvement cost him renomination as vice president in the 1872 election). Although the scandal absorbed a lot of Congress's attention, it also left legislators looking for an opportunity to do good, and Comstock's proposal neatly fit the bill.

The progress of the obscenity bill appeared to falter on the eve of adjournment, but according to Helen Lefkowitz Horowitz, the author of *Rereading Sex: Battles over Sexual Knowledge and Suppression in Nineteenth-Century America*, Jesup and fellow YMCA board member William E. Dodge sent a telegram to the Speaker of the House, James G. Blaine, urging the bill's passage. The bill was adopted in the wee hours of the morning on March 2, 1873, with virtually no debate, and was signed into law the following day by President Grant. Comstock left Washington not only victorious but further employed: he was appointed a special agent of the Post Office, which gave him the authority to carry out the mail-cleansing provisions of the new law.

To say that Comstock exercised his new powers with enthusiasm would be a gross understatement. He contemplated nothing less than the moral purification of the nation, a Sisyphean ambition that would eventually make him the most ridiculed man in America. But in the early years of his appointment, Comstock spread fear throughout the publishing and medical communities with his energetic efforts to stamp out vice and indecency, social ills that were almost entirely in his sole power to define.

Although the public was generally receptive, at least at first, to Comstock's efforts to clean up the seedier side of New York, concern quickly grew about the constitutionality of his investigative methods. In 1879, DeRobigne Mortimer Bennett, the publisher of an anti-Christian periodical called *The Truth Seeker*, published a lengthy exposé of Comstock called "Anthony Comstock: His Career of Cruelty and Crime." In it, he maintained that Comstock used a variety of duplicitous tactics to obtain evidence against alleged offenders, including mailing decoy letters under false signatures, posing as a woman when sending decoy letters, and inducing people to send contraband through the mails who might not otherwise have done so.

Bennett's charges against Comstock were often more inflammatory than factual, but his suspicions about Comstock's loose handling of the U.S. mails was bolstered by the fact that the year before, Comstock had been indicted in several jurisdictions for allegedly opening sealed packages in his search for evidence. The charges were eventually dropped, but there was a rising sense that Comstock was at best overzealous and at worst dangerous to fundamental liberties. The *Washington Post*, which thoroughly loathed Comstock from the start, was the first to report on the indictments and later proclaimed in an editorial:

> Reputable people have about come to the conclusion that this mean, meddlesome, pestilential fellow, this procurer of the commission of crimes in order to insure conviction, cannot be engaged in any work that a decent man ought to do. He possesses those elements of character most abhorrent to honorable

men and he pursues his vocation of spy by methods which are cordially detested among all who respect manliness.

Needless to say, Comstock did not take kindly to any suggestion that he violated the confidentiality of the mails or fraudulently induced the commission of a crime. In the Fifth Annual Report of the New York Society for the Suppression of Vice, delivered in 1879, he complained that opponents of the Comstock Act had spent much of the past year circulating a petition for its repeal, which charged "that monstrous outrages had been perpetrated under it by our Chief Special Agent, and that innocent men had been arrested and thrown into prison," and that a book purporting to be "the life of the agent" had been distributed as well.

The following year, Comstock wrote his first book, *Frauds Exposed: Or, How the People Are Deceived and Robbed, and Youth Corrupted*, in which he offered a spirited defense of his methods and emphatically denied ever tampering with the mails. "No person," he said, "could remain in the Post Office Department, or be retained in service one hour by the New York Society for the Suppression of Vice, who would be guilty of such tampering with the mails."

How, then, was it possible for Comstock to discern what missives contained illegal material? "By doing business with them," he said, "precisely as they invite the public to do by their printed advertisements and circulars."

> Do just as the scoundrel invites you to do—send the amount set opposite the article he has for sale as he directs, and he says he will send the article in return. Now, we so send, following the rules of evidence as laid down by "Greenleaf in evidence," and "Russell on crimes," and what do we accomplish?
>
> *First.* If what is advertised is obscene, or unlawful, and the scoundrel does as he says he will, we secure legal evidence of his guilt, and then—we secure the scoundrel.

In the short term, Comstock got the better of the argument. He successfully fought efforts by the National Liberal League and other free speech groups to persuade Congress to amend or even repeal the Comstock Act, and he continued his aggressive campaign against the

mailers of smut and other indecencies for another thirty-five years. And it is not an insignificant fact that more than a century after it was first adopted, the Comstock Act not only is still on the books but has been extended to the Internet, a technology Comstock could scarcely have imagined but undoubtedly would have loathed.

3

POPULATION, PUNCH CARDS, AND PRIVACY

The fierce debate over the need for a Bill of Rights and the sweeping language of the individual amendments make it unequivocally clear that the Framers and their political contemporaries were concerned about the autonomy and privacy of American citizens. But in their drafting of the Constitution itself, the Framers included a provision that unwittingly set in motion a train of events that threatens many of the privacy protections implicit in the Constitution and its first ten amendments.

One of the most contentious arguments at the Constitutional Convention, held in Philadelphia in 1787, concerned the structure of a national legislature to replace the ineffectual body created by the earlier Articles of Confederation. Prior to arriving in Philadelphia, Virginian James Madison drafted a plan that would have allocated representatives to the legislature based on each state's population of free men. Not surprisingly, this plan was backed by the bigger states (including Virginia, which was the most populous at the time). The smaller states preferred a plan put forward by New Jersey, which consisted of a legislature in which each state had a single vote. The debate grew so heated and the two sides seemed so intractable that some feared that it would doom the convention. But the Connecticut delegation saved the convention (and ultimately the new nation) by proposing a compromise that incorporated the significant elements of both provisions: a House of Representatives allocated proportionately by population, and a Senate in which each state would receive two votes.

One of the conditions for proportional representation, of course, is knowing how many people live in each state. In Article I, Section 2, of the Constitution, the convention laid out the formula for determining

how many representatives each state should have and provided for an enumeration every ten years.

The United States was the first country to make a regular count of its citizens a part of its fundamental governmental structure. The initial census, conducted in 1790, occurred more than a decade before the first comprehensive nose count in Great Britain and cost just over $44,000 (or roughly two cents, in today's dollars, for each of the 33 million people counted). Since then, twenty-one tallies of Americans have been conducted, with varying degrees of efficiency and controversy. The cost has risen somewhat: the 2000 census cost American taxpayers $6.5 billion, or about $23 per person counted.

A number of factors have contributed to the rising cost of the census over the years, but without question, the most significant is Congress's increasingly insatiable curiosity about where Americans are from, what their family lives are like, and what they do for a living. "Curiosity," the old saying goes, "killed the cat." Less than a hundred years after the nation was founded, the U.S. census nearly suffered the same fate.

HOW CONGRESS NEARLY KILLED THE CENSUS

The initial census in 1790 was conducted under the supervision of the U.S. secretary of state, Thomas Jefferson, and consisted of just six questions designed to satisfy the bare-bones requirements of Article I, Section 2, of the Constitution:

1. The name of the head of the household
2. The number of free white males under the age of sixteen
3. The number of free white males over the age of sixteen
4. The number of free white females
5. The number of other free persons
6. The number of slaves

Despite the limited number of questions, the idea of a national head count still met with some scattered resistance: Vermont enumerator Roger Waite, for instance, resigned his position as a census taker in 1790 after having been "dogbit, goose-pecked, cowkicked, briar-scratched, shot at, and called every 'fowel' that can be tho't of." A few

other households objected to being enumerated on biblical grounds, recalling that King David's census of Israel and Judah purportedly unleashed an epidemic that killed seventy thousand people (II Samuel 24:1–15). But on the whole, the first few censuses took place with little controversy.

In the early nineteenth century, Congress amended its census statute to require the census enumerators (assistant marshals from each of the U.S. judicial districts) to personally visit each household and collect not only demographic data, but for the first time, basic economic data about jobs and income. From 1810 to 1850, the core census questionnaire remained largely unchanged, although Congress experimented periodically with questions designed to collect property information, quantify the number of people over the age of twenty-one unable to read or write, and tally the number of people considered insane. The most significant change in the first sixty years of the census, from a technological perspective, was the introduction of standard printed forms for all enumerators in 1830. Since census takers were no longer using whatever scraps of paper they happened to have at hand, federal officials were able to more accurately tally the country's population.

By the middle of the nineteenth century, however, both Congress and the nation's growing business community were eager for more precise information about the makeup of the country and its residents. At the same time, the nation's leaders increasingly were convinced that the information generated by the census, particularly with respect to broader economic and social statistics, was essentially useless. The census of 1840, in particular, was widely criticized for its inaccuracies: Massachusetts congressman John Gorham Palfrey condemned it on the floor of the House as a "mortifying failure."

The widespread dissatisfaction with the results of the 1840 census persuaded Congress to follow the European example and create a central governmental bureau for planning, implementing, and tabulating statistical information about American citizens. The Census Board, as it was initially called, consisted of the secretary of state, the attorney general, and the postmaster general. After much wrangling and debate, the Census Board generated a questionnaire for the 1850 census that not only substantially increased the amount of information collected by the U.S. government but also generated the first

widespread objections to the federal census on invasion-of-privacy grounds.

Up to that time, only the name of the head of each household was written down by the enumerators. For the 1850 census, however, the new Census Board declared that all free persons would be listed individually and each person would be asked to provide the information requested by the census questionnaire. While this has proven to be a boon for genealogical researchers (although less so, unfortunately, for African Americans), it also represented a profound increase in both the quantity and the specificity of information collected by the government. The range of questions posed by the enumerators was expanded to include such topics as each person's age at the time of the census, the value of real estate he or she owned, whether the individual was "deaf-mute, blind, insane or 'idiotic,' " and whether he or she had attended school or had been married during the previous year. In previous censuses, the information collected by the enumerators had been publicly posted in each town to give the head of each household the opportunity to correct any errors. Now that the census was collecting information about specific individuals, however, that practice was stopped.

The 1850 census also marked the first time concerns were raised that some enumerators were misusing the information they were collecting. Thomas McKennan, who was in charge of the census during his brief eleven-day tenure as U.S. secretary of the interior (he resigned due to a nervous condition), warned census takers that they had a duty to treat the collected data properly:

Information has been received at this office that in some cases unnecessary exposure has been made by the assistant marshals with reference to the business and pursuits, and other facts relating to individuals, merely to gratify curiosity, or the facts applied to the private use or pecuniary advantage of the assistant, to the injury of others. Such a use of the returns was neither contemplated by the act [the Census Act of 1850] itself nor justified by the intentions and designs of those who enacted the law. No individual employed under sanction of the Government to obtain these facts has a right to promulgate or expose them without authority.

As the nation continued its enormous growth during the Industrial Revolution, the demand for demographic information and the concerns about its misuse kept pace. Congress made some minor improvements to the census in 1870, but thanks in large part to the lingering disruption of the Civil War and Reconstruction, it was not until 1880 that Congress substantially updated its census statutes.

At the urging of Dr. John Shaw Billings, the librarian for the surgeon general's office in Washington, the Senate Committee on the Census agreed to add a number of questions to the census designed to gather medical information about the country's population. For instance, enumerators were instructed to ask, "Is the person (on the day of the enumerator's visit) sick or temporarily disabled, so as to be unable to attend to ordinary business or duties? If so, what is the sickness or disability?" Enumerators were also instructed to ask each individual whether they were "maimed, crippled, bedridden, or otherwise disabled." An additional twenty-four questions helped make the 1880 census the largest and most inquisitive tabulation to date.

Anticipating that there might be some resistance to providing so much personal information, Congress adopted a provision that for the first time made it a crime for citizens to refuse to answer a census taker's questions. As superintendent of the census Francis A. Walker wrote in his instructions to the enumerators, "It is not within the choice of any inhabitant of the United States whether he shall or shall not communicate the information required by the census law." Failure to do so was a misdemeanor that carried a fine of $100.

At the same time, however, Congress recognized the need to establish greater legal safeguards for collected data. Each census taker hired for the 1880 census was required to take an oath of office, swearing that "I will not disclose any information contained in the schedules, lists, or statements obtained by me to any person or persons, except to my superior officers." Improper disclosure of information was also a misdemeanor, but could be punished with a fine of up to $500.

But as important as those legal developments were, the most significant aspect of the 1880 census from a privacy perspective was the sheer amount of data collected. During the preceding decade, the population of the United States had grown a remarkable 30 percent, from 38.6 million in 1870 to 50.2 million in 1880. The combination of a much larger population and a much more detailed census questionnaire resulted in a flood of data that essentially swamped the Census Office. Despite the services of Dr. Billings, one of the nation's earliest and most highly regarded statisticians, and a small army of nearly fifteen hundred clerks, the compilation and analysis of the census data was not finished for eight years. When it was finally completed, the 1880 census was published in twenty-two volumes containing a total of 21,458 pages. The entire process cost a rather remarkable $5.7 million.

As legislators and statisticians watched the long, slow, tedious tabulation of the 1880 census, it was widely feared—and generally acknowledged—that without a new system for tabulating results, it would not be possible to complete the 1890 census before it was time to start collecting data for the next one in 1900. One of the first to propose a possible solution was Billings himself, who suggested that the data collected about each individual "might be recorded on a single card or slip by punching small holes in it, and that these cards might then be assorted and counted by mechanical means according to any selected group of these perforations." Robert P. Porter, who served as superintendent of the 1890 census, later reported a conversation with Billings in which Billings argued that the 1880 census would be the last to be tallied without the aid of electricity. Eleven years later, Porter proudly announced that Billings's prediction was correct: electric tabulators counted the 1890 census in record time.

HOW HERMAN HOLLERITH SAVED THE CENSUS

Porter's ability to make that announcement was entirely thanks to the ingenuity of a civil engineer and mathematician named Herman Hollerith, a recent graduate of the Columbia University School of Mines who was hired to work as an engineer and special agent for the 1880 census. Hollerith was inspired by Billings's idea that the tabulation of census data could be performed more efficiently and accurately by electrical and mechanical means than by hand counting, and he set out to design and construct a suitable system.

Like most inventors, Hollerith drew his inspiration from a variety of sources. Reflecting on Billings's idea that an individual's data could be recorded by punching holes in a card, Hollerith recalled that he had seen railroad conductors using a similar method to keep track of which passenger was supposed to be sitting in each seat.

"One summer," Hollerith later wrote, "I was traveling in the West and I had a ticket with what I think was called a punch photograph. . . . The conductor . . . punched out a description of the individual, as light hair, dark eyes, large nose, etc. So you see, I only made a punch photograph of each person." The system was still in use in some parts of the country into the twentieth century: in 1901, for instance, Col. Henry Steel Olcott, the head of the American Theosophical Society, reported that on a trip to Southern California, his "punch photograph" was taken as follows:

PERSONAL DESCRIPTION OF PASSENGER

Male •	Light eyes •
Female	Dark eyes

Slim	Light hair
Medium	Dark hair
Stout •	Gray hair •

Young	Mustache •
Middle-aged	Chin beard •
Elderly •	Side beard •
	No beard

FIGURE I

Hollerith also was inspired by the design and operation of a mechanical weaving system developed by Joseph Jacquard, a French silk weaver and inventor. In 1801, Jacquard had demonstrated what was essentially the world's first programmable machine: a loom that used a long series of cards punched with holes to create a design in the woven fabric. The cards were strung together and fed through the loom in such a way that they controlled the movement of the loom's hooks and threads. By changing the order of the cards or by inserting cards with different arrangements of holes, the design of the fabric could be quickly and easily changed.

Jacquard's successful design for the programmable loom led Hollerith to initially design a tabulating system that used long, thin strips of paper punched with strategically placed holes to record data. Following the example of Jacquard's loom, Hollerith envisioned tallying the data by feeding the strips through a tabulating device. But the paper strips were both physically fragile and statistically awkward: they tore easily, specific data could not be found very easily, and errors were nearly impossible to correct without redoing the entire tape.

Hollerith realized that he could avoid many of his early system's problems by keeping Jacquard's basic idea of data cards, but separating the cards and treating each one as a separate storage unit. Building on this idea, Hollerith constructed a device that enabled census data clerks to transfer information from the handwritten census tally sheets to thin manila cards, each measuring just 6⅝ inches long by 3¼ inches high. The size of the card, like so many other parts of Hollerith's system, was a deliberate and thoughtful choice: it matched the size of paper currency in use at the time, which meant that the Census Office could store its millions of data cards in standard-sized cabinetry manufactured for the banking industry.

The data entry device, or keyboard punch, recorded census data by making small holes in various columns on the card—one each for gender, age, race, marital status, and so on. (Thus Hollerith gets credit for unintentionally inventing the notorious "hanging chad" that proved so problematic during the 2000 U.S. presidential election.) Despite the fact that the 1890 census posed even more questions than the notoriously inquisitive 1880 census, a single card was more than sufficient to record all of the information collected about each person. Moreover, the process proved remarkably efficient; with practice, a clerk could easily create a thousand census cards in a day.

The census cards were then placed, one by one, into Hollerith's most significant innovation: an electric tabulating machine that automated the compilation of census data. As each card was fed into the tabulation machine, a lever was pulled to press a number of steel pins against the card. Each steel pin matched one possible piece of data that could be recorded on the card. If there was no hole underneath a particular pin, then the pin would be blocked by the cardboard; but if a hole had been punched in that particular spot, then the steel pin would go through the card and touch a small cup of mercury below the card. By doing so, the pin completed an electrical circuit that caused a corresponding counter on the machine to increase by one.

To modern ears, it sounds like a cumbersome system, but it represented a profound leap forward in data processing capabilities. Between 1880 and 1890, the population of the United States had grown by another 25 percent; eventually, clerks for the twelfth census would punch out nearly 63 million census cards for the nation's inhabitants, containing an estimated one billion pieces of demographic data. But thanks to Hollerith's tabulation system, the Census Office was able to announce the total U.S. population of 62,622,250 on December 12, 1890, just six weeks after the census forms were returned to Washington. The compilation of the various schedules and tables of census data took somewhat longer, but the process was still vastly faster than the manual methods that had been used previously.

Even in its earliest form, Hollerith's electrical tabulation system offered glimpses of future data processing innovations. Rudimentary error correction was built into the system: incomplete cards, for instance, were automatically rejected and would not be tallied. The use of individual cards allowed for random access of information (the card of any individual could be quickly located, independent of any other), and a single card could be corrected without having to correct all the others. Moreover, through the use of electrical relays, Hollerith's machine could be configured to allow the sorting of the census cards by multiple criteria (for instance, winnowing out all cards of men aged thirty to thirty-four, or all Boston residents of Irish descent). Appropriately enough, the School of Mines graduate had effectively created the first efficient system for data mining.

In an article for the *Windsor Magazine* in 1910, Superintendent Porter described the transformation that occurred when Hollerith's cardboard cards were punched with an individual's census information. "These little cards," Porter wrote, "become endowed as it were with the attributes of living beings, whose life experience is written upon their face in hieroglyphic symbols, resembling in significance the traits of the human countenance. The grouping of these cards has been described as the division of an army from the corps to the battalion."

Despite Porter's enthusiasm for the Hollerith tabulation system, the 1890 census was widely criticized for allegedly undercounting the nation's population. In general, the blame was assigned to Porter, whom many regarded as an unqualified political hack who stacked the census enumerators with Republicans and jiggered the entire process to prevent Democratic-leaning cities from picking up additional representatives in the subsequent reapportionment. Hollerith himself largely escaped criticism, although the *New York Herald* ran a bold headline proclaiming "SLIPSHOD WORK HAS SPOILED THE CENSUS— MISMANAGEMENT THE RULE—Speed Everything, Accuracy Nothing."

But while the controversy over the census results eventually faded, the admiration for the speed with which the count was accomplished lingered. Building on his success, Hollerith founded the Tabulating Machine Company (TMC) in 1896 and was hired by the Russian government to assist with a national census the following year. Several other European censuses followed, as well as the 1900 U.S. census. By 1905, however, the Census Office was chafing under the cost of renting Hollerith's equipment and his rather stubborn resistance to making improvements in his design. After negotiations with Hollerith broke down, the Census Office decided to manufacture its own machines with the help of former TMC employees. Hollerith sued the government for breach of patent, but after seven years of litigation, his claim was rejected.

Perhaps anticipating defeat in the courts, or perhaps merely recognizing that his business was steadily declining, Hollerith sold TMC and its Washington factory in 1911 to a New York syndicate for $2.5 million. TMC was combined with three other tabulating companies under the somewhat awkward name Computing-Tabulating-Recording Company (CTR). Hollerith received half the sale price of TMC and a directorship in the new company, but both his health and his enthusiasm for the tabulating business were fading. CTR was on the verge of failing altogether in 1914 when a brash young salesman named Thomas J. Watson Sr. joined the company. Over Hollerith's objections, Watson pushed for improvements to the company's tabulating machines and upgraded the company's sales force. Uncomfortable with the direction the company was taking, Hollerith eventually retired in 1921 and took up farming until his death eight years later. In the meantime, Watson became general manager and then president of CTR. When the company began manufacturing machines overseas in 1924, Watson renamed the company International Business Machines Corporation (IBM). It would continue to play a central role in the evolution of personal privacy for decades to come.

THE BASHFUL PRESIDENT AND HIS YOUNG WIFE

Hollerith's remarkable "punch photographs" and his electronic tabulating machines were only two of the assaults on personal privacy occurring in the latter part of the nineteenth century. Thanks to a combination of technological innovations and increasingly fierce competition, the newspapers of that time were undergoing a dramatic shift. What were once primarily vehicles for partisan political debates and public notices were now becoming sources of entertainment for those segments of the population with more leisure time. As newspapers devoted more time and attention to social news, reporters and news photographers showed little regard for the privacy of both the famous and the relatively anonymous. The journalistic ethos of the era was best summed up in the motto for Joseph Pulitzer's *New York World:* "Spicy, Pithy, Pictorial."

One particularly savage example of the period's news coverage—and one that contributed significantly to the country's evolving views on personal privacy—was the 1884 presidential contest between Grover Cleveland, the Democratic governor of New York, and James G. Blaine, a Republican from Maine and the former Speaker of the House. Ostensibly, the main issue of the campaign was civil reform of the government. (Cleveland was nicknamed "Grover the Good" for his efforts at cleaning up New York's infamous Tammany Hall.) But instead, the campaign was thoroughly dominated by character issues and personal attacks.

Blaine, for instance, was widely accused of selling his influence as Speaker of the House to railroad interests. He had strenuously denied the charges when they were first made in 1876, but during the 1884 campaign, the issue resurfaced when a fresh batch of Blaine's personal correspondence with a Boston bookkeeper named James Mulligan was published. The contents were damning, as was Blaine's handwritten postscript to one note that read "Burn this letter." Blaine's letters gave rise to a popular chant at Democratic rallies: "Blaine, Blaine, James G. Blaine, continental liar from the state of Maine! Burn this letter!" During the height of the Mulligan letters controversy, Blaine repeatedly told reporters that there was an "innocent" explanation for his correspondence. However, as reporters were quick to point out, Blaine refused to provide the explanation, saying instead that it fell within his "sacred right to privacy."

Cleveland had his own vexatious problems with the press. In July 1884, the Buffalo *Evening Telegraph* reported that while Cleveland was practicing law in Buffalo, he had fathered an illegitimate child named Oscar Folsom Cleveland with a dry goods clerk named Maria Crofts Halpin. The paper went on to allege that after the baby was born, Cleveland had essentially kidnapped Halpin, committed her to an insane asylum, and put the unfortunate child up for adoption as an orphan.

As the paper's allegations rapidly circulated around the country (thanks to the telegraph and even the newfangled telephone), Cleveland gave his campaign wise counsel (all too rarely followed since): "Tell the truth." Although Cleveland was a notoriously private person, he heeded his own advice and admitted to having a sexual relationship with Halpin. However, Cleveland said that he could not be certain that the child was his, since Halpin had been involved with several other men at the time of Oscar's birth. He also admitted that he paid Halpin child support for a year in 1874, feeling it was his duty to do so as the only bachelor in Halpin's posse. However, Cleveland strongly denied the remainder of the *Telegraph*'s story. It was later learned that Halpin's turn in the asylum was due to alcoholism and that upon learning of her condition, Cleveland had helped to arrange a favorable adoption for the young boy.

Cleveland's forthright responses to the scandal helped diminish the political damage of the story, but the news nonetheless caused Republicans to coin one of the more memorable and derisive political slogans in American history: "Ma, Ma, where's my pa? Gone to the White House, ha, ha, ha!"

At least one newspaper, the *Evening Gazette* in Cedar Rapids, Iowa, was somewhat defensive about so brazenly trumpeting Cleveland's private affairs, but justified doing so in response to the partisan attacks on Blaine's integrity:

As the Democratic press opened the campaign by violent personal abuse of Mr. Blaine, it can not complain if the truth is published in regard to the private life of Mr. Cleveland. It is said that "people in glass houses should not throw stones," and if the Democratic Party wanted to prevent the smashup of glass in its wigwam, it should not have set us the example of heaving the first stone.

Even 125 years after the fact, however, it seems fair to ask whether unproven (and at the time, almost certainly unprovable) assertions that a bachelor attorney might have fathered a child out of wedlock were as serious or as relevant as well-documented charges of influence peddling by a Speaker of the House of Representatives. But given the amount of attention devoted to both scandals, it seems clear that in Victorian America, sexual propriety was as important, if not more important, than governmental ethics.

Cleveland's eventual victory (a relatively narrow 219–182 margin in the Electoral College) did not halt the press's interest in his private life; if anything, his personal affairs came under even greater scrutiny. Much of the attention centered on the speculation that the newly elected president, a long-confirmed bachelor, was planning to marry. By itself, the prospect of a first marriage in the White House would have excited popular interest, but the details of President Cleveland's courtship were particularly fascinating. The reported object of the president's fancy was Frances Folsom, a young woman twenty-seven years his junior and the daughter of his former Buffalo law partner, Oscar Folsom (the other man after whom Maria Halpin apparently named her illegitimate son). Cleveland had been a close friend of the Folsom family throughout Frances's life and had purchased her first baby carriage when she was an infant.

Public and journalistic interest in the president's courtship of Folsom was intense. "Is The President Engaged?" the *Washington Post* asked on April 16, 1886. The paper noted that Folsom had made "a very favorable impression in society circles" when she had visited Rose Cleveland, the president's sister and official hostess, during the previous summer. In a lengthier article just two days later, the *Post* reprinted a story by the *New York Sun* that not only confirmed the pending nuptials, but described at length Folsom's first serious romance, an engagement to a Charles Townsend that he broke off when he fell in love with another woman. Despite the obvious invasion of Folsom's privacy, the *Sun* (and the *Post*) piously argued that "the romantic episode is worth narrating, not only on account of its interest, but because it shows her rare good common sense on a trying occasion."

Throughout the fall of 1885 and spring of 1886, Frances Folsom toured Europe with her mother and thus largely escaped the increasingly heated speculation about the president's intentions. After landing in New York, however, Folsom traveled to Washington, D.C., with a persistent shadow of reporters. Understandably, the young woman found the incessant investigation into, and narration of, her personal life highly annoying. As the *Syracuse Standard* reported just a few weeks before her wedding to the president:

> It is more than whispered—in fact it is bawled that Miss Frances Folsom is losing her temper because newspapers and gossips use her name so freely. It is discreditable to the press that liberties with the sacredness of private life are taken and so lightly thought of; it is altogether to the young woman's credit that she resents the prying, peering and overhauling to which her affairs, even the purchase of her suppositional trousseau, are subjected.

The *Standard* acknowledged that a great deal of natural curiosity in the public resulted from the fact that one party to the wedding was the president of the United States ("our Chief Magistrate"), as well as what it coyly described as the "disparity in age and station." But it went on to say, "Still these concessions do not subtract very much from the impropriety of a great deal that is said or the impropriety of excess in the share of attention bestowed on the alleged engagement of Mr. Cleveland and Miss Folsom. . . . Miss Folsom is incensed against the meddlers, and her provocation is ample."

Grover Cleveland married Frances Clara Folsom on June 2, 1886, in the Blue Room of the White House. All journalists were barred from the Cleveland-Folsom nuptials.

A REVOLUTIONARY PROPOSITION

Interestingly, Frances Folsom's engagement and marriage to President Cleveland was not her first run-in with the press. The same *New York Sun* article that revealed Frances Folsom's broken engagement also reported that in 1885, Folsom hired a detective to find out the source of a "poor picture" of her that was published in a number of newspapers. "Her intention," the article said, "was to prosecute the originator of what she termed an outrage both civilly and criminally if it was possible."

The detective was unable to trace the photo to its source, and Folsom was forced to let the matter drop. But even if she had located the photographer, she would have been very unlikely to recover any damages or to interest a district attorney in the case: at the time, there was no recognition of a right to privacy in either common law or statutory law.

Whatever lingering privacy to which Folsom may have thought she was entitled quickly vanished following her marriage to Grover Cleveland. The vivacious and beautiful Mrs. Cleveland proved to be an enormously popular First Lady, and her image appeared not only in scores of newspapers and magazine covers but also on a dizzying array of unauthorized "endorsements" for various products, including liver pills, ashtrays, sweets of various kinds, soaps, ladies undergarments, and even an allegedly "safe" version of arsenic pills (which the manufacturer claimed was the secret of Mrs. Cleveland's flawless complexion).

According to one report, Rep. John R. Thomas (R-Ill.), a supporter of President Cleveland, "had his indignation greatly aroused recently on visiting a drug store to see the lithograph of the wife of the President of the United States, with a disagreeable superscription, used as an advertisement for a patent nostrum." Unfortunately, the precise nature of the superscription and the name of the patent nostrum were not reported. In any case, in March 1888 Thomas introduced legislation that would have penalized such behavior by providing that any corporation or individual

> who shall publicly exhibit, use or employ the likeness or representation of any female living or dead, who is or was the wife, mother, daughter or sister of any citizen of the U.S. without the consent in writing of the person whose likeness is to be used shall be guilty of high misdemeanor and shall upon indictment be fined not less than $500, nor more than $5,000, and stand imprisoned until fines and costs are paid.

Despite its innate paternalism, the bill was one of the first federal proposals to protect personal privacy, and it would have substantially reshaped privacy law in the United States if it had passed. However, the bill was rejected by the House, and in the wake of its defeat, advertisers actually increased their use of the First Lady's image in advertisements.

Undoubtedly, Frances Cleveland's experiences with privacy invasions both before and after becoming First Lady were a frequent topic of conversation among her circle of friends. As it happened, one of her close friends in Washington was Mabel Bayard Warren, the eldest daughter of Cleveland's secretary of state, Thomas F. Bayard. Mabel Warren was herself familiar with the intrusive nature of the press. As a descendent of three U.S. senators from Delaware (her father, grandfather, and great-grandfather) and the sister of a fourth, she held a prestigious position in Washington social circles, and her activities and those of her family were routinely covered by the media. When she married a promising young attorney named Samuel D. Warren Jr. on January 25, 1883, the wedding was covered in extensive detail by newspapers in Washington and New York.

In a paper titled "What If Samuel D. Warren Hadn't Married a Senator's Daughter? Uncovering the Press Coverage That Led to *The Right to Privacy*," University of Illinois College of Law professor Amy Gajda argued that it was the press's coverage of his wife that led Samuel Warren and his law partner, Louis D. Brandeis, to write their profoundly influential article "The Right to Privacy" for the December 1890 issue of the *Harvard Law Review*.

"Though Mr. Warren is clearly more famous today—thanks ironically to his publicized plea for privacy—in the 1880s it was, in fact, his wife who was the focus of media attention," Gajda wrote. "Samuel D. Warren married into what he would surely consider a media maelstrom. Indeed, if Samuel D. Warren had not married a United States Senator's daughter, *The Right to Privacy* would very likely never have been written."

It seems likely, because of both their general interest in the subject and Mrs. Warren's relationship with Mrs. Cleveland, that Samuel Warren and Louis Brandeis were familiar with the failed efforts in Congress to adopt privacy legislation in 1888. The timing of the publication of "The Right to Privacy" makes it probable that the two attorneys began drafting the article either while that legislation was under consideration or shortly after its defeat.

One other factor that unquestionably inspired Warren and Brandeis to draft their article was the rapid technological change occurring in photography. Despite the enormous popularity of both newspapers and photographs in the mid-nineteenth century, the two technologies had not yet merged. Somewhat ironically, just as they did in the U.S. census, holes punched in cardboard would play a role in the commercialization of photography as well.

In the mid-1870s, a young photographer named Stephen Henry Horgan was working for the New York *Daily Graphic*. In 1876, at the age of twenty-two, Horgan was put in charge of the *Daily Graphic*'s process department, the part of the newspaper operation responsible for laying out and printing the paper each day. It occurred to Horgan one day that the concept behind the then-popular "Berlin patterns"—embroidery designs that consisted of colored patterns of holes punched into stiff paper or cardboard—could be used to reproduce photographic images in a newspaper. The human eye, Horgan realized, can be fooled into seeing a series of tiny black dots of different sizes as varying shades of gray. By punching holes in a piece of cardboard and rolling black ink over it, Horgan was able to reproduce the myriad shades of gray in a black-and-white photograph.

Horgan eventually replaced the cardboard screen with a metal one, and on March 4, 1880, published the first newspaper photograph using what he called the "halftone" process. Although it would be some time before other newspapers followed suit, Horgan's innovation marked the start of photojournalism in the United States. By the end of the century, newspapers had figured out how to use halftone screens on high-speed rotary presses, thus dramatically increasing the number of copies that could be printed of any given image.

At roughly the same time, advances in photographic technology were making it dramatically easier and faster for the average person to take photographs. In 1883, the same year that Samuel Warren married Mabel Bayard, a Rochester, New York, inventor named George Eastman perfected a process for coating strips of paper with photographic emulsion. These rolls of film made it much quicker and simpler to take photographs, since hobbyists no longer had to carry around chemicals to coat glass slides before taking each photo.

Five years later, in 1888, Eastman sparked a second wave of popular enthusiasm for photography by introducing, under the brand name "Kodak," a one-button camera that was designed to take multiple photos using Eastman's rolls of film. Once the film was used up, consumers could send the camera back to Eastman's company, which would develop and print the pictures and return the camera with a fresh roll of film. Billed as "the latest and best outfit for amateurs," the camera was marketed with the popular slogan, "You press the button, we do the rest."

Eastman's invention helped turn what was generally considered a pleasant hobby into an active nuisance. Since his invention eliminated the need to muck about with chemicals and further reduced exposure times, no potential subject was safe from being photographed. The phrase "Kodak fiends" entered the vernacular (first appearing in the spring of 1890), along with many published complaints about the increased intrusiveness of amateur "snapshotters." In fairly short order, regulations were adopted prohibiting the unfettered use of cameras in the White House, on railroad lines and ferry services, and on private property. In response, some amateurs developed the "lunch basket racket," hiding their cameras inside a lunch basket with a hole in the side for taking photos. The illicit snapshots anticipated by more than a century the "upskirt" photos that are currently such a plague on the Internet.

Amateurs were not the only photographic opportunists; professional photographers took advantage of the faster exposure speeds as well to take photos of unsuspecting subjects (particularly attractive young women). Horgan's halftone process made it a relatively simple matter to publish those images in the society pages or use them for advertising, as in the case of Frances Cleveland. Whether such intrusions should be allowed, and what could be done to prevent them, quickly became a hot topic of discussion. In July 1890, attorney E. L. Godkin published an article titled "The Rights of the Citizen: IV. To His Own Reputation" in the popular magazine *Scribner's*, in which he argued that "privacy is a distinctly modern product, one of the luxuries of civilization, which is not only unsought for but unknown in primitive or barbarous societies."

Godkin identified curiosity as one of the chief enemies of privacy and noted the irony that as people withdraw from society to enjoy their privacy, the curiosity of their neighbors tends to increase proportionately. "Nobody quite likes to confess that he is eager to know all he can about his neighbor's private life," Godkin observed, "and yet the private lives of our neighbors form the staple topic of conversation in most circles in the absence of strong intellectual, political, or commercial interests."

As long as such gossip was primarily oral, Godkin argued, the chances of it reaching an audience unfamiliar with the subject were remote, and thus backyard news could be heard in the context of everything else that the listeners knew of their neighbor or fellow citizen. But with the rise of newspapers, the potential reach of gossip was virtually limitless. "It thus inflicts," Godkin said, "what is, to many men, the great pain of believing that everybody he meets in the street is perfectly familiar with some folly, or misfortune, or indiscretion, or weakness, which he had previously supposed had never got beyond his domestic circle."

That was a surprisingly modern observation. In their book *The Right to Privacy*, published 105 years later, Caroline Kennedy and Ellen Alderman describe two invasion-of-privacy cases involving voyeurism, one in which a young woman was videotaped having sex without her knowledge and one in which a couple discovered that they had been watched through a two-way mirror while on a romantic getaway at an Iowa resort. In both cases, the victims reported that the emotional injury was intensified both by the unwanted publicity and by the speed and distance with which it spread. As Kennedy and Alderman observed, "This kind of news transcended geographic boundaries."

At issue in 1880, just as it was a century later, was the sense that individuals had lost control over the information being spread about them. It is not entirely possible to control what one's neighbors say either, but at least when the gossip is localized, it is possible to correct the most egregious misstatements. When salacious information and unauthorized photographs are printed and published in regional or national media outlets, it is virtually impossible to recall them or to eliminate the impression they make. It was a point made by former U.S. secretary of labor Ray Donovan after being acquitted of larceny and fraud charges in 1987: "Which office do I go to to get my reputation back?"

Ultimately, Godkin argued, privacy is entirely about the ability to control information about oneself. "The right to decide how much knowledge of this personal thought and feeling," he said, "and how much knowledge, therefore, of his tastes, and habits, of his own private doings and those of his family living under his roof, the public at large shall have, is as much one of his natural rights as his right to decide how he shall eat and drink, what he shall wear, and in what manner he shall pass his leisure hours."

Godkin's concise and well-reasoned summary of the inherent right of each American to personal privacy and control of information about his or her life would prove remarkably influential. There is little doubt that the article was read that summer by one or both members of one of Boston's newest law firms, Warren & Brandeis. A decade later, it would be cited as an important source in what may well be the most influential law review article in American history.

4

PRIVACY IN STATE COURTS AND LEGISLATURES

Much of the contemporary debate about the right to privacy centers on whether it was appropriate for the U.S. Supreme Court to formally recognize the right at all, as it did in a series of decisions in the late 1960s and early 1970s. Conservative legal theorists argue that a new right can be established only by an amendment to the Constitution or by statute, and preferably by state statute rather than federal legislation. More liberal or progressive legal theorists, on the other hand, believe that it is entirely appropriate for the courts to recognize the evolution of a new legal right, particularly in the context of common law (legal principles derived from prior court decisions), when significant cultural or technological changes in society merit the innovation.

The issue is somewhat more complicated than the contemporary debate sometimes makes it out to be. Whether or not there is a common law or natural right to privacy is merely the first question. An equally important inquiry is this: against whom can a right to privacy, either common law or statutory, be enforced? For instance, it is an ancient right under common law to recover damages from an individual who commits an assault. However, until the passage of the Federal Torts Claim Act in 1946, lawsuits to recover damages for an assault committed by an employee or agent of the U.S. government were blocked by the doctrine of sovereign immunity. Conversely, the Fourth Amendment limits how the government can conduct searches and seizures, but does not impose similar limits on private employers, who can search the offices, desks, and computers of their employees with relative impunity.

To the limited extent that the concept of privacy makes any formal appearance in court decisions published before 1890, it is in the context of preventing or compensating for outside interference on or with one's property. The general genesis of the concept is the ancient doctrine cited so forcefully by James Otis in 1761, that "a man's house is his castle." It is an idea that ultimately can be traced back to the Magna Carta, the enumeration of individual liberties that England's King John was grudgingly forced to sign in 1215.

That inchoate sense of independence and personal autonomy woven by the Framers into the Bill of Rights also suffused the common law throughout the states of the new nation. Admittedly, however, the specific circumstances in which the concept of privacy was mentioned in early American cases were somewhat outrageous, given contemporary mores. They amply demonstrate how the "right to privacy" can be used not only as a sword for personal autonomy, but as a shield for domestic misconduct. Coincidentally, three particularly good examples of the darker side of personal privacy were all handed down by the North Carolina supreme court.

For example, the first use of the word "privacy" in a U.S. state court decision occurred in *State v. Mann* (1829), when the Supreme Court of North Carolina was faced with the question of whether a man could be indicted for shooting and wounding a female slave whose services he had leased for a year. A full generation before the Civil War, the court was sensitive to the risks of looking too closely at the private institution of slavery:

> We cannot allow the right of the master to be brought into discussion in the courts of justice. The slave, to remain a slave, must be made sensible that there is no appeal from his master; that his power is in no instance usurped; but is conferred by the laws of man at least, if not by the law of God. . . . No man can anticipate the many and aggravated provocations of the master which the slave would be constantly stimulated by his own passions or the instigation of others to give; or the consequent wrath of the master, prompting him to bloody vengeance upon the turbulent traitor—a vengeance generally practiced with impunity by reason of its privacy. The Court, therefore, disclaims the power of changing the relation in which these parts of our people stand to each other.

A year later, in *Burgess v. Wilson* (1830), the court displayed a genteel but unbending paternalism toward women in general when it said that a wife's testimony in a dispute over a will should be given "when in privacy, and with the self-collection which a timid female, in the presence of a crowd and overawed by the authority of her husband, might not be able to command in public."

A much more painful example occurred a generation later, when in *State v. Rhodes* (1868) the North Carolina supreme court declined to inquire too closely "whether the court will allow a conviction of the husband for moderate correction of the wife [that is, for three 'licks' with a stick the size of one of his fingers] without provocation."

> For, however great are the evils of ill temper, quarrels, and even personal conflicts inflicting only temporary pain, they are not comparable with the evils which would result from raising the curtain, and exposing to public curiosity and criticism, the nursery and the bed chamber. . . . We will not inflict upon society the greater evil of raising the curtain upon domestic privacy, to punish the lesser evil of trifling violence.

The willingness of courts and law enforcement officials to turn a blind eye toward domestic abuse in the name of privacy helps underscore the deep-seated nature of the right itself, at least with respect to activities within the home. It would be nearly a century before legislatures began working on ways to strike a better balance between domestic privacy and abuse.

In the meantime, society was changing, and there was a small but growing demand for federal and state legislation to protect an individual's privacy outside the home. As was discussed earlier, one such effort occurred in 1888, when John R. Thomas, the congressman from Illinois, tried to secure passage of legislation to protect Mrs. Cleveland from the use of her image in unauthorized advertisements. The following year, the state of Washington was the first to explicitly codify a right to privacy in its state constitution: "No person shall be disturbed in his private affairs, or his home invaded, without authority of law."

Since then, although Congress has never explicitly recognized the right to privacy by either statute or constitutional amendment, nearly a third of the states have added a privacy provision to their constitutions, and even more recognize a right to privacy in some form or other in their statutes. In each instance, an intellectual debt is owed to two young Harvard Law School graduates who, in a combined fit of legal foresight and personal pique, compellingly argued that invasions of personal privacy are as injurious as property trespass or physical assault.

"THE RIGHT TO PRIVACY"

Louis Dembitz Brandeis met Samuel Dennis Warren Jr. in the fall of 1875, when both were members of the Harvard Law School Pow-Wow Club, a student group that met to hold mock trials of cases argued before the Massachusetts appellate courts. There was a vast cultural and social gulf between them: Brandeis was a relatively impoverished student from a Jewish merchant family in Louisville, Kentucky, while Warren was a scion of an old and wealthy New England family.

Despite their differences, the two men quickly became fast friends, and they roomed together during their final year at Harvard. After graduation, Brandeis moved to St. Louis to practice law, but he quickly grew dissatisfied with the types of assignments he was given. When his friend Warren wrote to suggest a partnership, Brandeis gladly moved back to Boston, and the two young lawyers formed the firm of Warren & Brandeis in the summer of 1879. Although the firm quickly prospered and the reputation of the two attorneys spread rapidly, their partnership was fairly short-lived. On May 11, 1888, Warren's father died, after which Warren left the practice of law to help run S. D. Warren Paper Mill Company, the family's extensive paper manufacturing business. Nonetheless, he remained in close contact with Brandeis and collaborated with him on three articles for the *Harvard Law Review* after his retirement from active practice: "The Watuppa Pond Case" (December 1888), "The Law of Ponds" (April 1889), and "The Right to Privacy" (December 1890).

It is the last of these that secured Samuel Warren and Louis Brandeis a permanent place in American legal history in general and the history of the right to privacy in particular. "The Right to Privacy" was that rarest of law review articles: a treatise so well reasoned and so compellingly argued that it helped to reshape American legal theory.

The foundation of the article is a concept at the core of the modern privacy debate: that "political, social, and economic changes entail the recognition of new rights, and the common law, in its eternal youth, grows to meet the new demands of society." To illustrate their central theme, Warren and Brandeis traced the changing response of the common law to infringements on personal space, beginning with protection from actual assaults by fist or sword and evolving to include mere threats of attack, damage to property (trespass), damage to reputation (libel and slander), and even infringements on intangible property (copyright, trademark, and trade secrets).

None of these developments, they argued, required legislative enactments. Instead, they were part of the natural evolution of the common law. "Thoughts, emotions, and sensations demanded legal recognition," Warren and Brandeis wrote, "and the beautiful capacity for growth which characterizes the common law enabled the judges to afford the requisite protection, without the interposition of the legislature."

Warren and Brandeis argued that the time had come for the courts to recognize a common law right to privacy—or a "right to be let alone"—for two main reasons. First, they pointed out, technology was making privacy invasions much easier than ever before:

> Instantaneous photographs and newspaper enterprise have invaded the sacred precincts of private and domestic life; and numerous mechanical devices threaten to make good the prediction that "what is whispered in the closet shall be proclaimed from the house-tops." For years there has been a feeling that the law must afford some remedy for the unauthorized circulation of portraits of private persons; and the evil of invasion of privacy by the newspapers, long keenly felt, has been but recently discussed by an able writer.

Second, in a plaintive passage almost certainly written by the notoriously proper and reticent Warren, the attorneys argued that the excesses of the press, unfettered by a compensable right to privacy, were threatening the very underpinnings of American society:

The press is overstepping in every direction the obvious bounds of propriety and of decency. Gossip is no longer the resource of the idle and of the vicious, but has become a trade, which is pursued with industry as well as effrontery. To satisfy a prurient taste the details of sexual relations are spread broadcast in the columns of the daily papers. To occupy the indolent, column upon column is filled with idle gossip, which can only be procured by intrusion upon the domestic circle. The intensity and complexity of life, attendant upon advancing civilization, have rendered necessary some retreat from the world, and man, under the refining influence of culture, has become more sensitive to publicity, so that solitude and privacy have become more essential to the individual; but modern enterprise and invention have, through invasions upon his privacy, subjected him to mental pain and distress, far greater than could be inflicted by mere bodily injury.

Law review articles, however compelling, do not typically command much attention from the mainstream press, and "The Right to Privacy" was no different. The article received favorable or matter-of-fact notice from a handful of papers, and one particularly critical summary from the editorial staff of the *Galveston Daily News*. The Texas paper dismissed the concerns of "ladies and gentlemen, criminals, and people of sensitive respectability" and lamented:

The matter has come to such a point that an enterprising journal can not reproduce the photograph of a gentleman's daughter without running the risk, somewhat remote, of a call, and a more or less spirited remonstrance from the parent. The feelings of these thin-skinned Americans are doubtless at the bottom of an article in the December number of the *Harvard Law Review*, in which two members of the Boston bar have recorded the results of certain researches into the question whether Americans do not possess a common-law right of privacy which can be successfully defended in the courts.

The publication of "The Right to Privacy" marked the end of the formal collaboration between Warren and Brandeis. But despite their steadily growing political differences (the aristocratic Warren grew increasingly conservative, and Brandeis grew steadily more progressive), the two remained good friends.

One legacy of their partnership, however, had a dark and tragic effect. During their partnership, Warren asked Brandeis to set up a trust to handle the revenues of S. D. Warren and Company and distribute profits from the business among the heirs of S. D. Warren. During the 1890s, however, revenues from the company steadily dropped, and the amounts paid to the Warren siblings and other heirs through the trust were correspondingly reduced. Warren's brothers, Ned and Fiske, alleged that Brandeis had structured the trust to discriminate against them in favor of his former law partner, Samuel. On February 18, 1910, with the family business in increasing decline and a widely publicized intrafamily lawsuit pending in court, the intensely private Samuel Warren spent an afternoon chopping wood at a Bayard family home known as Karlstein and then shot himself in the head. The *New York Times* discreetly reported that "Samuel Dennis Warren died of apoplexy to-day at his home in Dedham." He was fifty-nine at the time of his death.

Six years later, during his confirmation hearings for a seat on the U.S. Supreme Court, Brandeis came under intense and hostile questioning for his role in the trust and the later lawsuit among the family members. The opposition was so strenuous (including a petition by fifty-four prominent Boston attorneys denouncing Brandeis) that the hearings on his nomination lasted four months. In the end, however, Brandeis was confirmed on June 1, 1916, by a relatively narrow 47–22 vote. During his twenty-three years on the Supreme Court, Brandeis would prove to be one of its most passionate defenders of personal privacy, although unfortunately, he would not live to see the Court's ratification of the legal right he and Samuel Warren proposed.

THE FLOUR SACK GIRL SUES FOR PRIVACY

As important as "The Right to Privacy" ultimately was to the development of privacy law in the United States, its immediate impact was largely limited to the lawyers and judges who read the article in the august pages of the *Harvard Law Review*, a publication not known for its extensive mass-market circulation. In typical fashion, the real boost for the concept of an enforceable "right to privacy" occurred when newspapers latched on to the plight of an attractive young woman who objected, much as Frances Cleveland had, to the unauthorized use of her image in advertising.

In 1900, an eighteen-year-old Rochester, New York, woman named Abigail Roberson went to a local studio to have some photographs of herself taken. Her boyfriend at the time asked whether a friend could use the photographs to draw a portrait of her, and Roberson agreed. Unbeknownst to her, however, the friend had been commissioned by the Rochester Folding Box Company to create a drawing of an attractive young woman for use in advertisements for Franklin Mills Flour. Roberson's image, appearing under the banner "Flour of the Family," was reproduced on twenty-five thousand posters and advertisements.

When Roberson discovered that her image had been used without her permission, she filed a lawsuit against the Rochester Folding Box company, alleging that she had suffered such emotional distress from the taunts of neighbors that she had taken to her bed and received medical treatment. She sought an injunction to stop any further distribution of her likeness, and also asked for $15,000 in damages, which was a remarkable sum for the time (roughly equivalent to $363,000 today).

The Rochester Folding Box Company's first response was to file a demurrer to the complaint (essentially a motion to dismiss), arguing that Roberson had failed to state a cause of action. The trial court overruled the demurrer, using language similar to, and in some cases drawn directly from, Brandeis and Warren's law review and their quotations of E. L. Godkin's article:

> The privacy of the home in every civilized country is regarded as sacred, and when it is invaded it tends to destroy domestic and individual happiness. It seems to me, therefore, that the extension and development of the law so as to protect the right of privacy should keep abreast with the advancement of civilization. When private and domestic life is invaded, which brings pain and distress of mind and destroys the pleasure and happiness of domestic life the courts ought to have power to protect the individual from such an invasion.

The trial court's ruling was upheld the following summer by the Appellate Division, and an appeal was filed with the Court of Appeals, New York's highest court. In a narrow 4–3 decision, the Court of Appeals reversed the lower courts and ruled that there was no common law right of privacy in the state of New York.

The majority opinion was written by chief judge Alton Brooks Parker, a Democrat who had been appointed to the court in 1898. Parker began his opinion by noting that there is no mention of a "right to privacy" in any legal treatises prior to 1890, when "it was presented with attractiveness and no inconsiderable ability in the *Harvard Law Review* in an article entitled, 'The Right of Privacy.'" If the court were to recognize such a right, Parker argued, it would open up the courts to potentially endless litigation for perceived invasions of privacy. The appropriate course of action, he suggested, would be for the legislature to prohibit the use of a person's likeness without consent. "In such event," Parker noted, "no embarrassment would result to the general body of the law, for the rule would be applicable only to cases provided for by the statute."

Parker's objection to any expansion of the law by the court to encompass personal privacy was met with eloquence by his fellow judge, John Clinton Gray, who argued in dissent that the twin forces of social progress and judicial equity not merely permitted but compelled the recognition of a right to privacy:

> In the social evolution, with the march of the arts and sciences and in the resultant effects upon organized society, it is quite intelligible that new conditions must arise in personal relations, which the rules of the common law, cast in the rigid mould of an earlier social status, were not designed to meet. It would be a reproach to equitable jurisprudence, if equity were powerless to extend the application of the principles of common law, or of natural justice, in remedying a wrong, which, in the progress of civilization, has been made possible as the result of new social, or commercial conditions.

Judge Gray also had the prescience to recognize that the claim for a right to privacy was not merely capricious preference, but also an issue of personal safety:

Security of person is as necessary as the security of property; and for that complete personal security, which will result in the peaceful and wholesome enjoyment of one's privileges as a member of society, there should be afforded protection, not only against the scandalous portraiture and display of one's features and person, but against the display and use thereof for another's commercial purposes or gain.

The decision by the Court of Appeals sparked considerable comment, not merely in New York but in papers across the country. A week after the court's decision, the *New York Times* published not one but two editorials on the topic. In one, the *Times* assessed Judge Parker's opinion as "a sane and conservative judicial interpretation of the equities," but worried that the case would "break down all barriers between the individual seeking modest privacy and a public supposed to be consumed by a morbid appetite for the portraits of people who do not care to be made notorious." But in the second, under the heading "Topics of the Times," the court's decision that there is no right to privacy was described as "a terrifying statement": "Most would be inclined to say, we think, that any man or woman, young or old, has a just grievance when his or her picture is thus appropriated to the real or imagined benefit of another in whom he or she is not interested."

News of the decision spread quickly by post and telegraph across the nation, with summaries of the decision appearing in the *Colorado Springs Gazette*, *Atlanta Constitution*, *Des Moines Capital*, *Hayward* (Calif.) *Review*, *Modesto Evening News*, and *Racine Daily Journal*, among others. Most reported the outcome of the case without discussion, or at most with a brief excerpt of chief judge Parker's opinion, but a few papers offered pithy comments criticizing the court.

For instance, the *Racine Daily Journal* opined that as a result of the decision, "every citizen, male or female, in whatever condition of life cannot help himself or herself if they find their picture being used in some advertising device, and must submit to the detestable cruelty of it." The *Modesto Evening News* agreed, writing that "it is coming to a hard pass when it is no longer possible for a beautiful woman to avoid having her pictures sent broadcast over the country, posted on barrels, tacked up in public places in order to attract attention to an advertisement."

In typical Wild West fashion, the *Colorado Springs Gazette* suggested that in the absence of a legal remedy, offended privacy victims could take matters into their own hands: "Newspapers will hereafter feel free to print pictures of people in general without permission. When a person feels that his rights are trampled upon, there will always remain the one consolation that the public has always had when it has felt itself injured by the newspaper—go to and lick the editor."

While there are no reports of vigilante justice against beleaguered newspaper editors, intrepid photographers did run the risk (much as they do today) of being forcibly ejected from private property if the owner did not desire their presence.

THE RIGHT TO PRIVACY SPREADS ACROSS THE COUNTRY

Chief Judge Parker's suggestion that the right to privacy was a legislative matter did not fall on deaf ears. On January 22, 1903, New York state senator Nathaniel Elsberg introduced a bill that fell somewhat short of recognizing a right to privacy (even today, New York has no such statute), but instead barred the use of the "name, portrait, or picture" of any living person for commercial purposes. The bill established a penalty of up to a year in prison and a fine of up to $1,000, and it also established the right of the injured party to recover damages. The bill became law on April 6 and took effect on September 1 of that year.

But one final twist remained in the *Roberson* case. In the summer of 1904, Alton Parker was nominated by the Democrats to run for president against the Republican incumbent, Theodore Roosevelt, and resigned from his seat on the Court of Appeals. His nomination brought a steady stream of reporters and photographers to Rosemount, Parker's country home in Esopus, New York (a small town on the Hudson River south of Albany). Initially, Judge Parker welcomed the surge in publicity, but by mid-July, he had run out of patience with the "camera fiends."

"I reserve the right," Parker humorously argued to the *New York Times*, "to put my hands in my pockets and assume comfortable attitudes without being everlastingly afraid that I shall be snapped by some fellow with a camera." The newspaper reported that "Esopus has been fairly overrun with photographers," including some that lurked about trying to photograph the nominee in his bathing suit during his regular morning swim in the Hudson.

Parker's claim of a right to privacy did not go unnoticed by one particularly interested person. A few days later, Abigail Roberson sent a letter to the *New York Times,* pointing out that the former judge was asserting a right that he and three other judges had denied to her, and one which was not covered by New York's new law:

> I take this opportunity to remind you that you have no such right as that which you assert. I have very high authority for my statement, being nothing less than a decision of the Court of Appeals of this State wherein you wrote the prevailing opinion.
>
> I had never appeared before the public in any capacity nor solicited any favor at its hands. You, on the other hand, are a candidate for the highest office in the gift of the people of the United States, and that fact makes you the legitimate centre of public interest. You are asking the suffrage of the American public, and the American public would seem to have some legitimate right of investigation. Your candidacy is something more than voluntary, and it may fairly be said that you have invited the curiosity which we have both found to be somewhat annoying.

Roberson's letter caused considerable amusement around the country, although there was some suspicion that it had actually been written by one of her attorneys in her name. In any case, the publicity did not help Parker's presidential campaign; that fall he suffered a stinging defeat, losing to Roosevelt by 2.5 million votes (out of 13 million cast) and by more than a 2–1 margin in the Electoral College (336–140). Parker retired from public life—and the much-hated "camera fiends"—and spent the rest of his life quietly practicing law.

Although Abigail Roberson did not receive any relief from New York's highest court, the decision in her case did set off a slowly simmering debate in state courts and legislatures around the country over the concept of a "right to privacy." Some courts, like the New York Court of Appeals, concluded that there was no legal basis to announce such a right and that any protection of the right to privacy required legislative action. For example, in the case of *Henry v. Cherry & Webb* (1909), the Rhode Island Supreme Court ruled against a man who claimed that his right to privacy was violated when a department store published a photo of him in an advertisement reading "THE AUTO COATS WORN BY ABOVE AUTOISTS ARE WATER-PROOF. MADE OF FINE QUALITY SILK MOHAIR—10.50—IN FOUR COLORS." After a lengthy analysis, the court concluded that it was "unable to discover the existence of a right of privacy."

The Supreme Court of Georgia, in the case of *Pavesich v. New England Life Insurance Company* (1905), was the first to reach the opposite conclusion. Pavesich's photograph, like those of Roberson and Henry, was used without his permission in an advertisement, in this case a pitch for life insurance. The company ran an advertisement contrasting a healthy-looking man (Pavesich) with a sickly-looking individual (unidentified); below Pavesich's photograph was an implicitly attributed statement reading, "In my healthy and productive period of life I bought insurance in the New England Mutual Life Insurance Co., of Boston, Mass., and to-day my family is protected and I am drawing an annual dividend on my paid-up policies." The caption underneath the other photo suggested that the pictured chap's decrepit condition stemmed from not buying insurance. Pavesich sued for $25,000, alleging that the use of his photograph and the false statement "was malicious and tended to bring him into ridicule before the world."

The court was not fazed by the originality of Pavesich's claim. "The novelty of the complaint is no objection," associate justice Andrew Jackson Cobb wrote for a unanimous court, "when an injury cognizable by law is shown to have been inflicted on the plaintiff. In such a case 'although there be no precedent, the common law will judge according to the law of nature and the public good.'" And the right to privacy, Cobb declared, is just such a natural right: "Each individual as instinctively resents any encroachment by the public upon his rights which are of a private nature as he does the withdrawal of those of his rights which are of a public nature. A right of privacy in matters purely private is therefore derived from natural law."

In a lengthy historical analysis stretching back to basic principles of Roman law, Cobb cited numerous legal protections for individuals that are aspects of contemporary privacy: freedom from nuisances like noise, prohibitions against trespass and eavesdropping, protection from unreasonable searches and seizures, and so forth. He also discussed at length the article written by Warren and Brandeis, which he said "ably and forcefully maintained the existence of a right of privacy."

Justice Cobb paid particular attention to the New York Court of Appeals decision in *Roberson*, which he correctly noted was the only other American high court decision that previously had addressed the issue. Although he expressed admiration for the thoroughness of Judge Parker's analysis and agreed that there were no clear precedents for the "right to privacy," Cobb disagreed with his conclusion that the right should not be recognized:

> The desire to avoid the novelty of recognizing a principle which had not been theretofore recognized was avoided in such cases by the novelty of straining a well-recognized principle to cover a state of facts to which it had never before been applied. This conservatism of the judiciary has sometimes unconsciously led judges to the conclusion that because the case was novel the right claimed did not exist. With all due respect to Chief Judge Parker and his associates who concurred with him, we think the conclusion reached by them was the result of an unconscious yielding to the feeling of conservatism which naturally arises in the mind of a judge who faces a proposition which is novel.

Instead, Cobb said, the proper analysis was presented by Judge Gray in his dissent, which Cobb cited at length and with high approval. "The effect of the reasoning of the learned judge whose words have just been quoted," Cobb said, "is to establish conclusively the correctness of the conclusion which we have reached, and we prefer to adopt as our own his reasoning in his own words rather than to paraphrase them into our own."

In what may have been a backhanded reference to Judge Parker's own difficulties with the press the year before, Cobb said that it might well be that a candidate for public office "impliedly consents" to the taking of his photograph, but added that the court was not willing to go even that far:

It would seem to us that even the President of the United States in the lofty position which he occupies has some rights in reference to matters of this kind, which he does not forfeit by aspiring to or accepting the highest office within the gift of the people of the several States. While no person who has ever held this position, and probably no person who has ever held public office, has ever objected, or ever will object, to the reproduction of his picture in reputable newspapers, magazines, and periodicals, still it can not be that the mere fact that a man aspires to public office or holds public office subjects him to the humiliation and mortification of having his picture displayed in places where he would never go to be gazed upon, at times when and under circumstances where, if he were personally present, the sensibilities of his nature would be severely shocked.

So thoroughly satisfied are we that the law recognizes within proper limits, as a legal right, the right of privacy, and that the publication of one's picture without his consent by another as an advertisement, for the mere purpose of increasing the profits and gains of the advertiser, is an invasion of this right, that we venture to predict that the day will come when the American bar will marvel that a contrary view was ever entertained by judges of eminence and ability.

To a great extent, Justice Cobb's graciously optimistic prediction regarding the evolution of American privacy law has come to pass, at least with respect to the misappropriation of one's actual image for commercial purposes. But as we'll see in the latter portion of this book, where the law has failed to keep pace is with the changing definition of "one's picture." Where once one's picture was measured by the resolution of a photograph, now it is marked by the number of bits of data that make up one's digital profile. Both legislatures and the courts have yet to fully grapple with that development.

THE BIRTH OF THE EXCLUSIONARY RULE

Since federal law generally does not protect against the types of personal torts or injuries that concerned Brandeis and Warren, it would be many years before the federal courts would catch up to the state courts in their explicit discussion and recognition of the right to privacy. But federal law, including the Constitution, does govern the actions of federal agents. Thanks at least in part to the widespread concern about the heavy-handed methods of Anthony Comstock, which coincidentally overlapped the growing concern about journalistic invasions of privacy, the federal courts began looking at the concept of personal privacy in the context of the Fourth Amendment—the prohibition against unreasonable searches and seizures. It was particularly fitting that they should do so, since that amendment, perhaps more directly than any other, was a response to the privacy invasions of the British government before the Revolution. Ultimately, it was federal Fourth Amendment jurisprudence, rather than misappropriated images, that led to the recognition by the Warren Court of a constitutional "right to privacy" in the 1960s.

To be fair, none of the Fourth Amendment cases decided during Comstock's professional career (1873–1915) mention him directly. But opposition to Comstock and his methods helped galvanize liberal—and liberating—forces in a number of different fields, including politics, medicine, and art, so it is not surprising that law was affected as well.

The Supreme Court took a glancing look at the Fourth Amendment in the case of *Ex Parte Jackson* (1877), when the Court was presented squarely with the question of whether the provisions of the Comstock Act that prohibited the mailing of certain items were constitutional. The Court ruled unanimously that they were, but noted in passing that a person's correspondence can be opened only with a warrant issued pursuant to the terms of the Fourth Amendment: "No law of Congress can place in the hands of officials connected with the postal service any authority to invade the secrecy of letters and such sealed packages in the mail; and all regulations adopted as to mail matter of this kind must be in subordination to the great principle embodied in the fourth amendment of the Constitution."

The next Fourth Amendment case arose nine years later (and just four years before Warren and Brandeis wrote "The Right to Privacy"), when the Supreme Court, in *Boyd v. United States* (1886), was presented with the question of whether a person's failure to produce certain papers could be held against that person at trial. In a revenue enforcement statute first adopted in 1863, Congress gave U.S. Attorneys (the federal government's prosecutors) the authority to ask for a court order compelling defendants or claimants to produce "any business book, invoice, or paper belonging to, or under the control of, the defendant or claimant" if it was the U.S. Attorney's belief that the material would "tend to prove any allegation made by the United States." E. A. Boyd & Sons was charged with importing glass without paying customs duty, and the U.S. Attorney obtained an order requiring the company to produce its invoices for the glass. The company challenged the law, arguing that it was a violation of both the Fourth Amendment and the Fifth Amendment (the latter guarantees freedom from self-incrimination).

Writing for a 7–2 majority, associate justice Joseph Bradley declared that the central question before the Court was whether a compulsory production of documents constitutes an unreasonable search and seizure within the meaning of the Fourth Amendment. Noting James Otis's challenge to the writs of assistance more than a century earlier, Justice Bradley concluded that the law unquestionably was unreasonable:

> The act of 1863 was the first act in this country, and, we might say, either in this country or in England, so far as we have been able to ascertain, which authorized the search and seizure of a man's private papers, or the compulsory production of them, for the purpose of using them in evidence against him in a criminal case, or in a proceeding to enforce the forfeiture of his property. Even the act under which the obnoxious writs of assistance were issued did not go as far as this. . . . The search for and seizure of stolen or forfeited goods, or goods liable to duties and concealed to avoid the payment thereof, are totally different things from a search for and seizure of a man's private books and papers for the purpose of obtaining information therein contained, or of using them as evidence against him.

Justice Bradley went on to argue that the memory of the general writs of assistance and Otis's brilliant opposition to them was still fresh in the minds of the Framers, having occurred less than twenty years before. The Framers also had in mind, Bradley said, the opinion of Charles Pratt, 1st Earl Camden, in the case of *Entick v. Carrington* (1765), in which he awarded judgment against four messengers of

King George III for breaking into the home of John Entick and forcefully seizing his private papers during a search for an allegedly seditious newspaper.

"As every American statesmen, during our revolutionary and formative period as a nation, was undoubtedly familiar with this monument of English freedom," Bradley said in his opinion, "and considered it as the true and ultimate expression of constitutional law, it may be confidently asserted that its propositions were in the minds of those who framed the Fourth Amendment to the Constitution, and were considered as sufficiently explanatory of what was meant by unreasonable searches and seizures."

The upshot, the Court said, was that the Framers who later served in the nation's early Congresses could never have consented to the passage of the challenged law. "The struggles against arbitrary power in which they had been engaged for more than twenty years," Bradley said, "would have been too deeply engraved in their memories to have allowed them to approve of such insidious disguises of the old grievance which they had so deeply abhorred."

While the *Boyd* case can be considered the formal beginning of Fourth Amendment jurisprudence, it was a later decision, *Weeks v. United States* (1914), that went one step further and introduced the exclusionary rule to federal case law. (The exclusionary rule prohibits the introduction of evidence that is obtained illegally or unconstitutionally.) Significantly, given the quasi-hysterical environment created by Comstock, *Weeks* was one of the first cases to challenge not a federal law but the actions of a federal agent.

During an investigation into an illegal lottery in Kansas City, Missouri, a U.S. marshal entered a suspected lottery agent's dwelling without a warrant and seized various letters and papers of the defendant, who unsuccessfully applied to the trial court for their return to prevent their being used as evidence. The Supreme Court ruled that the trial court had erred by turning down the application and held that it was unconstitutional under the Fourth Amendment to permit the introduction of evidence seized during a warrantless search by a federal agent.

Despite having been written nearly a century ago, the central holding of associate justice William Rufus Day remains a compelling summary of privacy rights under the U.S. Constitution:

The effect of the Fourth Amendment is to put the courts of the United States and Federal officials, in the exercise of their power and authority, under limitations and restraints as to the exercise of such power and authority, and to forever secure the people, their persons, houses, papers and effects against all unreasonable searches and seizures under the guise of law. This protection reaches all alike, whether accused of crime or not, and the duty of giving to it force and effect is obligatory upon all entrusted under our Federal system with the enforcement of the laws. The tendency of those who execute the criminal laws of the country to obtain conviction by means of unlawful seizures and enforced confessions, the latter often obtained after subjecting accused persons to unwarranted practices destructive of rights secured by the Federal Constitution, should find no sanction in the judgments of the courts which are charged at all times with the support of the Constitution and to which people of all conditions have a right to appeal for the maintenance of such fundamental rights.

It is likely that Fourth Amendment jurisprudence would have developed along these lines even without Comstock, the New York Society for the Suppression of Vice, and the vice hunters around the country who emulated him. But unquestionably, his well-publicized excesses and his willingness to skirt constitutional boundaries not only spurred judicial interest in the Fourth Amendment but also sparked a growing public concern about the possible dangers of government investigations and information gathering. Those concerns would only intensify as federal and state governments, desperately scrambling to cope with the combined perils of world wars and international economic crises, began collecting unprecedented amounts of personal information.

5

NO MORE GENTLEMEN

The Rise of Governmental Espionage

In the history of the right to privacy, the distinction between the telegraph and the telephone can be seen clearly by virtue of the fact that for the first seventy-five years or so of its existence, the telegraph did not generate a single significant court ruling on privacy. The telephone, however, thanks in part to its ubiquity and in part to the relative ease with which law enforcement could eavesdrop on personal conversations, quickly sparked legal controversies that substantially shaped the development of the law of privacy.

In theory, the invention of the telephone in the late nineteenth century should have been a positive development for the privacy of personal communications. The transmission of one's voice directly to the ear of a listener meant that there was no writing involved that could go astray or be read en route by someone other than the intended recipient. And whereas sending a telegram necessarily required presenting the message to the telegraph operator, when using the phone there was no need to reveal the content of one's conversation ahead of time to the phone company, and thus no need to trust that the conversation would remain secure in the company's records. Even the casual eavesdropping that can occur in the street or in a shop was largely eliminated by the marvelous new invention.

But in reality, the telephone inflicted grave and permanent damage to the concept of personal privacy. Part of the reason was the end of a certain amount of psychological solitude: to a degree never matched by the silent letter or even the telegram delivered to the door, the telephone was a self-inflicted breach in the wall of the subscriber's castle. Once a phone was installed, its demanding jangle could sound at any moment. As numerous commentators grumpily noted at the time, whatever its other merits, Bell's telephone sadly reduced the peace and serenity previously enjoyed in one's home.

But the most significant impact of the telephone on personal privacy was the launch, once and for all, of the era of electronic exhibitionism and voyeurism. The inherent characteristics of the new technology made it remarkably easy for nosy neighbors and aggressive law enforcement officers to listen in on virtually any telephone conversation. The growth of both casual and intentional eavesdropping that accompanied the invention of the phone permanently changed not only society but the law that governs it.

A brief technical overview is helpful. In its most basic configuration, a telephone line consists of little more than two twisted copper wires that form a lengthy electrical circuit between the speaker and the listener. When someone talks into the microphone of a telephone handset, the sound of the voice causes a small diaphragm in the handset to vibrate, which in turn causes an electromagnet to move back and forth in a matching pattern. As the magnet moves, it increases or decreases the strength of the electrical current moving through the phone wire.

At the other end, a corresponding electromagnet moves back and forth to varying degrees depending on the strength of the current coming through the telephone wire. The magnet in the receiver is attached to a diaphragm of the speaker within the handset, which as it vibrates reproduces the sounds made by the caller. When telephones were introduced, wiretapping a phone was no more complicated than connecting the wires of a handset to the corresponding wires of a particular phone line somewhere along the circuit. Although adding an additional handset necessarily reduced the voltage going through the line, the reduction was typically minimal and hard for the conversers to detect. The handset could then be used to listen quietly to the conversation taking place.

The tapping of telegraph wires had been a popular activity with the criminal element since before the Civil War, but it was difficult to target specific businesses or individuals, since so few of them had their own telegraph lines. In order to intercept a particular individual's telegram, an eavesdropper would have to know which telegraph office the target was going to use and roughly when the telegram would be sent. Even assuming the correct line and approximate time were known, the eavesdropper would no doubt have to transcribe dozens or even hundreds of telegrams to find the one sent by the target.

But the telephone was a far more enticing target for illicit listeners. Since the telephone was marketed from the outset as an affordable and convenient personal technology, first to businesses and then to individual subscribers, it was much easier to identify a particular telephone line used by the target of an eavesdropping campaign. And since telephone users could typically talk as long as they wanted (at least on local calls) without incurring additional charges, a tapped telephone line tended to produce far more information than the typical terse telegram.

Racecourses, bookies, gambling dens, and stockbrokers were among the establishments most commonly tapped, but the growing household use of phones opened up new possibilities for electronic snooping. As early as 1911, for instance, a suspicious husband hired a private detective to tap his own home phone and transcribe conversations between his wife and their chauffeur. "The stenographer's notes," a paper drily reported, "which were read in court, told of more or less intimate talks between Mrs. Sagal and the chauffeur."

As we'll see, over the next half century the practice of wiretapping telephones would become one of the most controversial and challenging legal and political issues in the United States. But in the early days of the telephone system, the vast majority of the eavesdropping that occurred was a direct result of the design and implementation of the phone system itself.

PARTY LINES AND "HELLO GIRLS"

The expiration of the Bell Telephone Company's main patents in 1893 and 1894 unleashed a period of tremendous competition and innovation in the fledgling telephone industry. In the seventeen years since Alexander Graham Bell barked "Mr. Watson—come here—I want to see you" into his experimental telephone apparatus, roughly 260,000 telephones had been installed in the United States. According to Claude S. Fischer's *America Calling: A Social History of the Telephone to 1940*, roughly two-thirds of the early subscribers were businesses, mainly due to the high cost of the new technology. But once the telephone industry was freed from the need to pay licensing fees to Bell Telephone for its patented technology, thousands of independent phone companies sprang up around the country. By the time the United States entered World War I on April 6, 1917, there were more than ten million telephones in use across America.

One of the main reasons for the phenomenal growth of telephone subscriptions in the first two decades of the twentieth century was the introduction of the shared service line, or "party line," an innovation that enabled a phone company to spread the cost of running a phone line among multiple subscribers—typically four to eight, but sometimes as many as thirty. When a call was received by a person on a party line, the conversation could be heard by anyone else on the line who picked up the receiver. Each subscriber was assigned a unique ring sequence so that he or she could tell which calls to answer and which to leave alone. Columnist Donnie Johnston, reminiscing in the *Free Lance–Star* (Fredericksburg, Virginia), said that everyone knew his own ring, but knew everyone else's ring as well. "So when the phone dinged," Johnston said, "you knew just who was getting a call. If you wanted to listen in, you just quietly picked up the receiver as soon as the ringing stopped."

Telephone companies issued earnestly worded pamphlets urging subscribers to respect each other's privacy, but human nature being what it is, it was still fairly common for people to listen in on each other's phone calls. One technical feature of party lines made it amusingly difficult to listen in undetected: as each receiver was lifted off the hook, the voltage on the line decreased, which lowered the volume of the call. If too many people decided to eavesdrop on a call, the speakers would end up having to shout at each other in order to be heard. It was a good sign that unwanted guests had joined the party.

"Party lines could destroy relationships," Johnston wrote. "If you were dating someone on the party line and got a call from another girl, well, the jig was up. Five minutes after you hung up, everybody in the neighborhood—including your girlfriend—knew about the call. In fact, there were times when the girlfriend butted in and chewed both the caller and the callee out. Watch what you say."

Thanks to their efficient use of lines and corresponding low cost, party lines quickly became the primary form of telephone service for a majority of Americans, particularly those in more rural areas. By 1920, over 60 percent of rural telephone subscribers were on party lines, compared to just 10 percent of urban subscribers. Shared service lines lingered well into the twentieth century before phone companies finally began phasing out the last ones and replacing them with single-subscriber lines that offer modern conveniences unavailable on a shared service, such as the ability to use an answering machine or voice mail, call waiting, and so on.

Nosy neighbors were not the only ones who might be listening in on a phone conversation. For a short time, at least, the telephone also perpetuated the casual (and occasionally not so casual) corporate surveillance that began with the telegraph industry. In the early days of the telephone system, all calls were routed through manual switchboards staffed by telephone operators. When a call came in to the switchboard, the telephone operator, or "hello girl," would ask the caller for the number of the person being called. The operator would then use a patch cord to connect the caller's line directly to the phone line of the receiving party (for a local call) or to a trunk line (for a long-distance call to another town or state). As with the telegraph system, the nature of the phone system made it impossible to call someone in complete privacy. The operator not only would know who was calling whom at any given time but could easily listen in on any conversation. Once a telephone circuit was successfully connected, operators were supposed to turn off their headsets to allow the callers to speak in private, but it was widely believed that operators often eavesdropped out of nosiness or mere boredom.

It was one person's suspicion about eavesdropping that led to the eventual elimination of the manual switchboard. In Kansas City, Missouri, an undertaker named Almon Strowger became convinced that the local switchboard was redirecting his business calls to a rival undertaker. (His suspicions were heightened by the fact that one of the "cord operators" was his rival's wife.) Using a combination of electromagnets and hat pins, Strowger invented a device to automatically handle the switching of telephone calls. He was awarded a patent on his invention in March 1891, and the first system went into operation in LaPorte, Indiana, on November 3, 1892, with much fanfare.

It would be many years before Strowger's automatic exchanges completely replaced the "hello girls," but the improvements in speed, labor costs, and consumer privacy made a compelling case for telephone companies to make the switch. In most cases, Strowger's invention reduced the time required to make a telephone connection from minutes to mere seconds. And as Strowger envisioned, the automation of the switching process reduced the likelihood of eavesdropping by telephone company employees. Telephone privacy still was not absolute, of course: phone lines were still susceptible to wiretapping; party lines remained in relatively common use through the end of the twentieth century; and telephone companies soon began maintaining, first manually and later electronically, lists of numbers dialed by each subscriber (for billing purposes, although it didn't take long for the lists to be subpoenaed for other reasons). Nonetheless, the introduction of automated switches definitely enhanced telephone privacy, at least as far as the general public was concerned.

THE NEW YORK CHARITY WIRETAPPING CASE

The loss of privacy due to party lines or switchboards was often amusing and occasionally embarrassing, but rarely harmful. Wiretapping, on the other hand, was a much more serious matter. Criminals were not the only ones eavesdropping on conversations. Law enforcement had always tried to keep up with the technical innovations of crime, and wiretapping was no exception. If anything, law enforcement authorities were even more eager than the average criminal to use wiretapping techniques, since they could be used not only to fight the crime of wiretapping itself but to gather information about other types of crimes that were being planned or committed. In the late nineteenth century and early twentieth century, there were very few laws regulating wiretapping, and the practice quickly became a popular tool for both state and federal law enforcement officials. It is impossible to know just how many police departments and federal agencies gathered information by listening in on conversations. Were it not for a particularly complicated and nasty battle over public charities in New York City, the practice of official wiretapping might have gone undisclosed for decades.

In 1914, John P. Mitchel, the newly elected "Boy Mayor" of New York (he was just thirty-four), appointed John A. Kingsbury to serve as the city's commissioner of charities. At the time, all private charities were under the supervision of the State Board of Charities, which among other things issued certificates authorizing the placement of dependent children. Kingsbury believed that municipalities in general, and New York in particular, should have supervisory authority over the charities within their borders, particularly with respect to living conditions. He alleged that the state board had been derelict in its inspection duties and persuaded New York governor Charles Whitman to appoint a special commission, headed by Charles H. Strong, to hear his allegations.

In the spring of 1916, a number of Catholic Church officials made the explosive allegation that their telephones had been tapped during the charities investigation. The Reverend William B. Farrell, rector of the Church of SS. Peter and Paul in Brooklyn, told reporters:

> Time after time during the investigation [by the Strong Commission], counsel have asked questions regarding the substance of phone conversations, which could be obtained only by eavesdropping on telephone conversations.
>
> The matters which have been discussed over the telephone in the hearing of eavesdroppers have mainly concerned questions of matrimony and other sacred subjects of private life. These were all taken down in shorthand, we have positive knowledge, at a police station. If such things are to be permitted, no man's private affairs are safe. This is the most contemptible and mean infringement on personal rights that has ever occurred in this country.

At the request of the church, New York county district attorney Edward Swann began a separate investigation of the charges to determine whether New York's 1893 antiwiretapping law had been violated. The police were authorized to conduct wiretapping of criminals or criminal conversations, he said, but if officers were merely seeking information or misused the information they obtained, then it would be up to a jury to determine whether the law had been broken.

Just four days after the initial wiretapping allegations were raised, Mayor Mitchel admitted to a *New York Times* reporter that he had authorized the eavesdropping on Catholic officials in response to a charge by Commissioner Kingsbury that the officials had perjured themselves during testimony before the Strong Commission. "On information that a crime had been committed, lodged by the Commissioner of Charities," Mitchel said, "the police listened to telephone conversations over three telephone wires. No other telephones whatsoever were interfered with. This the police did under authority of law."

On May 3, 1916, a grand jury in Kings County, New York, (now the borough of Brooklyn) began investigating whether New York City officials had violated the state's wiretapping law, which the state assembly had adopted thirteen years earlier. After hearing nearly three weeks of testimony, the grand jury indicted Kingsbury and William H. Hotchkiss, special deputy corporation counsel for the city of New York. Neither Mayor Mitchel nor police commissioner Arthur Woods were indicted, although the grand jury suggested that it had thought long and hard about doing so:

> If, as does appear, they approved of the conduct of those who were responsible for the tapping of the wires in question for no other purpose than to furnish counsel in private and personal litigation with information, and to gratify private curiosity, and not for the detection and prevention of crime, the conduct of the Mayor and Police Commissioner merits most severe condemnation.
>
> The danger which this system can be subjected to by officials with ulterior purposes must be apparent, and this Grand Jury condemns those officials who, in violation of their oaths, arbitrarily intrude, by means of tapping telephone wires, into the private affairs of law-abiding citizens without warrant in the law.

In the meantime, the news of the wiretapping in New York City attracted the attention of the Thompson Committee, a joint legislative group conducting a wide-ranging investigation of New York public utilities under the direction of state senator George F. Thompson. In mid-May, John L. Swayze, an official for the New York Telephone Company, told the Thompson Committee that police wiretapping was far more extensive than previously imagined. The New York police department, he said, had been wiretapping phones as part of criminal investigations for twenty years, beginning in the administration of Mayor William Strong. Swayze also told the committee that in the last two years, the police commissioner had authorized the tapping of 350 different telephone wires in New York City. He said that in each case the police commissioner asserted that the wiretap was necessary to detect or prevent a crime.

The following day, at his own request, Commissioner Woods appeared before the Thompson Committee to defend the police department's use of wiretapping. His unapologetic arguments are a catalog of the justifications claimed for every intrusive investigative technique since: "If you confine your detectives in their work against criminals to methods which should be used with honest men, you are making it impossible for them to get results and deliver the goods in the class of work that you set them to do. The old saying of 'Set a thief to catch a thief' is a pretty good saying. The detective works with the thief's methods and uses the thief's weapons."

Woods asserted that a variety of unsavory techniques were a necessary part of law enforcement, but assured the committee that these methods were employed with the greatest care. Under close questioning from the state senators, however, it became increasingly clear that the decision to conduct electronic surveillance was solely in the police commissioner's discretion, with little or no judicial oversight. That conclusion bothered at least one member of the committee, state senator Robert R. Lawson, who told Woods: "This all leads me to the conclusion, Mr. Commissioner, that some innocent person whose wire you may have tapped, who feels justly aggrieved, may proceed to test the question, and if it reaches the point of the United States Supreme Court, I am wondering whether they wouldn't declare that listening-in is unconstitutional."

Woods was singularly unconcerned: "Well, of course, I don't know. You can never tell what lawyers will do when they are let loose."

Later that month, in an interview with the weekly magazine *The Outlook*, Commissioner Woods reiterated his defense of the practice of wiretapping by the police:

> Much detective work, at best, is disagreeable. It involves methods that no one likes to use. It involves eavesdropping, shadowing, looking through windows, listening to conversations. It would be wholly unjustified to do this sort of thing willfully where law-abiding citizens are concerned, but it would be equally a neglect of duty on the part of a police department if it failed to use these measures against thieves.

Woods argued that the police department took the "most stringent precautions" to insure that the rights of honest people were protected, although he conceded that the police department "may unwittingly, or by an error in judgment, listen to the conversation over telephone wires of law-abiding citizens." Woods hastened to assure readers that "the record of such conversation, however, would be immediately destroyed and forgotten." At the same time, however, the commissioner urged people to remember that "telephone conversations from their very nature cannot be private in the way that letters can be, since the employees of the telephone company cannot help hearing parts of conversations and may, if they are inclined, easily hear all."

While not specifically referencing Woods's arguments, the *Washington Post* offered a stirring and sarcastic rebuttal in a scornful editorial titled "Why Not Tap the Mails?"

The mails carry more secrets than are carried on the wires. Why do the police of New York permit criminals to use the mails? What is the United States secret service thinking of that it fails to open and inspect private correspondence? How do we know that the most far-reaching conspiracies and diabolical plots are not being hatched through the use of the mails? Criminals are cautious in the use of the telephone, but they do not hesitate to take advantage of the inviolability of the mails.

Espionage of the mails is as justifiable as espionage of telephone messages. If peeping and prying and eavesdropping is to be legalized, let us do the work thoroughly. Let no man be trusted. Let Congress repeal the law which penalizes violation of the privacy of the mails. Let censors be installed in the post-offices, so that no missive may pass without inspection. Put into effect the most scientific system of spying that European or Oriental craft has ever evolved. We Americans should have the best.

It might be well also to shadow private citizens and their families. Detectives in the hallways and cellars might find a lot of criminality that now goes undetected. Peeping Toms and sneaks could thus perform great service for the state.

But until a government spying system is substituted for

the present system of protecting personal liberty, we insist that wire-tapping is as vicious and indefensible as opening the mail.

As noble as those sentiments were, however, there was little or no chance that they would be honored. The temptation for law enforcement to use wiretapping as an investigative tool was simply too great, even in a state that actually had criminalized unlawful wiretapping. And the limited deterrent effect of the law against wiretapping depended on the ability of a district attorney to successfully prosecute violations.

In that regard, the charities wiretapping case was not encouraging. In the spring of 1917, the wiretapping trial of John Kingsbury and William Hotchkiss began in Brooklyn. After just a week of testimony, the case ended abruptly when the trial judge directed a verdict for the two defendants. While acknowledging that "the police cannot arbitrarily nor without just cause interfere with the right of privacy of the owner of a telephone line," the court concluded that neither Kingsbury nor Hotchkiss had the requisite intent to be found guilty.

"While I believe that the District Attorney was justified in conducting the investigation which he has made and presenting this case for trial," the judge said, "I am convinced that the proof does not, under the rule of law, show the bad faith and evil intent of the defendants necessary to constitute the crime of which they were charged."

It seems that New York voters disagreed. In the wake of the police wiretapping scandal, Mayor Mitchel lost his reelection bid to county judge John F. Hylan, a candidate backed by the infamous Tammany Hall and the equally notorious newspaper magnate William Randolph Hearst. An early critic of the Mitchel administration for its handling of the charities investigation, Hylan promised shortly after his election that wiretapping would be limited to criminal investigations and closely regulated, although he offered the usual caveat. "During my administration, I will permit no wiretapping except to detect crime, and even then only upon permission being given by some judicial officer or the District Attorney. Anyone permitting wiretapping under other conditions will be prosecuted to the full extent of the law." In his first interview following his inauguration, Hylan went even further: "Personally, I abominate such listening in to other people's talk. . . . In addition to being annoying and embarrassing, such an unlicensed privilege in the hands of the police easily becomes a very grave menace."

As gratifying as New Yorkers no doubt found the mayor's comments, the charities wiretapping case did not spark the wide-ranging debate about law enforcement eavesdropping that one might have expected. By the time the Kingsbury and Hotchkiss trial had ended, the United States was at war with the Central powers that were trying to overrun Europe. Whatever harsh and unflattering light might have been shined on official eavesdropping was extinguished for the time being by the various international crises of the day.

THE BLACK CHAMBER AND PROHIBITION

As happened during the Civil War, the onset of hostilities in World War I almost immediately led to an increased interest in reading, translating, and deciphering intercepted messages, both domestic and foreign. But in the half century after Fort Sumter fell, a growing variety of unregulated and unprotected forms of communication offered the federal government far more opportunities to intercept messages than Lincoln could ever have imagined. Although primitive and somewhat scattered, the government's efforts to take advantage of those interception opportunities helped lay the groundwork for the extensive global eavesdropping that takes place today.

The first step was to exert direct censorship control over foreign communications. Just three weeks after Congress's declaration of war on April 6, 1917, Woodrow Wilson issued Executive Order 2604, which prohibited the transmitting of messages outside the United States except under regulations issued by the secretary of war or the secretary of the navy. Six months later, in October, Wilson went even further and established a Censorship Board to monitor and control "communications by mail, cable, radio, or other means of transmission passing between the United States and any foreign country," regardless of whether the foreign country was friendly or antagonistic.

The membership of the Censorship Board amply illustrated its intention to reach all forms of communication: representatives of the secretary of war, the secretary of the navy, the War Trade Board, the chair of the Committee on Public Information, and the postmaster general. In addition to his supervisory role on the Censorship Board, the postmaster general was also charged with establishing regulations requiring a complete translation, with accompanying affidavit as to accuracy, of any foreign language publication intended for distribution through the U.S. mails. Although Wilson's order did not specifically say so, the implication was clear that the postmaster could refuse, as his predecessor Montgomery Blair had done, delivery of any publication that was considered subversive or disloyal.

One by-product of the increased interest in intercepting electronic communications and the limited number of legal restrictions on doing so was the birth of U.S. signals intelligence, or SIGINT. According to a history of U.S. army signals intelligence published by the U.S. Army Center of Military History in 1993, no branch of the U.S. government conducted cryptanalytic activities prior to the start of World War I. In the months prior to the U.S. declaration of war in 1917, however, a young government telegrapher named Herbert O. Yardley was working as a code clerk for the U.S. Department of State. Yardley had an amateur interest in cryptography and occupied his spare time trying to break the codes used by the State Department to transmit President Wilson's various communications overseas. To Yardley's dismay, it took so little time for him to decipher the U.S. messages that they might just as well have been sent in plain text.

Following the declaration of war, Yardley persuaded Col. Ralph Van Deman to establish a new military intelligence section—MI-8 —to crack the diplomatic and military codes used by other nations. Yardley's section grew rapidly and in just over a year was staffed by eighteen officers, twenty-four civilian cryptographers and cryptanalysts, and more than a hundred stenographers and typists. MI-8 did not have any particularly spectacular successes during World War I, but its successor organization earned itself a permanent place in U.S. espionage lore.

Following the end of armed hostilities in 1918, Yardley was asked to reorganize MI-8 and continue its operations. The new organization was known as the Black Chamber. In order to give it a lower profile, the entire unit was moved to New York—first to 22 East Thirty-eighth Street and then to 52 Vanderbilt Avenue—where it operated under the purposefully bland and seemingly innocuous name of "Code Compilation Company." The group's primary goal following the war was breaking a series of difficult message codes used by the Pacific's newest naval power, Japan. During the course of two years' intense work, Yardley and his staff succeeded in cracking several different Japanese codes.

Although the Black Chamber's code-breaking efforts played a pivotal role in U.S. negotiations with Japan at the important Washington Naval Conference in late 1921 and early 1922, the group's influence steadily waned in the years afterward. Direct interception of foreign transmissions by the American military was still in its infancy, and communications companies like Western Union and Postal Telegraph were reluctant, out of concern that their increasingly international economic interests would be damaged, to simply provide the Black Chamber with copies of messages sent to and from foreign governments. At the same time, more and more of Yardley's own attention was occupied with decidedly nongovernment activities, including code consulting work for private companies, the creation and sale of commercial codes, and even real estate sales.

In the late 1920s, long after World War I had ended, the Black Chamber was asked to perform one rather minor bit of code breaking that was part of a more ominous development in government eavesdropping. During the course of its long-running efforts to enforce Prohibition, the U.S. Coast Guard discovered that bootleggers and rum-runners were using coded radio signals over unlicensed frequencies to coordinate pickups and deliveries in international waters. Initially, the intercepted codes were sent to Victor Weiskopf, one of Yardley's top cryptanalysts in the Black Chamber. Weiskopf moonlighted with the U.S. Department of Justice, and it was through that agency that the decoded messages were redistributed to various law enforcement agencies in the U.S. government.

However, the Black Chamber's involvement in the antiliquor effort was brief. As the battle against contraband liquor intensified, the Coast Guard set up its own intelligence office, with the help of the U.S. Bureau of Prohibition, and hired Elizabeth S. Friedman as a cryptanalyst. Through the end of the 1920s, the Coast Guard's cryptanalytic unit (which consisted solely of Friedman and a clerk) decoded thousands of intercepted messages and turned the information over to a wide range of American law enforcement agencies, including the

Bureau of Internal Revenue, the Coast Guard, the Bureau of Prohibition, the Bureau of Investigation, and the Narcotics Division of the U.S. Department of the Treasury. It was a graphic demonstration of how the resources and tools of military and foreign intelligence could easily be redirected toward domestic issues.

Despite their brief involvement in Prohibition enforcement efforts, dissatisfaction with the Black Chamber and Yardley was rapidly rising. There was some discussion in military circles about the possibility of consolidating all code services in a single department. But before any action could be taken, secretary of state Henry L. Stimson received his first batch of decoded Japanese diplomatic messages from Yardley after taking office in January 1929. The aristocratic and accomplished Stimson was reportedly furious to learn about the Black Chamber's activities and demanded that it be shut down immediately, saying that "Gentlemen don't read each other's mail."

Another thing that gentlemen are not supposed to do is "kiss and tell," but Yardley broke that rule as well. With the Great Depression in full swing, his cryptanalytic skills were in low demand. To support his family, Yardley wrote an extensive exposé about his code-breaking work called *The American Black Chamber.* The book sold well (particularly in Japan) but infuriated members of the American intelligence community—in part because it compromised the ongoing operations of various U.S. agents, and in part because it revealed to a number of previously unsuspecting countries that the Americans were reading their signals. Federal laws were quickly passed to prevent a repeat occurrence, and Yardley's next manuscript, "Japanese Diplomatic Secrets: 1921–1922" (which was actually ghostwritten by Marie Stuart Klooz), was seized by the Department of Justice before it could be printed.

Despite their limited operational successes and relatively brief existence, Yardley's MI-8 and Black Chamber are generally acknowledged as distant but important forebears of the National Security Agency, the intelligence-gathering organization secretly established by President Truman. Stimson's protestations aside, the chief legacy of the Black Chamber and the Coast Guard's cryptanalytic unit was the acknowledgement that federal agents, whether or not they were gentlemen or ladies, did in fact read foreign mail and listen to foreign radio broadcasts. Left unanswered was whether federal agents could also listen to American telephone conversations without violating the Bill of Rights. That question could be answered by only one court.

OLMSTEAD V. UNITED STATES (1928)

In the early part of the twentieth century, the practice of eavesdropping on domestic conversations was chiefly the tool of local law enforcement, which effectively meant that the practice could not be challenged in federal court. But that changed on January 29, 1920, when the provisions of the Eighteenth Amendment formally took effect and the United States officially went "dry."

In retrospect, the grand experiment that became known as Prohibition (or as it might be known today, the "War on Alcohol") was a losing battle from the start. Among its more pernicious effects were the strengthening of organized crime, growing disdain and disrespect for legal authority, and the rampant hedonism that gave the decade its evocative nickname, "the Roaring Twenties." But one then-unsuspected effect still lingers: the damage that the "War on Alcohol" did to the right to privacy.

The use of the country's signals intelligence capabilities and cryptanalytic resources is one example of the lengths to which the government was willing to go to shut the liquor tap. But far more extensive and intrusive was the rise in federal wiretapping and eavesdropping that occurred during the thirteen years of Prohibition. Thanks in large part to the greater sensitivity to Fourth Amendment issues inspired by Anthony Comstock a generation earlier, it did not take long for such activities to be challenged in federal court.

Shortly after Prohibition began, federal law enforcement agents learned of a massive bootlegging operation based near Seattle, Washington. As many as ninety-one people were involved in the production and distribution of illegal liquor, which was manufactured on a ranch outside the city limits and stored in a number of underground caches in the area. The liquor was smuggled north across the Canadian border into British Columbia and south by boat down the coast of the Pacific Northwest. All told, the business generated a minimum of $2 million per year in total sales (approximately $25 million in today's dollars).

The ringleader for the bootlegging business was a man named Roy

Olmstead, who ran the operation from an office building in downtown Seattle. Olmstead's office had three different phone lines, which connected to outside lines through the building's basement. During the course of the investigation into the bootlegging conspiracy, federal agents tapped the office phone lines in the basement, as well as some of the phone lines of various conspirators on the poles near their homes. Over the course of several months, the agents transcribed a large quantity of information about the conspiracy from the wiretaps and used it to indict Olmstead and several others. Olmstead appealed his conviction, arguing that the use of wiretaps constituted an unreasonable search and seizure and thus violated his rights under the Fourth Amendment.

The U.S. Court of Appeals for the Ninth Circuit overruled Olmstead's constitutional challenge, holding that the language of the Fourth Amendment had never been interpreted to exclude the introduction of evidence obtained by mere listening. "The purpose of the amendment is to prevent the invasion of homes and offices and the seizure of incriminating evidence found therein," the court ruled. "Whatever may be said of the tapping of telephone wires as an unethical intrusion upon the privacy of persons who are suspected of crime, it is not an act which comes within the letter of the prohibition of constitutional provisions."

The U.S. Supreme Court agreed to hear Olmstead's appeal from the Ninth Circuit decision, but the result was the same. In an opinion written by chief justice (and former president) William Howard Taft, the Court rejected Olmstead's privacy argument on several grounds. First, Taft said, the language of the Fourth Amendment is limited to "material things"—a person, his house, his papers, or his personal effects. Since an individual's spoken words are not "material," he or she has no privacy interest in them as they travel over the phone wires.

Second, Taft noted, a spoken conversation does not enjoy the same level of protection guaranteed by Congress to private letters:

It is plainly within the words of the [Fourth] Amendment to say that the unlawful rifling by a government agent of a sealed letter is a search and seizure of the sender's papers or effects. The letter is a paper, an effect, and in the custody of a Government that forbids carriage except under its protection.

The United States takes no such care of telegraph or telephone messages as of mailed sealed letters. The Amendment
does not forbid what was done here. There was no searching.
There was no seizure. The evidence was secured by the use of
the sense of hearing and that only. There was no entry of the
houses or offices of the defendants.

If Olmstead's argument is upheld, Taft warned, it would effectively extend the provisions of the Fourth Amendment to the whole
world through the telephone wires reaching from Olmstead's office.
"The intervening wires," the chief justice said, "are not part of his
house or office any more than are the highways along which they are
stretched. The reasonable view is that one who installs in his house
a telephone instrument with connecting wires intends to project his
voice to those quite outside, and that the wires beyond his house and
messages while passing over them are not within the protection of the
Fourth Amendment."

Any remedy, the Court concluded, would have to come from Congress, which has the authority "to protect the secrecy of telephone
messages by making them, when intercepted, inadmissible in evidence in federal criminal trials." Absent such legislation, Taft said,
the Court has no obligation to exclude evidence, regardless of how
unethically it may have been collected (and the Court conceded that
the federal agents had broken Washington state law by listening to
Olmstead's conversations without a warrant). The Court's decision
established what can only be described as a low bar for governmental
conduct: "A standard which would forbid the reception of evidence if
obtained by other than nice ethical conduct by government officials
would make society suffer and give criminals greater immunity than
has been known heretofore."

Chief Justice Taft managed to get through his entire opinion without using the word "privacy," a remarkable omission
given the actions of the federal agents. But one of his fellow justices was uniquely qualified to correct the oversight: associate justice Louis Brandeis, who had coauthored "The Right to Privacy"
thirty-eight years earlier and who was then serving his twelfth year
on the high court. Along with his fellow justice Oliver Wendell
Holmes, Brandeis drafted a dissent that was, according to *Time* mag-

azine, "as vitriolic as any ever read into the records of the Supreme Court."

As an initial matter, Justice Brandeis dismissed the idea that the Court was incapable of applying the provisions of the Fourth and Fifth Amendments to new technology. "Clauses guaranteeing to the individual protection against specific abuses of power," Brandeis said, "must have a similar capacity of adaptation to a changing world." He noted that the Fourth Amendment was specifically designed to address abuses of privacy by the British government involving breaking and entering into colonial homes. The Fifth Amendment was intended to prevent self-incrimination by the only means then available to a hostile government: physical force and torture.

But over the decades, Brandeis pointed out, the ability of the government to obtain incriminating information directly from suspects had grown immensely. In a remarkably foresighted passage, he laid out a compelling case for an organic and adaptive interpretation of the Bill of Rights:

> Subtler and more far-reaching means of invading privacy have become available to the Government. Discovery and invention have made it possible for the Government, by means far more effective than stretching upon the rack, to obtain disclosure in court of what is whispered in the closet.
>
> Moreover, "in the application of a constitution, our contemplation cannot be only of what has been but of what may be." The progress of science in furnishing the Government with means of espionage is not likely to stop with wire-tapping. Ways may some day be developed by which the Government, without removing papers from secret drawers, can reproduce them in court, and by which it will be enabled to expose to a jury the most intimate occurrences of the home. Advances in the psychic and related sciences may bring means of exploring unexpressed beliefs, thoughts and emotions. "That places the liberty of every man in the hands of every petty officer" was said by James Otis of much lesser intrusions than these.

The purpose of the Fourth and Fifth Amendments, Brandeis argued, is not to punish the mere physical invasion of home and hearth (although hopefully that is discouraged as well); instead, the two amendments are intended to protect the "sacred right" of "personal security, personal liberty, and private property," all of which are supposed to be free of governmental invasion in the absence of an authorized intrusion.

What made the *Olmstead* case even more problematic, Brandeis noted, is that the wiretaps by the federal agents were a clear violation of Washington state law, which prohibited wiretaps. Although Brandeis conceded that the criminal acts were the responsibility of the individual officers and not the U.S. government, he said that the government accepted "moral responsibility" for them when it decided to introduce the evidence obtained by the wiretaps. The concluding paragraph of Brandeis's dissent is a condemnation not merely of the government's illegal tactics in 1925 but of numerous unconstitutional invasions since. The current Supreme Court would do well to heed his call:

> Decency, security and liberty alike demand that government officials shall be subjected to the same rules of conduct that are commands to the citizen. In a government of laws, existence of the government will be imperiled if it fails to observe the law scrupulously. Our Government is the potent, the omnipresent teacher. For good or for ill, it teaches the whole people by its example. Crime is contagious. If the Government becomes a lawbreaker, it breeds contempt for law; it invites every man to become a law unto himself; it invites anarchy. To declare that in the administration of the criminal law the end justifies the means—to declare that the Government may commit crimes in order to secure the conviction of a private criminal—would bring terrible retribution. Against that pernicious doctrine this Court should resolutely set its face.

Despite Brandeis's passionate dissent, as well as the fact that by this time a majority of states (twenty-eight) had laws prohibiting wiretaps, the Court's decision in *Olmstead* opened the floodgates for wiretapping by Prohibition agents. The outcry over the practice grew so intense, however, that the Expenditures Committee of the House of Representatives announced that it would hold hearings on the issue in January 1931.

During testimony before the House panel, U.S. attorney general William DeWitt Mitchell said that just four days after the hearings were announced, he had issued an order authorizing limited wiretapping by all agencies within the U.S. Justice Department. Mitchell said that the order was intended to eliminate inconsistencies within the department, since Prohibition agents would conduct wiretapping without penalty, while other federal agents faced discipline for doing so. He also argued that "wiretapping as a general practice ought not be permitted," but in light of the fact that lawbreakers use all available resources to commit crimes, he suggested that law enforcement "should not be handicapped by flat regulations." Attorney General Mitchell's defense of wiretapping outraged congressional opponents of Prohibition, known collectively as "wets"; but despite repeated efforts over several years, they were unable to muster the votes for an outright ban on the practice by federal agents.

While both Congress and the Supreme Court, even today, may fall short of Brandeis's vision of the proper relationship between government and citizen, his unwavering enunciation of the privacy rights inherent in telephone conversations was eventually vindicated—but not until the Court's decision in *Katz v. United States* (1967), which was handed down more than a quarter century after Brandeis's death. Nonetheless, the "Right to Privacy" article that he wrote with his friend Samuel Warren and his years of passionate and compelling reasoning on behalf of individual privacy while on the Court continue to set the loftiest aspirations for the constitutional protection of privacy in the United States.

6

THE PEEPING TOMS OF PUBLIC LIFE

No president in the modern media era has ever benefited more fully from the concept of personal privacy than Franklin Delano Roosevelt. Throughout his political career, and particularly during his twelve years as president, the members of the press corps helped Roosevelt keep secret two significant aspects of his private life: his challenging physical disability and the renewal of a long-suspended extramarital relationship.

The veiling of Roosevelt's disability was the more remarkable of the two omissions, since it required the tacit cooperation of so many people in both the press and the government over such a long period of time. In 1921, while vacationing at his family's summer house on Campobello Island in New Brunswick, Roosevelt contracted a serious and debilitating infection. While there is some debate in the medical community about whether Roosevelt contracted infantile paralysis (more commonly known as polio) or another neurodegenerative disease known as Guillain-Barré syndrome, the end result was the same: the tall, athletic, fiercely competitive tennis player and swimmer was permanently paralyzed from the waist down and lost the ability to walk.

Roosevelt's illness came in the midst of what was already a very promising political career for the New York Democrat. Beginning in 1913, he had served as assistant secretary for the navy for seven years under Woodrow Wilson, and in 1920 he ran unsuccessfully for vice president with Democratic presidential candidate James M. Cox. Despite the seriousness of the viral attack that he suffered the following year, neither he nor his formidable wife, Eleanor, were inclined to let his illness interfere with his political ambitions; while Franklin recuperated and taught himself to "walk" short distances by twisting his upper body to swing his iron-braced legs, Eleanor traveled to political meetings throughout the state of New York, assuring all who would listen that her husband would soon be back in the arena.

Roosevelt made a courageous return to public life in 1924, when he attended the Democratic National Convention in New York to nominate his longtime friend, New York governor Alfred E. Smith, for president. Over the course of the fifteen-day convention, Roosevelt rose repeatedly to speak on behalf of Smith, and the papers frequently noted that the proceedings were briefly delayed while Roosevelt, on crutches, was assisted to the podium. Roosevelt's fortitude, however, was unavailing; the Democrats, in the first of what would be a history of contentious conventions, deadlocked between Smith and Californian William McAdoo. In the end, a compromise candidate, John W. Davis, was sent off to ignominious defeat in the fall at the hands of the incumbent president, Calvin Coolidge.

From that point forward, there were only a handful of brief mentions in the press of Roosevelt's disability, all of which downplayed his daily struggles and regular use of a wheelchair. In July 1932, in the midst of his first campaign for president, the *New York Times* cheerfully reported that "today, Roosevelt is in good health. He has discarded his crutches and is able to walk with the use of canes and the steel braces which have been fitted to his lower limbs." In a *Washington Post* profile of the new president in November, the reporter noted, "Neither Roosevelt nor any member of his family has ever publicly acknowledged his condition to be an affliction." During the campaign, Roosevelt's son James pointed out that the presidency is, "after all, a desk job."

Throughout Roosevelt's time in the White House, according to Doris Kearns Goodwin in *No Ordinary Time: Franklin and Eleanor Roosevelt: The Home Front in World War II*, the American public had absolutely no idea of just how immobile he was. The press made no mention of the fact that Secret Service agents routinely lifted him in and out of automobiles, pushed his wheelchair, and gave him the support and momentum necessary to "walk" to a lectern or podium. And even as visual imagery became an increasingly important part of both media and politics, Goodwin notes, the deference to the president's privacy held:

There was an unspoken code of honor on the part of the White House photographers that the president was never to be photographed looking crippled. In twelve years, not a single picture was ever printed of the president in his wheelchair. No newsreel had ever captured him being lifted in or out of his car. If, as occasionally happened, one of the members of the press corps sought to violate the code by sneaking a picture of the president looking helpless, one of the older photographers would "accidentally" block the shot, or gently knock the camera to the ground.

The "veil of silence," as Goodwin describes it, was not limited to Roosevelt's physical condition. It extended as well to a series of secret meetings between Roosevelt and an old flame, Lucy Page Mercer Rutherfurd, that occurred toward the end of his life. In 1913, shortly after Roosevelt was appointed assistant secretary of the navy, Eleanor Roosevelt hired Lucy Mercer as a social secretary. Five years later, Eleanor discovered a packet of letters in her husband's luggage that revealed an intense affair with Mercer. The couple decided that a divorce was impractical for both financial and political reasons, but Roosevelt promised his wife that he would never see Mercer again.

That promise may have been broken as early as 1941, Goodwin speculates, when a "Mrs. Paul Johnson" visited the White House to have dinner with the president on several occasions. One of Roosevelt's Secret Service agents, William Simmons, later said that Lucy Rutherfurd (she had married Winthrop Rutherfurd in 1920) was given the code name "Mrs. Johnson." But certainly, the two old friends renewed their acquaintance in 1944, shortly after Winthrop Rutherfurd's death, when Lucy Mercer Rutherfurd was openly listed among the guests for an April 28 dinner at Hobcaw, financier Bernard Baruch's mansion in South Carolina (a dinner that Eleanor did not attend). Over the next nine months, with the active help of his daughter, Anna, Roosevelt and Rutherfurd met secretly more than a dozen times for private dinners and day trips.

Since these were nonofficial events, no formal guest lists or announcements were given to the press; but given how closely the activities of the president and the White House were monitored by reporters even then, it is highly unlikely that no members of the press were aware of Rutherfurd's visits with FDR. Nonetheless, the "veil of silence" persisted. According to Goodwin, Eleanor herself did not learn of Rutherfurd's surreptitious visits until the day of her husband's death in Warm Springs, Georgia; Rutherfurd, along with three other guests, was with the president when he suffered a cerebral hemorrhage and died. (Eleanor's discovery of her daughter's role in the deception caused a lengthy strain between the two women.) Public reports of Roosevelt's initial affair and renewed relationship with Rutherfurd were even slower to emerge; they did not begin to circulate until the 1960s, an era when the press began taking a much more critical look at public figures in general.

There is more than a little irony in the fact that Roosevelt had so much help in preserving the privacy of the personal aspects of his life. During the course of his twelve years in office, the actions taken and the programs started by his administration resulted in unprecedented intrusions on the privacy of average Americans. And thanks to a combination of unforeseen commercial and technological developments, the intrusions of the Roosevelt administration, seemingly minor at the time, helped make possible the endless and increasingly daunting privacy invasions that occur today.

THE BLACK COMMITTEE AND THE "DEATH SENTENCE" CLAUSE

The first great privacy controversy of the Roosevelt administration was not a direct result of the new president's policies, although it was a by-product of one of his most vigorous legislative battles. As part of his campaign to pull the United States out of the throes of the Great Depression, Roosevelt argued that the era's enormously powerful public utility holding companies should be strictly regulated or, ideally, eliminated altogether. (Then as today, a holding company was a shell corporation that owned or "held" one or more subsidiary businesses.) Roosevelt believed that the utility holding companies artificially raised the cost of water and electricity for consumers and represented an excessive and even dangerous concentration of financial resources and political influence.

According to a report prepared by the National Power Policy Committee in early 1935, just thirteen utility holding companies controlled 75 percent of the privately owned electric utility industry. Historian Arthur M. Schlesinger Jr., in his 1960 book *The Politics of Upheaval*, traced the development of holding companies to "bankers and speculators" and offered a description of their activities that foreshadowed contemporary economic problems: "The whole dizzy process of pyramiding [holding companies on top of operating companies] enabled an astute promoter to build a gaudy empire on a trivial investment of his own cash."

On February 6, 1935, Rep. Sam Rayburn of Texas introduced the Public Utility Holding Company Act, which called for the regulation and eventual elimination of the holding companies. In the Senate, Burton K. Wheeler of Montana introduced a similar bill, and the resulting legislation was often referred to as the Wheeler-Rayburn bill. The most controversial part of the bill was known as the "death sentence," a section giving the Securities and Exchange Commission the authority to dissolve any holding company unless, by January 1, 1940, the company could prove its economic benefit to utility customers.

The threat to disband holding companies set off a titanic legislative struggle in the spring of 1935, one that nearly ignited a constitutional crisis in the process. Within days of the introduction of the Wheeler-Rayburn bill, the public utility lobby began organizing a letter-writing and telegram campaign to protest what one utility president told shareholders was an "unnecessary and destructive measure."

The size of the power lobby offers some indication of why Roosevelt perceived holding companies to be such a threat. According to one contemporary count by the Scripps Howard News Service, utility lobbyists in Washington actually outnumbered the members of Congress (660 to 527). Tales of undue influence and outright bribery were rife. Within days, members of Congress were deluged with what Senator Wheeler described as a "flood of misleading propaganda." By mid-March, a spokesperson for utility investors said that at least half a million messages had been delivered to Congress. Senator Wheeler estimated that he himself was receiving several hundred letters and telegrams a day on the legislation, as were many other senators. However, the senator said, it was obvious that much of the correspondence was from a common source.

The aggressive campaign by the utilities sparked a sharp response from Roosevelt, who sent a sternly worded message to Congress protesting the fact that the utilities were using "investors' money to make the investor believe that the efforts of the Government to protect him are designed to defraud him." In response, a whispering campaign was launched against Roosevelt himself, suggesting that his passionate push to rein in the holding companies was a sign of incipient mental illness.

The campaign was the idea of E. P. Cramer, an advertising executive for the Thomas A. Edison Company, who later was summarily fired when he was identified as the source of the rumors. Nonetheless, the story gained a certain amount of traction in the media. *Time,* for instance, reported that Washington correspondents were being quizzed on Roosevelt's condition: "He had, according to the tales roaring through the country in whispers, grown mentally irresponsible. Hadn't you heard that during a Press conference he had a fit of laughter, had to be hurriedly wheeled out of the room?" Apart from sparking a rare mention of the president's disability in the press, the whispering campaign did little more than give Roosevelt some amusement.

Despite the propaganda and letter-writing campaigns, the Wheeler-Rayburn bill (with the "death sentence" included) narrowly passed the Senate on June 11, 1935. The battle then shifted to the House; with Democrats outnumbering Republicans by a remarkable 322–103, Roosevelt expected the bill to be easily approved. But the publicity campaign of the power lobby was having an effect. Although the White House lobbied the House strongly, the "death sentence" provision was struck down on July 1 by a vote of 216–146. While the bill that was later passed by Congress made significant improvements in the regulation of holding companies, including the first registration requirement for federal lobbyists, it was well short of what Roosevelt and his administration had been seeking.

In the wake of the stinging defeat of the "death sentence" clause, investigations of utility lobbying practices and whether they wielded undue influence were launched by both the Senate and the House. The lead figure in the drama was Senator Hugo Black, a Democrat from Alabama and an attorney with a fondness for aggressive investigations and sharp questions. But few anticipated just how aggressively Black would go after the utility lobbyists. Armed with an initial budget of $50,000, Black and the Senate Lobby Committee (which most people quickly referred to as the "Black Committee") leaped into action. Even before Black opened the first public hearing on July 12, 1935, he sent investigators to raid the office of Philip H. Gadsden, chair of the Committee of Public Utility Executives. When Gadsden arrived at work that morning, he found federal agents reviewing his files and correspondence; the agents told him he was expected on the Hill and delivered him for a day of intensive questioning by Senator Black.

The revelations that spilled out of Black's investigation were startling: the power lobby had not only spent an enormous amount of money fighting the Wheeler-Rayburn bill (at least $1 million, and perhaps as much as $5 million) but also had engaged in the systematic forgery of telegrams and letters that purported to oppose the legislation. Rep. D. J. Driscoll (D-Pa.), for instance, reported receiving more than one thousand identical telegrams, with the names of senders apparently selected in alphabetical order from the phone book in Warren, Pennsylvania. Black's antagonism toward the power lobby was only heightened when it was discovered that a Western Union employee, at the direction of a power utility employee, had burned the originals of the telegrams sent to Driscoll. The normal practice, the manager of the Western Union branch told the Black Committee, was for originals to be held for a year.

Following the discovery that fake telegrams had been sent and then burned, the scope of Black's inquiry rapidly expanded, and the impact on privacy was profound. At the request of the Senate committee, the Federal Communications Commission (FCC), which had oversight authority over the telegraph companies, demanded that each company provide information under oath about the number of forged telegrams sent to influence legislators on the Wheeler-Rayburn bill. More chillingly, Senator Lewis B. Schwellenbach (D-Wash.), a member of the Lobby Committee and an ardent supporter of the New Deal, suggested that the committee should expand its inquiry into the tax returns of the nation's steel companies, which were opposed to tax code changes proposed by Roosevelt.

Roosevelt took that idea one step further, issuing an executive order on July 31, 1935, that instructed the secretary of the treasury to turn over to the committee all "income, excess profits, and capital tax returns . . . for the purpose of, and to the extent necessary in the investigation of lobbying activities in connection with the so-called

'Holding Company Bill,' or any other matter or proposal affecting legislation." Senator Black wasted little time obtaining the tax returns of the central figures and companies in the lobbying inquiry, and he used the financial information extensively in questioning witnesses.

Even greater privacy intrusions were in the works. In January 1936, with a national election looming in the fall, a group of conservative Democrats called the American Liberty League invited former New York governor Alfred E. Smith to give a speech. Roosevelt's once-close friend gave a rousing denunciation of the New Deal, warning his fellow Democrats that they could either "take on the mantle of hypocrisy or take a walk, and we will probably do the latter."

Just three days later, the Senate Lobby Committee announced that it was launching a new phase of its investigation to determine whether any "dummy donors" had contributed to the American Liberty League and a variety of other groups opposed to the New Deal in general and the Wheeler-Rayburn bill in particular. A questionnaire was prepared by committee counsel and sent to several hundred individuals and organizations, ordering them to report "under oath" as to whether they had contributed to the groups in question and whether those contributions had been reimbursed by someone else. Committee members dismissed the idea that the questionnaire was sent out in response to Smith's anti–New Deal speech, but the timing was certainly suspicious.

Public outrage and opposition to Black's methods began building in early March of that year, when various corporate law firms discovered that the Senate Lobby Committee was in possession of confidential telegrams sent to and from their clients. Western Union conceded that the bulk of the telegrams had been turned over the previous year, when Congress was in recess. After having responded without objection to more than one thousand subpoenas from Black's committee, Western Union announced that it would henceforth inform its customers that copies of their telegrams had been requested. Upon receiving notice that his firm's telegrams were among the subpoenaed documents, Chicago attorney Silas Strawn obtained a preliminary injunction in federal court blocking the committee's request.

"It is alarming, indeed," Strawn said at the time, "that we are required to invoke the protection of a court order in order to safeguard our constitutional rights and those of our clients. To acquiesce in the invasion of such rights so clearly defined and so long established is to invite tyranny and encourage despotism."

The invasion was much greater than Strawn realized. The very next day, it was learned that the FCC, without even the issuance of a subpoena by the Senate Lobby Committee, had helped the committee copy over thirteen thousand telegrams from various telegraph companies, including every telegram sent to and from the American Liberty League. The league's president, Jouett Shouse, angrily denounced the actions of the FCC and the Lobby Committee, and told listeners of an NBC radio broadcast that every Washington, D.C., telegram between February 1 and December 31, 1935, had been read by federal investigators. "Now get that: I do not mean telegrams about legislation or public business," he said. "I mean that if you, wherever you live, sent any telegram, however private, out of Washington to any one in the world, on any subject, your telegram has been subject to the prying eyes of the representatives of the New Inquisition."

Throughout the Lobby Committee's work, the press had largely been silent about the privacy invasions that were occurring. But the news that the committee had engaged in the wholesale collection of private telegrams, without any semblance of legal process, horrified many observers. Arthur Krock, the esteemed Washington bureau chief for the *New York Times*, speculated that the telegram seizures would become a campaign issue later that fall. "Congressional committees bent on inquiry," Krock wrote, "have generally revealed total disregard of the rules of evidence and rights of privacy."

Three weeks later, a *Times* editorial under the heading "The Right to Privacy" quoted the opening lines of the Fourth Amendment and then stated firmly: "If that amendment is more than a meaningless set of words, if it is directed against anything at all, it is directed against precisely the kind of activities in which the Black lobby committee has recently been engaged."

After citing various cases condemning governmental "fishing expeditions" for potential evidence, the editorial presented its conclusion:

That the seizures ordered by the Black committee were so sweeping as to constitute a mere fishing expedition is so plain that it does not need to be argued. If such inquisitorial tactics were to be freely permitted the right of privacy would disappear, and critics of this or any future Administration would be exposed to ruthless reprisals. If telegrams that a Senator does not like can be seized and published without restraint, even if they advocate or involve nothing illegal, then there is no reason why private letters cannot be seized out of the mails.

This is the issue that is presented by the methods of Senator Black and his committee. It cannot be confused or obscured by denunciations of public utility companies or of a particular publisher. The primary question in relation to the Black committee is whether a plain defiance of the intent of the Constitution is to be allowed to pass unchallenged.

A month later, the *Times* was joined by the other members of the American Newspaper Publishers Association, which voted unanimously at its annual meeting that both civil damages and criminal charges should be sought against "all involved in the odious affair."

Black was both defiant and unrepentant. Accusing his detractors of conducting "a malicious campaign of misrepresentation," Black argued that his committee was operating in the same manner as every congressional investigative committee since 1792. That was the year in which the House authorized a special committee to investigate a significant military loss in the campaign against Native Americans, giving its members the power to "call for such persons, papers, and records, as may be necessary to assist their inquiries."

"If the time ever comes," Black warned, "when the courts issued injunctions to prevent the production of papers, the power of the Senate to conduct investigations is completely lost."

Much to the dismay of Black's opponents, his view prevailed. Although the field work of the Lobby Committee wrapped up at the end of March, a lawsuit filed by publisher William Randolph Hearst against Hugo Black and the committee continued throughout the summer. Hearst alleged that the committee's use of the FCC to obtain and read telegrams between him and his employees that had nothing to do with the subject of the inquiry was a violation of his First, Fourth, and Fifth Amendment rights.

The U.S. Court of Appeals for the District of Columbia agreed that Hearst's rights and those of his employees had been violated by Black's high-handed methods:

The property right in private telegrams is in no material respect different from the property right in letters and other writings; nor is there any good reason why the right of privacy in the one should be any greater than in the other. Telegraph messages do not lose their privacy and become public property when the sender communicates them confidentially to the telegraph company.

The court went on to say that the "dragnet seizure" conducted by the Black Committee was the type of activity that a federal court, acting in equity, could order stopped, provided that it was alerted to the seizure beforehand or even while it was happening. But Hearst's claim foundered on a shoal that has sunk innumerable privacy claims since: the reluctance of courts to act to protect information that is no longer private. In this case, the court said, its ability to act was limited further by the need to respect constitutional separation of powers: "If a court could say to the Congress that it could use or could not use information in its possession" regardless of how it obtained such information, "the independence of the Legislature would be destroyed and the constitutional separation of the powers of government invaded."

"NOT FOR IDENTIFICATION PURPOSES"

The appeals court decision was a warning shot across the bow to Congress on its investigative tactics. But as destructive and alarming as the inquiries of the Black Committee were, their impact on personal privacy was relatively short-lived; once the committee ceased operating, telegrams regained their tenuous privacy. If anything, the committee's excesses made people more sensitive, at least temporarily, to the potential abuses of legislative committees. Although it was not widely appreciated at the time, far more significant privacy invasions would result from what is perhaps Roosevelt's most famous policy initiative.

On August 14, 1935, after considerable congressional debate, Roosevelt signed into law the Social Security Act, which provided for the payment of retirement, unemployment, and death benefits to American workers. Since the funds for the system were based on a payroll tax divided between employees and their employers, it immediately became apparent that a system was needed to distinguish between the wages earned by different people with the same name and to track each individual's earnings accurately throughout his or her lifetime.

The legislation that established the Social Security program authorized the creation of a system to ensure an accurate record of earnings for each employee, but did not specify a particular method for doing so. In December 1935, the Associated Press reported that the government was considering a system to assign a number to each of the nation's 28 million employees. "With thousands of John Smiths in the country," the article noted, "it was explained that the New York John Smith might try to pass himself off as the Chicago Smith and receive greater benefits the Chicagoan was entitled to, because he had worked longer and contributed more."

Just under a year later, on November 5, 1936, the Treasury Department adopted a new regulation, known as "Treasury Decision 4704," which ordered that a Social Security number be issued for each employee covered by the government program. (A separate system of employer identification numbers was created to distinguish among the country's similarly named businesses.) Unwittingly, Treasury Decision 4704 set in motion a long series of events that have radically reshaped personal privacy in America: for the first time, each person in the United States had a unique identification number.

Roosevelt's proposal to provide old age and disability protection was controversial in its own right, but the idea of issuing each worker a unique number was particularly disturbing to many. Republicans seized on the numbering scheme as a potentially powerful issue in the 1936 presidential campaign; in the week before the national election, the Republican National Committee (RNC) released an advertisement depicting a mock-up of the Social Security registration form and a photo of a man wearing a metal dog tag with a Social Security number. The advertisement was published nationwide in the Hearst newspaper chain, which at the order of its owner was openly hostile to both President Roosevelt and his New Deal.

According to the RNC, the federal government was planning to require each employee to reveal a wide variety of personal information, including "whether the worker had been divorced, his church membership, union affiliation, physical defects, reasons for leaving other position, references other than former employer, registration number and employer." In a speech in Boston the night before the advertisement ran, RNC chair John D. M. Hamilton held up a metal tag and said models had been prepared and submitted to the new Social Security Board. "Will fingerprinting be next?" he demanded.

One small piece of Hamilton's charge was accurate: an overeager company, the Addressograph-Multigraph Corporation, actually had prepared a sample Social Security dog tag and sent it to the commissioner of the Social Security Board, Arthur J. Altmeyer. Commissioner Altmeyer immediately rejected the idea, but kept the prototype as an amusing souvenir until his retirement, when he donated it to the Social Security Administration (the successor organization to the original Social Security Board).

The other RNC charges were dismissed as "fabrications" by Anna M. Rosenberg, a regional director of the Social Security Board. Rosenberg, who was one of the people involved in drafting the registration forms, stated categorically that "the administration of the Social Security Act requires information concerning only a few simple questions such as the name, age, address, and present place of employment of the applicant." She described the form created by the RNC as a "palpable and misleading forgery . . . designed to misrepresent the board's intentions and to deceive the public by deliberate falsehood."

The RNC's efforts to scare up opposition to the Social Security Act (and by extension, Roosevelt) on privacy grounds were a complete failure, as was much of the party's 1936 election strategy. Roosevelt and his vice president, John N. Garner, won a landslide victory, carrying all but two states (Maine and Vermont) and capturing nearly 61 percent of the popular vote. The Social Security program went into effect the following year, and has proven to be one of Roosevelt's most enduring legacies.

As the government rushed to accomplish the phenomenal task of registering America's workers in the Social Security system, privacy concerns did not entirely disappear. Hundreds of women, for instance, called the Social Security Board during the registration period to ask worriedly whether their employers would be told their age or marital status, information that women at the time often had to falsify in order to get or keep a job. Regional Director Rosenberg assured each caller that the Social Security Board would not release a worker's information to his or her employer and that if privacy was a concern, the caller should send her registration card directly to Washington rather than handing it to her boss.

Gender issues were not the only source of privacy worries. Labor leaders, who played a significant role in helping the government with the launch of the Social Security program, feared that employers would be able to use Social Security numbers to permanently blackball employees who had been fired. Again, Rosenberg assured unions that the Social Security Board would work to prevent businesses from misusing Social Security numbers, and she reminded workers that they could apply for a new Social Security number at any time. Employees were also reassured that they were not required to carry their cards at all times; to the contrary, they were encouraged to keep the cards safe in an envelope at home so that they would not tear or wear out.

By February 8, 1937, more than 22 million workers had registered for retirement benefit accounts. The Social Security Board stored each application numerically as it came in, and then created a punch card for each worker, with a ledger to record the annual earnings on which retirement benefits were calculated. The sheer volume of paper and storage required to handle what many described as "the largest bookkeeping operation in the world" posed a serious logistical challenge. After calculating the weight of the records and the space needed to process them, the Social Security Board determined that there was no building in Washington large enough or strong enough for the new agency. But a suitable building was found in Baltimore—the Candler Building, a former Coca-Cola bottling factory located on the city's harbor. The building's large open spaces and sturdy construction comfortably housed the Social Security agency until it moved to its current headquarters in Woodlawn, Maryland, in 1960.

As the first Social Security checks were sent out in 1938, a new problem arose: identity theft. The current plague of identity theft stems from a combination of the inherent limitations of the Social Security number as an identification tool and the vast number of uses to which the number has been put over the years. The true scope of the problem has become evident only in the last decade or so; but even when the Social Security number was introduced, the federal government warned that its own system for assigning Social Security numbers and distributing the associated cards was inherently insecure. Not only was it relatively easy to falsify an application for a new number, but the vast number of Social Security checks and cards mailed each month turned mailbox and identity theft into flourishing criminal enterprises.

In 1943, Secret Service chief Frank J. Wilson warned that "anyone can get a Social Security card in somebody's name in just a few minutes. Social Security cards are by no means reliable identification." His comments came in the wake of the arrest of five teens for looting mailboxes for Social Security checks, which they cashed using Social Security cards as identification. In an effort to cut down on check-cashing fraud, the Secret Service launched a nationwide campaign to urge merchants to "Know Your Endorser." In addition, as a reminder to individuals and businesses of the Social Security card's inherently insecure nature, the Social Security Board began printing "For Social Security Purposes—Not for Identification" in bold letters at the bottom of each card.

It does not appear that either measure was a tremendous success. By the end of 1946, postal authorities estimated that the use of Social Security cards to cash stolen checks was one of the leading forms of fraud in the United States. Peter Kasius, a regional director for the newly renamed Social Security Administration (SSA), told the *New York Times* that "the Social Security account number card is worthless as a means of identification for check-cashing purposes."

Kasius added that the SSA had issued repeated warnings to business and banks that the card should not be used as identification, and he noted that the agency did not have the manpower to investigate the actual identity of applicants. The *Times* article, which reported that mailbox thefts had risen 100 percent over the previous twelve months, also detailed a number of cases in which thieves had successfully stolen and cashed thousands of dollars' worth of government checks.

It was technology that eventually began to turn the tide in the battle against Social Security card fraud. In September 1959, the *Washington Post* reported that a woman had been arrested for cashing a check using a false Social Security card. The fraudulent transaction was photographed by the merchant using a new device, a dual-lens camera called the Regiscope: one lens photographed the check casher, while the other photographed the check and the Social Security card.

(The Regiscope company is still in operation and markets an updated version of the technology today.) When the check was returned as a forgery, the merchant contacted the Secret Service, which then used the Regiscope photographs to locate the woman.

Although the Regiscope provided a solution to one problem— fraudulent check-cashing—it heralded another: a growing interest in photographic and even video identification technologies that would grow steadily more intrusive.

THE 1940 CENSUS: "NONE OF THEIR DAMNED BUSINESS"

The third major privacy battle during the Roosevelt administration concerned the 1940 census, which came under particularly harsh attack from those who felt it was too inquisitive. Leading the charge was Senator Charles William Tobey, a sharp-tongued Republican from Temple, New Hampshire. Despite having been elected to the Senate just two years earlier, Tobey wasted little time in becoming the most persistent and outspoken foe of the nation's sixteenth census.

His campaign against the census began with the release of a letter sent on February 1, 1940, to Harry Hopkins, who as secretary of commerce was responsible for overseeing the upcoming census. One of Tobey's complaints was that politically appointed census takers would be asking for sensitive income information and might pass it on to "their political bosses." Hopkins flatly rejected Tobey's concerns, writing that "your fears about the invasion of people's privacy and misuse of confidential information by the census-takers will hold up only so long as you labor under the delusion that this activity is something new." Hopkins went on to point out that many of the questions planned for the 1940 census had first been asked sixty, seventy, or even ninety years earlier.

A few days later, President Roosevelt sought to calm fears over the census (and respond to Tobey's charges) by issuing a proclamation calling for the cooperation of every American in answering the census questions. The president's reassurances illustrate the concerns that were circulating at the time:

> The sole purpose of the census is to secure general statistical information regarding the population, business activities and resources of the country, and replies are required from individu-

als only to enable the compilation of such general statistics. No person can be harmed in any way by furnishing the information required. The census has nothing to do with taxation, with military or jury service, with the compulsion of school attendance, with the regulation of immigration or with the enforcement of any national, State, or local law or ordinance. There need be no fear that any disclosure will be made regarding any individual or his affairs.

But Roosevelt's proclamation did little to satisfy angry legislators. House Republicans, who described the census as a "menace to the liberties of America," seized on the issue as an opportunity to embarrass Roosevelt, who at the time was considering the possibility of running for an unprecedented third term as president. The Republicans even engineered a vote by the House to withhold the $5 million needed to conduct the census. During the debate, Rep. Dewey Jackson Short (R-Mo.), an ardent Roosevelt foe, shouted on the floor: "What difference does it make to Harry Hopkins whether the bathtub in my home is used by me exclusively or shared by a friend? My constituents will tell the questioners very plainly that it's none of their damned business!"

In an editorial the following morning, the *Washington Post* offered a prescient warning: "As the Government requires more and more information regarding the lives of its citizens, it should be increasingly scrupulous in the methods employed to collect that data." The *Post* agreed that the use of political appointees as census takers was "particularly unfortunate."

Less than a month before the scheduled start of the census, Senator Tobey sponsored a resolution ordering the Census Bureau to drop any questions about wages or earnings from its questionnaire. Thanks to a series of radio speeches by Tobey criticizing the intrusiveness of the census and the proposed penalties for refusal to answer, members of Congress were receiving large amounts of negative mail on the subject. Given the fact that Germany had launched World War II by invading Poland the previous September, many both in and out of Congress saw the specter of totalitarianism in the proposed census. As Senator Warren Austin (R-Vt.) put it, "In view of the present condition of the world and in our country it is very important that we satisfy our people we are not on the road to tyranny and that we do not want to take away their rights of privacy." Rep. William Jennings Miller (R-Conn.) was even more blunt, warning that it would be unwise to ask intrusive questions during a period of "disturbed world conditions and loose talk about a dictatorship in the United States."

In testimony before the Senate Commerce subcommittee considering Tobey's resolution, three influential women warned the committee that housewives across the country were irate about the prospect of answering the census takers' intrusive questions. All three—Catherine Curtis, national director of Women Investors in America; Mrs. William C. Uhrhan, of Buffalo, New York; and Mrs. Norman Nock, a representative of the American War Mothers—told the committee that legislation would be needed to enlarge the nation's jails if the census went forward as planned.

The threat that housewives might refuse *en masse* to answer census questions was particularly disturbing to the Census Bureau, which anticipated that many, if not most, of the people answering the door during the day would be women. Census Bureau officials assured the public that the information would be kept confidential and was being collected only to provide government officials with the first "complete picture of the extent and effect of unemployment and underemployment" in the United States. As the *Alton Evening Telegraph* noted during the height of the controversy, the challenged questions were included in the census questionnaire not at Roosevelt's urging but at the request of major business and nonprofit organizations, including the Rockefeller Foundation; Sears, Roebuck and Company; the Metropolitan Life Insurance Company; and the National Association of Manufacturers.

Nonetheless, Tobey continued his outraged campaign against the census, claiming that the push for income information was leading to the formation of "anti-snooping" clubs around the country. He warned that the government was seeking information about income to increase taxes and asking about physical capabilities to gather information for war mobilization efforts. And remarkably, given the state of the law at the time, Tobey became one of the first lawmakers to suggest that there is a constitutional right to privacy.

"If you stand upon your constitutional rights," Tobey said in a nationally broadcast radio address, "and refuse to answer the questions which violate your right of privacy as guaranteed under the Constitution, you will have plenty of company. Thousands have already expressed their determination to resist these questions. Congressman [Daniel] Reed of New York and Senator [Bennett] Clark of Missouri have both publicly expressed their intention to refuse to answer such questions, and I shall do the same."

A few days later, the Senate Commerce Committee narrowly approved Tobey's resolution calling for a condemnation of the income questions. Both the Committee's vote and Tobey's radio broadcasts opposing the census elicited a sharp response from Secretary Hopkins, who described the New Hampshire senator's crusade as "a menace to the processes of self-government."

"The spectacle of a United States Senator calling for resistance to the authority of the Government," Hopkins said, "appealing for civil disobedience, urging an informational sit-down strike against the Government is un-American." He pointed out that the census was being conducted pursuant to an act of Congress and that the vote of the Commerce Committee was merely advisory, since it could not amend or overturn a previously adopted law. He also noted that a census is required by the Constitution and reminded Tobey of his senatorial oath to uphold that document.

Hopkins was not the only one to think that Tobey had gone too far in calling for civil disobedience. The editorial board of the *Washington Post*, for instance, said that Tobey could have launched a very compelling attack against the census without challenging the good faith of the Census Bureau.

"Unfortunately," the *Post* continued, "the Senator has chosen to incite people to refuse to answer by standing upon an assumed 'constitutional' right to privacy. In thus arousing public suspicion and resentment, he has done irreparable damage. For the census-takers can succeed in their work only if they have the willing cooperation of those interrogated."

Despite muttered threats by Tobey that he would file lawsuits to delay the start of the census, the national enumeration was launched without a noticeable hitch on April 2, 1940. "Senator Tobey has fought a losing fight," the *Washington Post* observed the following day. "He has failed to convince either the Census Bureau or the Senate that any question should be eliminated. The sportsmanlike course for him to take is to recognize his defeat and cooperate to make the census a success." The *Post* also called on every family to do the same, arguing that "there is every reason to believe that such cooperation can be freely given without fear that confidential information will be exposed to promiscuous examination or put to improper use."

The threatened housewife rebellion failed to materialize, and the census proceeded smoothly through the late spring and summer of 1940. Census Bureau officials reported that there were few, if any, objections; in fact, the biggest problem was that people kept asking the census takers in to chat or have a bite to eat. As the data collected by the census takers flowed into Washington, the bureau increased its staff to a peak of seven thousand people. After a massive computational effort, it reported in late November that the population of the United States was 150,362,326, representing an 8.6 percent increase since the 1930 census.

Given the overall smooth operation of the 1940 census, it is hard to say that the American people as a whole shared the privacy concerns raised by Senator Tobey and other congressional Republicans. The more reasonable inference, given the politics of the time, was that Republicans were less concerned about personal privacy than they were about Roosevelt serving a third term. But it made little sense for the Republicans, typically viewed as the "law and order" party, to advocate civil disobedience, particularly given the extent to which cooperation with the census was seen as a civic duty.

HOOVER AND THE FBI DEFEND WIRETAPPING

One significant privacy intrusion that Congress did try to stop in the 1930s was the practice of wiretapping private conversations. Following the 1927 *Olmstead* decision (discussed in Chapter Five), which upheld the legality of wiretapping, the rise of surveillance by federal agents in Washington grew so pronounced that one writer compared it to the work of the Soviet Union's much-feared state police.

"Make no mistake about it," *Washington Post* reporter Douglas Warrenfels said, "Uncle Sam now has a mailed fist and he isn't pulling his punches. . . . It is an open secret around town that investigators almost invariably pry into the personal affairs and background of aspirants for posts of public trust. One recent occupant of the White House used to pigeon-hole automatically all applications of persons found to be disciples of John Barleycorn."

One of the rising stars of the new surveillance regime was J. Edgar Hoover, who headed a team of four hundred agents for the Justice Department's Bureau of Investigation. Although a superb organizer and institutional leader, Hoover was also deeply worried, to the point of outright paranoia, about the threat of subversive elements in American society. In ways both large and small, he used the growing power of the bureau to gather and collect information about potential threats from enemies within and without.

Born on New Year's Day, 1895, in Washington, D.C., Hoover worked at the Library of Congress following graduation from high school. There is a much-repeated but apparently undocumented story that during his time at the library, Hoover studied the crime-fighting methods of Anthony Comstock, whom he allegedly admired for his long, persistent struggles against pornographers, abortionists, and other purveyors of vice. It is not implausible that Hoover would have known of Comstock, whose activities were widely publicized right up to his death in September 1915. Moreover, Hoover was taking night classes at George Washington University with a concentration in law, so Comstock would have been a logical figure to study. But while the precise extent of the old vice hunter's influence on the young Hoover is unknown, the two shared similar attitudes toward muscular law enforcement and a willingness to dispense with constitutional niceties in the exercise of their perceived duties.

Hoover's own federal law enforcement career was marked by rapid advancement. In 1919, just two years after joining the Justice Department, Hoover was appointed head of the General Intelligence Division (GID). At the instruction of attorney general A. Mitchell Palmer, Hoover and the GID conducted a series of infamous raids on people (mostly resident aliens) who were viewed as political dissidents and potential terrorist threats. Hoover's campaign against subversives earned him a promotion to the Bureau of Investigation. He was appointed as the bureau's sixth director by President Calvin Coolidge on May 10, 1924, and held the position until his death on May 2, 1972.

Throughout his long career, Hoover was an ardent supporter of surveillance technology, which frequently brought him in conflict with Congress and the Supreme Court. In 1927, Congress passed the Radio Act in an effort to organize and more efficiently allocate radio broadcast frequencies. But the supervisory body created by the act, the Federal Radio Commission (FRC), proved too ineffectual to monitor the burgeoning industry. In an effort to stay ahead of the technological curve, Congress passed the Communications Act of 1934, which transformed the FRC into the Federal Communications Commission.

Congress also used the Communications Act as an opportunity to respond to the Supreme Court's *Olmstead* decision, in which the Court had ruled that a wiretap by federal agents did not constitute a "search" within the meaning of the Fourth Amendment. Section 605 of the Communications Act specifically provided that "no person not being authorized by the sender shall intercept any radio communication and divulge or publish the existence, contents, substance, purport, effect, or meaning of such intercepted communication to any person."

In two separate decisions, the Supreme Court held that Section 605 barred federal courts from permitting the introduction of evidence obtained by federal agents through wiretaps. The first was *Nardone v. United States* (1937), in which the Court ruled 7–2 that by adopting Section 605, Congress had intended to block the practice of federal wiretapping, regardless of its benefit for law enforcement.

"Congress may have thought it less important," the Court said, "that some offenders should go unwhipped of justice than that officers should resort to methods deemed inconsistent with ethical standards and destructive of personal liberty. The same considerations may well have moved the Congress to adopt [Section] 605 as evoked the guaranty against practices and procedures violative of privacy, embodied in the Fourth and Fifth Amendments of the Constitution."

Joining the majority in the *Nardone* decision was the newest associate justice, Hugo Black, the former Alabama senator known for his own somewhat cavalier attitudes toward privacy as head of the Black Committee. Black had been nominated to the Court by President Roosevelt earlier that year in appreciation for his staunch work in the Senate on behalf of the administration and the New Deal.

Two years after the *Nardone* case, the Court considered the question of whether Section 605 barred federal wiretapping of intrastate calls as well. This time, in *Weiss v. United States*, the decision was unanimous that by adopting the Communications Act, Congress intended to prohibit the unauthorized interception of telephone conversations.

Despite the rulings of the Supreme Court, Hoover remained a staunch defender of wiretapping. Whatever wiretapping had been done by federal agents, Hoover said in March 1940, occurred "only in extraordinary situations and in an entirely legal manner." Nonetheless, a few days later Hoover recommended to U.S. attorney general Robert H. Jackson that the Department of Justice ban the practice altogether. Jackson agreed and issued a statement announcing the change: "Notwithstanding it will handicap the FBI in solving some extremely serious cases, it is believed by the Attorney General and Director of the Bureau that the discredit and suspicion of the law enforcing branch which arises from the occasional use of wire tapping more than offsets the good which is likely to come of it."

While the editors of the *Washington Post* may not have agreed with Senator Tobey that the Constitution contains a "right to privacy," that's not to say that the paper did not support the concept of privacy in general. In an editorial eight days after Jackson's statement titled "No More Wire-Tapping," the *Post*'s editorial board praised Attorney General Jackson for the change in the Justice Department's policy. At the same time, however, the *Post* (and others) criticized the attorney general for his slowness in responding to the Supreme Court's decisions, particularly in *Weiss*, which had been handed down over four months earlier. "The Court's decision," the paper said, "should have been followed by prompt abandonment of wire-tapping by the FBI, without waiting for agitation by Congress."

Neither Jackson's statement nor the Court's decisions brought an end to the wiretapping debate. In the years to come, as the United States entered another world war and then settled into the simmering hostility and surveillance race that marked the Cold War with the Soviet Union, the pressure on federal agencies (particularly the FBI) to conduct wiretapping would only intensify.

Even in the spring of 1940, as the *Post* pointed out, Attorney General Jackson and others were urging Congress to specifically authorize wiretapping in cases "of kidnapping, extortion, and racketeering, which involve special use of the telephone." But the problem, as the *Post* editors sagely observed, is that "if encroachment upon the privacy of wire messages is permitted for one purpose, it is likely to be used for other purposes, as Justice Black once demonstrated." Some, at least, had not forgotten the privacy depredations of the Black Committee.

Indeed, much of the remaining story of the right to privacy is about the use of information for purposes other than originally intended, whether collected by federal agents or by corporations. Over the course of the next decade, an unforeseen mix of government-issued numbers, bank-issued credit, and computers would intensify the erosion of each person's ability to control the spread of information about his or her life.

7

THE GREAT RED THREATS TO PRIVACY

Credit Cards and Communism

The 1950s were a bad decade for personal privacy. In the years following the end of World War II, Americans were caught up in the heady emotions of global victory and the nation's confirmed status as one of the world's leading superpowers. After years of sacrifice, there was a hunger to live the American dream for which the war had been fought—and the nation's burgeoning class of advertising executives (the men in the gray flannel suits) were happy to describe exactly how that dream should be furnished and equipped, from the snappiest car models to the latest labor-saving devices. At the same time, however, the United States felt threatened by the rise of Communism; increasingly, protecting the American dream was interpreted as using whatever means were necessary to identify and root out Communist sympathizers in American society. Personal privacy was frequently the first casualty in the search for subversive "Reds" in government, the military, and the arts.

Two great social waves also gathered steam after victory in Europe: the baby boom, the single largest population bubble in American history, and the credit boom, a surge in deferred payment for purchases that may only now be cresting. The baby boom quietly slowed at the end of the 1950s (although most demographers mark the formal endpoint in 1963 or 1964). The credit boom, however, grew steadily from the early 1950s and has never looked back. Over the decades, the combined use of the Social Security number as the primary consumer identifier and the staggeringly large national credit card system caused a significant, albeit largely undetected, erosion of consumer privacy.

The development of the credit card actually predates the Social

Security number by more than two decades. Although there is a long history of individual businesses tracking store credit for trusted customers, the telegraph company Western Union was the first multistate business to create a credit system for its customers. The company issued stamped steel cards, known as "metal money," that allowed customers to defer payments for telegrams, interest free, at any Western Union office. A decade later, in 1924, the General Petroleum Corporation introduced its own metal money to allow its employees to pay for gasoline and other automotive services. The idea proved so popular that the company extended it to preferred customers and eventually to the general public. The concept might have gained more traction had the Great Depression not intervened.

By the late 1930s, as the country was slowly crawling its way out of the Depression, various businesses began issuing single-purpose credit cards. For instance, in 1939 AT&T rolled out the Bell System Credit Card, which was essentially a calling card for business travelers. Rather than fishing in a pocket or purse for change, a traveler could simply read off a string of numbers and have the cost of the call put on his or her monthly bill. A wide variety of other businesses— department stores, railroad lines, delivery companies, and so on— issued their own cards. But since each card could be used only in the business that issued it, the impact of these types of cards on personal privacy was not much greater than the older system of a scrawled sheet of paper listing a month's purchases in the village store. The one significant difference was that with the rise of multistate corporations, information about a person's credit and purchasing activity was beginning to travel far outside his or her local community.

The nascent growth of the credit industry came to a grinding halt once again just before World War II, when the Federal Reserve Board announced new regulations governing consumer credit. Purchasers were required to pay off credit charges for goods and services within forty days following the last day of the month in which the item was purchased. For installment purchases, the board raised the down payment to one-third of the total price for the good or service and ordered consumers to pay off the balance within twelve months.

The credit industry began to return to normal after December 1, 1946, when those restrictions were eased. With the war over, both government and industry were eager to convert the nation's excess military manufacturing capacity to the production of consumer goods. There was a general recognition that a loosening of credit rules would help jump-start the general economy, in turn helping to create much-needed jobs for America's returning military forces.

THE INVENTION OF CARDBOARD MONEY

The true start of the modern credit card industry can be traced to a moment of forgetfulness. In December 1949, commercial credit specialist Frank X. McNamara had just finished a pleasant meal in a midtown Manhattan restaurant when he realized that he had left his wallet and all of his cash at home. He called his wife, who graciously agreed to make the forty-five-minute drive from Long Island to bring McNamara his wallet. While waiting for her to arrive, it occurred to McNamara that there might be a better way to a pay a restaurant tab than with cash. He sketched out some thoughts on a napkin and the following year founded the Diners Club charge card company with partners Ralph E. Schneider and Casey R. Taylor.

After an investment of $250,000 and nearly a year's hard work lining up restaurants, car rental companies, hotels, and florists willing to accept the Diners Club card in lieu of cash, McNamara and his partners began issuing their first cardboard charge cards in September 1950. Cardholders agreed to pay a five-dollar annual fee to use the card, and Diners Club charged merchants 7 percent for the convenience of their patrons and promotional benefits.

On September 26, 1950, the company ran its first ad in the *New York Times*:

> Say "Charge It" At any of the fine restaurants listed below!
>   Yes, your Diners' Club Card is a master credit card at these, and one hundred other superb eating places in the metropolitan New York area, Chicago and other key cities. Receive one monthly statement reflecting all charges.

The Diners Club Card program was specifically aimed at the business community—one of its chief benefits was easier tracking of expenses—but it was pitched in expressly egalitarian terms. "You don't have to be a top executive to enjoy the many benefits of this man-about-town charge account privilege," the ad promised. "Any responsible business man or woman, executive or employe [*sic*], can have this Diners' Club Card simply by applying by mail or phone today for an application or further particulars."

Since the program's name and its advertising were specifically designed to evoke the sense of belonging to a select organization, the resulting loss of privacy should have come as no surprise. There is a constant tension between how much an organization knows about someone and the level of service it can provide in return; many high-end hotels, for instance, keep detailed files on the preferences of their frequent customers. The illusion being offered by Diners Club, and countless club programs since, was that those perks are available to people who don't regularly frequent the Plaza Hotel on New York's Central Park South or the Savoy on the Strand in central London.

In its first month, Diners Club handled just $1,200 in billings, but just over a year later, it reported that its monthly billings exceeded $700,000. The company also predicted that its monthly charges would exceed $1 million in the spring of 1952 (a goal that it easily met). In light of its success with restaurants, Diners Club announced that it would expand its charge service to airlines, a preliminary step to expanding the New York–based card's coverage across the entire United States. By the fall of 1953, the monthly billings for Diners Club were over $2.2 million and rising steadily.

In an interview with the Associated Press in December 1951, McNamara unwittingly illustrated the impact the new financial tool was already having on personal privacy. "The largest tab we had," McNamara said, "was for a $25,000 party thrown by a business firm in Los Angeles, but we have at least 50 members whose monthly charges come to $1,000 to $1,500. But in this business, you can expect anything. We've got one member whose only charges each month are for chocolate sodas."

While amusing, McNamara's awareness that one of his subscribers had a chocolate soda habit illustrates the origin of much of the contemporary privacy conflict: the willingness of people to trade information about what they do and what they buy to complete strangers in exchange for the convenience of making a single monthly payment or simply carrying less cash. (Keep in mind that in 1950, the cost of a chocolate soda was somewhere between a nickel and a dime.) Information that was once limited to an anonymous chocolate-loving

New Yorker and his or her favorite soda jerk was now national interview fodder at best and a cross-marketing opportunity at worst. Of course, back then, when the charge and credit card industry was in its infancy, Diners Club subscribers had little reason to worry that their dining habits would be tabulated and sold to other potentially interested merchants. Today, however, the soda sipper would undoubtedly be deluged with advertisements from rival chocolate companies, other nearby soda fountains (if any still exist), and weight-loss programs.

The success of McNamara's general-purpose charge card was the beginning of a great American love affair with the concept of consumer credit. From the start, the driving forces were the ease with which credit cards were issued and the lure of "buy now, pay later": as one reporter wrote in late 1955, "With the right cards, one can go almost anywhere and enjoy the trip with all its trimmings, without immediately feeling the financial strain."

Although the Diners Club card could be used to make purchases at a variety of different businesses, true general-purpose credit cards were still some years away. But there was clearly a growing consumer interest in deferred or installment payments, so a large number of businesses began issuing their own single-purpose card. By the end of the decade, it was not unusual for a salesman or executive to carry around twenty or thirty different charge cards for use in specific hotel chains, restaurants, department stores, auto rental agencies, airlines, and so on.

The rapidly growing credit industry accelerated the loss of consumer privacy. This should not have come as a big shock: approval for even the most basic department store card typically required the applicant to furnish a name, home address, employer's name and address, and banking and store references to verify creditworthiness. As a result, each and every card carried its own privacy tax, both in terms of the original application and the ongoing record of activity. Remarkably, however, it would be nearly twenty years before people began worrying about just how much information was being collected and stored by businesses and credit card companies.

The tremendous surge in credit cards spurred the growth of an industry that has had an even greater impact on personal privacy: the nation's credit bureaus. Although credit bureaus date back to the beginning of the twentieth century, when merchants were looking for a way to determine whether their out-of-town vendors and customers were financially reliable, their influence and importance increased dramatically in the early 1950s. In 1952, the American Credit Bureau Association reported that 1,703 local credit bureaus were on its membership rolls and estimated that another 300 or so were not members. Altogether, the 2,000 credit bureaus maintained detailed files on the financial activity and creditworthiness of seventy million people.

Even in a noncomputerized age, it is remarkable how much information was collected by the bureaus about consumers. In September 1953, *New York Times* reporter Pierce Fredericks visited a bureau to learn more about how the credit industry functioned. "At a bureau," he said, "there is a card for everyone in the area who has ever had a charge account or bought on time." The card contained information stored in a variety of categories, including residential history (house value or rental payment), business and resources (including the jobs of other family members), bank, and litigation. The card also contained a listing of every store or merchant with which the consumer had done business, along with a numerical record of the consumer's payment history: "30" for the most favored monthly payers, "30–60" for the slightly slower but still okay, "60–90" for the potentially problematic, and bright red stickers for the defaulters or "skips."

The accumulation of all that data helped give rise to the nascent data mining industry. Without computers, which were only just beginning to make their way into nongovernment organizations, there were limits on just how much information could be derived from the stacks and stacks of cards; but that didn't stop bureaus from forming some general conclusions. For instance, Fredericks said, one bureau compiled a list of the occupations most likely to have skips in their ranks. The bureau said that it had no explanation why some jobs wound up on the list and not others; the list (which, unfortunately, Fredericks did not publish) was simply a reflection of the bureau's experience.

Similarly, the bureau interviewed by Fredericks said that based on the data in its files, it could divide its problem accounts into six general categories: (1) people who were in financial trouble due to illness or job loss, (2) "loaders"—"women planning a divorce who stagger their husbands' accounts with a ten years supply of lingerie and jewelry," (3) first-time credit users who overlooked the repayment part of the arrangement, (4) women who hid credit bills from their husbands, (5) "unhappy women" who used credit charges to punish their husbands, and (6) people who simply suffered from poor financial sense.

American spending habits kept the credit bureaus busy. By the beginning of the 1960s, total consumer debt had risen to $51.1 billion, nearly ten times what it had been at the end of World War II (roughly $5.6 billion). For the first time, credit and banking executives were beginning to worry publicly about "too much credit," and a rise in uncollectible accounts and credit card fraud schemes caused many companies to lower their credit limits and tighten credit policies. (By comparison, America's consumer debt in the summer of 2008 was $14 *trillion*—a 27,450 percent increase in less than fifty years.) An inevitable by-product of the concern about rising debt levels was more record keeping, more inquisitive applications, and greater information sharing among businesses and credit card companies. And in just a few years, companies would have a new tool—the massive data storage and mining capacity of mainframe computers—to help them analyze and profit from all of that data.

THE RED SCARE

At the same time that American consumer privacy was experiencing its first serious assault from growing credit bureau files, citizen privacy was coming under particularly fierce attack. The period's most aggressive invader of personal privacy was the infamous Joseph McCarthy, a Republican senator from Wisconsin, who rose to fame on the strength of his repeated accusations that the government was harboring known Communists and "perverts." On February 9, 1950, McCarthy gave a famous speech before the Republican Women's Club of Wheeling, West Virginia, in which he alleged that the State Department was infested with "known Communists" who were helping to shape U.S. policy. In a letter to President Truman a few days later, McCarthy demanded that Truman investigate the charges and warned that "failure on your part will label the Democratic party as being the bed-fellow of international communism."

McCarthy was a particularly powerful and effective demagogue, and his charges tapped into deep-seated anxieties among the American public that untold numbers of Communist sympathizers were secretly biding their time, waiting for the right moment to strike at the pillars of American society. Over the course of that summer, McCarthy and the Republican Party expanded their charges to include the threat of "sexual deviancy" (that is, gays). Republican National Committee chair Guy George Gabrielson solemnly warned that "perhaps as dangerous as the actual Communists are the sexual perverts who have infiltrated our Government in recent years. The State Department has confessed that it has had to fire ninety-one of these. It is the talk of Washington and of the Washington correspondents corps."

The hysteria whipped up by McCarthy and the Republicans in 1950 led to a series of background investigations of federal employees and helped spur the adoption of particularly oppressive legislation. In response to McCarthy's taunts that Democrats were soft on Communism, President Truman proposed a series of measures aimed at improving domestic security, including the registration of Russian-trained spies and saboteurs. In a message to Congress, he agreed that "present law is inadequate to permit proper supervision of deportable aliens and should be strengthened"; however, Truman expressed disapproval of a pending proposal that would allow the attorney general to detain certain aliens for an indefinite period of time, "not pursuant to a conviction for crime, but on the basis of an administrative determination."

The president's proposals, however, were insufficient for many legislators. In August, Senator Pat McCarran (D-Nev.), the chair of the Senate Judiciary Committee, proposed a far more comprehensive antisubversive package that pulled together elements of several existing pieces of legislation. The omnibus bill, known formally as the Subversive Activities Control Act of 1950 and colloquially as the McCarran Act, was adopted after contentious debate on September 20, 1950. Among other things, the act barred Communists from working for the U.S. government, denied passports to members of Communist organizations, and required Communist organizations to register with the U.S. attorney general and provide information about their officers, finances, and membership. Most disturbingly, the law authorized the president to apprehend and detain in an internment camp "each person as to whom there is reasonable ground to believe that such person probably will engage in, or probably will conspire with others to engage in, acts of espionage or of sabotage."

Despite the fact that Truman himself was eager to get tough against domestic Communists, the McCarran Act was more than he could stomach. He vetoed the bill on September 22 and returned it to Congress with a lengthy message dissecting the bill's various flaws. "The application of the registration requirements to so-called Communist-front organizations," Truman said, "can be the greatest danger to freedom of speech, press and assembly since the Alien and Sedition Laws of 1798."

Arguing that governmental stifling of opinion is "a long step toward totalitarianism," Truman offered a resounding rejection of the bill's incipient thought control:

> We can and we will prevent espionage, sabotage, or other actions endangering our national security. But we would betray our finest tradition if we attempted, as this bill would attempt, to curb the simple expression of opinion.
>
> This we should never do, no matter how distasteful the opinion may be to the vast majority of our people. The course proposed by this bill would delight the Communists, for it would make a mockery of the Bill of Rights and of our claims to stand for freedom in the world.

Truman's veto set off another tremendous debate in Congress. With the 1950 midterm elections just six weeks away, legislators were eager to get back to their districts to campaign and even more eager to demonstrate to their constituents that they were doing something about the threat of Communism. The House of Representatives, under the firm leadership of Speaker Sam Rayburn (D-Tex.), quickly overrode Truman's veto by a wide margin, 286–48.

In the Senate, however, a small group of liberal senators launched a noble but ultimately futile filibuster against the veto override. Led by Senator Hubert H. Humphrey (D-Minn.), seven senators talked through the night of September 22 and into the early afternoon of the twenty-third; one of them, William Langer (R-N. Dak.), actually had to be carried off the floor of the Senate when he suddenly collapsed at his desk at five in the morning, after more than five hours of uninterrupted oratory against the bill. It was, at the time, the third longest continuous Senate session in history. Despite such heroics, however, the dissidents were ultimately unable to prevent the vote from occurring, and the Senate overrode President Truman by a vote of 57–10.

Among its various provisions, the McCarran Act imposed a requirement on President Truman to establish a Subversive Activities Control Board (SACB), which was charged with holding hearings to determine whether certain organizations, like the Communist Party of America, were actual Communist-run organizations or merely Communist front groups. In a speech given to the Brooklyn Bar Association a short time later, SACB chair Peter Campbell Brown acknowledged the risk that such investigations might go too far, arguing that the federal courts and lawyers must learn to distinguish between "sincere liberalism" and communism. "We all abhor the witch hunt and must neither persecute nor prosecute anyone for holding unpopular beliefs," Brown said. "We must at all times remain true to the spirit of the Declaration of Independence and the Constitution, but we must take steps to protect our people from that which goes beyond discussion and tends to incite efforts to overthrow our Government by force."

Congress, however, was not about to back away from its efforts to control Communism in the United States. In 1954, despite the concerns of President Eisenhower, Congress made the issue of registration moot by passing the Communist Control Act, which outlawed the existence of the Communist Party and made it a criminal offense for anyone to belong to or support the group.

In 1968, Congress repealed the registration requirements of the McCarran Act. The remainder of the law, at least as it applied to Communist action or Communist front groups, was repealed in 1993. The Communist Control Act remains on the books, but its constitutionality has never been ruled on by the Supreme Court, in large part because no federal administration has ever attempted to enforce the law by prosecuting someone for allegedly belonging to the Communist Party.

THE BATTLE OVER LEGALIZING WIRETAPPING

Despite the fact that Congress had forbidden wiretapping in the Communications Act of 1934, and the Supreme Court had ruled at least twice that evidence collected through wiretaps was inadmissible in federal court, it was clear a decade later that federal agents had not stopped listening in on phone conversations. On the contrary, given the advances in electronic technology, particularly the miniaturization of listening devices, there was widespread concern that the federal government in general, and J. Edgar Hoover's FBI in particular, were conducting far more surveillance than they admitted.

Renewed attention was focused on the practice of FBI wiretapping during the trials of Judith Coplon, an employee in the foreign agents registration unit of the Department of Justice. She was allegedly recruited to spy on American counterintelligence efforts by the Soviet intelligence and secret police force, the People's Commissariat for State Security (NKGB), in 1944. Five years later, she was arrested during a rendezvous with a known NKGB official in New York; a search revealed that she was carrying secret U.S. information at the time.

Coplon was tried twice, once for espionage in 1949 and once for conspiracy in 1950, and was convicted in both cases. However, both convictions were overruled due to FBI wiretapping improprieties—the first because the FBI destroyed its wiretap records prior to trial, and the second because the bureau actually eavesdropped on Coplon's conversations with her attorney, Leonard Boudin. The FBI's position was not aided by the fact that federal agents lied about whether wiretapping had occurred. Such conduct led the *Washington Post* to opine, "We need an eternally vigilant police force; we need also to be eternally vigilant against attempts by the police to go beyond their proper powers."

The head of the Justice Department, attorney general J. Howard McGrath, tried to reassure the public that he had "fully reviewed" the FBI's wiretapping activities and promised that they were well within the guidelines set by former attorneys general Robert H. Jackson and Tom Clark (both of whom, incidentally, had since taken seats on the Supreme Court). However, McGrath justified the "limited" use of wiretapping in light of "the emergency which still prevails and the necessity of protecting the national security." In the Justice Department's view, even if evidence collected through wiretapping could not be introduced in court, the investigative leads obtained from listening to conversations were too valuable to pass up.

FBI director Hoover chimed in on the debate, saying that the FBI had just 170 phones in the United States under surveillance and that the use of the technique was entirely justified. "I dare say," Hoover said, "that the most violent critic of the FBI would urge the use of wiretapping techniques if his child were kidnapped and held in custody. Certainly there is as great a need to utilize this technique to protect our country from those who would enslave us and are engaged in treason, espionage and subversion, and who if successful would destroy our institutions and democracy."

Law-and-order advocates in Congress made repeated attempts to overturn the Supreme Court's decisions by passing legislation explicitly authorizing wiretapping in various circumstances. A bill to permit federal agents to conduct wiretapping had been introduced in 1941, shortly after the Supreme Court rulings in *Nardone* and *Weiss*, but failed in large part due to opposition by President Roosevelt, who viewed it as too sweeping an infringement on civil liberties. A decade later, in 1950, Rep. Kenneth B. Keating (R-N.Y.) introduced similar legislation that would have given wiretapping authority not only to the FBI but also to military investigative units.

The ability to tap wires, Keating asserted, was critical to protecting national security. "Otherwise," he said, "we are saying to spies that they are free to use telephones in their espionage activities, but the government is forbidden to tap those wires in its counter-espionage work. What an absurd and dangerous result!"

During the course of the debate over the Keating wiretapping bill, another disturbing privacy trend emerged: the growth of corporate and consumer wiretapping and eavesdropping. In a groundbreaking article published in December 1952 in the *Reporter*, a liberal biweekly newsmagazine, William Fairfield and Charles Clift investigated and described widespread private surveillance. Much of it, they said, required specialized training from a telephone company, but increasingly, advances in electronic devices were making it possible for anyone with enough money to conduct sophisticated eavesdropping.

An investigation by the New York City Anti-Crime Committee in early 1955 revealed a wide range of legal and illegal eavesdropping techniques in use around the city, ranging from an "off the premises" extension installed by a phone subscriber to induction-coil listening devices and battery-powered radios transmitting phone taps. The committee also noted that microphone technology, particularly parabolic mikes, could be used by investigators and eavesdroppers to overhear and record conversations taking place three football fields away. Overall, the committee concluded, the practice of eavesdropping was getting steadily easier for the average person.

In the 1954 midterm elections, the Democrats gained a narrow advantage that they would hold for the next forty years. The chair of the House Judiciary Committee, Rep. Emmanuel S. Celler (D-N.Y.), was a passionate advocate of civil rights who played a central role over the next decade in drafting the Civil Rights Act of 1964, the Voting Rights Act of 1965, and the Civil Rights Act of 1968. He was also deeply opposed to wiretapping (which he described as a "vicious cancer," a phrase unconsciously echoed twenty years later by John Dean when describing the cover-up of the Watergate bugging). In 1955, in the wake of the revelations from New York City on the extent of both government and private surveillance, Celler held a series of hearings on several bills designed to ban the practice outright.

One of the more interesting sessions occurred on May 3, when New York wiretap specialist Bernard Spindel testified before Celler's subcommittee and demonstrated a variety of different listening devices. He attached a tiny "bug" to a phone in the hearing room, which recorded Celler's voice when he talked into the handset and also recorded the voices in the hearing room after the phone was hung up. Other tools of the trade included tiny thumbtacks that could be pushed into drywall to pick up signals from a telephone circuit box, induction coils that could be used to listen to conversations in adjoining rooms, an army surplus "beaming receiver" that could pick up conversations over long distances, and a cigarette-pack-sized sound receiver that Spindel said was actually "king-sized" compared to other, more miniaturized devices. At his request, the committee went into executive session to see demonstrations by Spindel of even more complex and invasive surveillance tools. Eventually, the subcommittee recommended legislation that would have outlawed all wiretapping except as provided by state law or in the case of federal agents authorized by a court-issued search warrant. However, the full House Judiciary Committee did not take any action on the proposal, and it languished.

Whatever Spindel demonstrated to lawmakers behind closed doors, it is hard to imagine that it was much more remarkable than the innovations being introduced by the electronics industry. In January 1957, for instance, New York City police and FBI agents were treated to a demonstration of a wireless microphone that could transmit sounds clearly to a listener three or four blocks away, even in central Manhattan. The primary purpose, the inventors said, was for use on the stage or at sporting events, where wires would be inconvenient. There was little question, however, that the sensitive and discreet transmitters would find a market in law enforcement. "Any thinking man," *New York Times* reporter Meyer Berger wrote, "must regard it with suspicion and with sadness. It disrobes privacy and leaves him nude."

The legal battle over the use of wiretap evidence intensified later that year, when the Supreme Court took its earlier wiretapping rulings one step further. In *Benanti v. United States*, the Court announced that henceforth the federal courts could no longer admit evidence obtained through wiretaps by state officials, even where such wiretapping was authorized by state constitution or statute. Section 605 of the Communications Act of 1934, chief justice Earl Warren said, "created a prohibition against any persons violating the integrity of a system of telephonic communication," and "evidence obtained in violation of this prohibition may not be used to secure a federal conviction."

The *Benanti* decision infuriated federal and state law enforcement officials, who not unreasonably saw the ruling as interfering with their ability to investigate and prosecute criminal activity. The impact of the Court's ruling was felt almost immediately in New York City, where federal prosecutors were forced to drop pending perjury charges against Teamster leader Jimmy Hoffa, because the case was based in large part on secret wiretaps obtained by the Manhattan district attorney's office. After the *Benanti* decision, calls in Congress for legislation to officially authorize the use of wiretap evidence intensified, notwithstanding the equally fervent objections of Congressman Celler.

What one might fairly describe as the "wiretapping decade" ended with a well-received book, *The Eavesdroppers*, by former Philadelphia district attorney Sam Dash, law professor Robert E. Knowlton, and electrical engineer Richard F. Schwartz. The book was the culmination of eighteen months of research on electronic eavesdropping tactics and tools in the United States. Much of the research was conducted in New York City, where police officers told Dash that as many as twenty thousand illegal wiretaps were conducted each year. Dash later testified to a Senate committee that he and his coauthors found evidence of illegal wiretapping in nearly every major city in the United States.

One of Dash's more explosive revelations came from an interview of a former Federal Communications Commission investigator, who told him that in 1935 or 1936, FCC officials conducted a raid on a building not far from the U.S. Supreme Court. They discovered wiretap apparatus that was connected to phone lines running into the chambers of the justices. No wiretapper was apprehended, but the investigator told Dash that the equipment had clearly been used recently. A large business with an important case before the Court was suspected of having arranged the wiretapping, but there was insufficient evidence to pursue charges, and the Court apparently was not informed of the discovery until publication of Dash's book.

In addition to conducting field research into the prevalence of wiretapping, Dash and his research team also confirmed the wide variety of new technologies being used to conduct electronic surveillance. Electronic listening devices were steadily shrinking in size, Dash said, at the same time that their ability to pick up and transmit voices was growing. One commonly available device was no larger than a matchbook and could easily be concealed in a wastebasket or on the underside of a desk; another was small enough to hide on the back of a painting or print.

In his section of *The Eavesdroppers*, Schwartz described in detail the process of tapping phones, both through direct wire connections and with remote devices like induction coils and tape recorders. He also described the wide range of concealed microphones (both wired and wireless) available for surveillance, as well as parabolic and tube microphones capable of listening to conversations hundreds of feet away.

Some of the devices discussed by Schwartz must have seemed like science fiction to readers and to members of Congress: microwave and ultrasonic beams that could record the vibrations caused by sound on a window or a wall, metal detectors, infrared cameras, closed-circuit surveillance cameras, and magnetic transmitters to track vehicles. But if anything, it seems likely that Dash and his team barely scratched the surface of emerging electronic surveillance tools: after all, the National Security Agency was still a well-kept secret at that point. But remarkably, the investigation detailed in *The Eavesdroppers* did little to rattle American complacency with respect to privacy, and Congress apparently saw no need to press forward with privacy legislation. It would not be the last time that Congress elected to ignore the impact of technology on privacy.

THE MARCH OF THE "BIG BRAINS"

The final factor that made the 1950s such a bad decade for privacy was more foreshadowing than actual plot development: the slow but steady introduction of mainframe computers into government agencies and large businesses (particularly insurance companies). In the years immediately following the end of World War II, J. Presper Eckert and John W. Mauchly began work on the first general-purpose computer, the Electronic Numerical Integrator and Computer (ENIAC). In 1949, the U.S. Census Bureau approached Eckert and Mauchly and asked them to design a computer that could be used to help crunch the numbers for the upcoming 1950 census.

The resulting machine, called the Universal Automatic Computer I (UNIVAC I), was delivered to the Census Bureau on March 31, 1951, and formally dedicated to government service ten weeks later. By modern standards, it was a massive and expensive ($1 million) device. Altogether, its various components took up more than 380 square feet of floor space and weighed just under fifteen tons. Each UNIVAC I had approximately five thousand temperamental and short-lived vacuum tubes and performed calculations at a rather pedestrian clock speed of 2.25 megahertz. The coverage of the government's new million-dollar tabulator was glowing; one paper noted, "In one-sixth of a second the electronic device can classify an average citizen as to sex, marital status, education, residence, age group, birthplace, employment, income, and a dozen other classifications."

The Census Bureau was so impressed with the operation of the first UNIVAC I that it ordered a second one to be installed three years later to help tally information received from a census of the nation's agricultural industry. In a sign of things to come, the bureau announced that because of its new computing capabilities, it would not need to hire as many temporary employees as it had in the past.

Another significant player in the mainframe computer industry was IBM. In 1952, it introduced the IBM 701 Electronic Data Processing Machine, the company's first commercially available scientific computer. Initially designed for the U.S. government to assist the military during the Korean War, the machine was also marketed to private defense and aircraft firms. Within a short time, IBM had eighteen orders for its new device. As the company's newly appointed president, Thomas J. Watson Jr., sagely observed, "We knew that we were in the electronics business and that we'd better move fast."

The 701's initial client list was a veritable who's who of the military-industrial complex: Lockheed, Douglas Aircraft, General Electric, Convair, the U.S. Navy, United Aircraft, Boeing, and North American Aviation, all within two years of the machine's release. One other early customer—the National Security Agency—is listed today on IBM's historical Web site for the 701, but was not mentioned during early press coverage of the new computer. However, one contemporary press report noted that the "Brain," as the 701 was known, was capable of translating Russian to English at the rate of two and a half lines per second. It is not difficult to imagine which customer might have found that useful.

Both of the other major government collectors and processors of private data—the Social Security Administration and the Internal Revenue Service—entered the computer age in the 1950s as well. In 1956, the SSA installed an updated version of IBM's mainframe, the 705, which it used to post earnings records and calculate benefits. The 705 offered several technical advantages over the 701, the most notable of which was the replacement of vacuum tubes with magnetic core storage, which was both faster and cooler. In addition, the output of the 705 could be stored on large reels of magnetic tape, each capable of holding five million bytes of data. The new storage technology was badly needed: the SSA was on the verge of outgrowing its capacity to physically store data cards about the American population. Since each reel of tape could store the data from between twenty-five thousand and fifty thousand punch cards, the space savings were impressive.

The IRS was somewhat slower to enter the computer age, but in 1958, it announced that any taxpayer earning less than $10,000 could use the simplified Form 1040A, which consisted of a single card with approximately fifteen questions on the front and back. The IRS commissioner, Russell C. Harrington, said at the time that as many as seventeen million Americans would qualify to use the simpler form, which would make it much easier for the IRS to begin processing returns by computer.

Given its decennial data processing challenge, the Census Bureau naturally remained at the forefront of government computer use. Frustrated by the tedious process of transferring census information from forms to the same type of data cards that Herman Hollerith had introduced seventy years earlier, the bureau began work in the 1950s on a system to speed up the process. The system it developed, called the Film Optical Sensing Device for Input to Computers (FOSDIC), was first deployed for the 1960 census. Census data was recorded on specialized forms ("FOSDIC schedules") with filled-in ovals for each piece of information. At the Census Bureau, the forms were photographed onto microfilm, which was then fed into the FOSDIC machines. The machines were designed to read the filled-in ovals from the microfilm and convert the information to electronic data, which was stored directly on magnetic tape. The computers then read the data off the magnetic tapes and performed the necessary calculations.

The 1960 census was notable not merely for the introduction of the highly successful FOSDIC system (which was used for the next three censuses as well) but also for being the first census in which individual households filled out the census form themselves. Census takers then visited each home to verify the information before transferring it to the machine-readable forms.

Unlike some earlier censuses, the 1960 count was relatively non-controversial. There was a brief flap over a proposed question about religious belief, which was dropped after some religious organizations objected. Other questions were proposed by various business groups but were rejected by the Census Bureau as being either too trivial or too personal. For instance, the cosmetics industry lobbied for a question about hair color, while the garment industry wanted the bureau to query each person for their weight and personal measurements. The bureau also declined to inquire about pets and cemetery lot ownership.

By the end of the decade, various agencies within the federal government were using an estimated 250 electronic brains to handle an ever-increasing array of calculations, ranging from tracking satellites to designing bridges and highways to analyzing air traffic patterns. Although most were performing the types of mathematical calculations and modeling not easily done by slide rule, others were being used to compile, store, and analyze increasingly large amounts of private information about American citizens.

Admittedly, in those early days of the computing revolution the big boxes were not doing much that was significantly different from what had been done before; they were simply doing it much, much faster and in smaller spaces. But these behemoths laid the groundwork for a new and much more invasive era of data collection and data mining that would permeate every level of government and business. The irony is that they quietly did so at a time when both Congress and the Supreme Court were demonstrating their strongest support yet for the concept of the right to privacy.

CY'S GOLDEN HOUR

arren Court

When George Orwell's dystopian book *1984* hit the bookshelves in June 1949, it was instantly acclaimed as a brilliant and darkly bleak look at an all-too-possible future. "A great work of kinetic art," said *New York Times* reviewer Mark Schorer in a summary titled "An Indignant and Prophetic Novel." The most frightening aspect of Orwell's world was "the complete abolition of privacy," the *Washington Post* editorialized on June 20. "Every waking moment of the lives of the inhabitants is under the scrutiny of the dreaded Thought Police. Among the devices employed for this purpose is a kind of two-way television, whereby all symptoms of discontent, such as changes of facial expression or lack of enthusiasm at the daily mass calisthenics or hate programs are instantly noted."

The embodiment of Orwell's surveillance-blighted future was Big Brother, a creation so plausible and so frightening that he instantly took his place alongside other literary metaphors for human ingenuity run amok, including Mary Shelley's Frankenstein and his monster, Jules Vernes's Captain Nemo and the Nautilus, and even Robert Louis Stevenson's Dr. Jekyll and Mr. Hyde. In remarkably short order, "Big Brother" began appearing as shorthand for uncontrolled and increasingly invasive surveillance, an epithet aimed chiefly at the government but also at any individual or organization with the capacity and desire to pry into one's personal affairs.

Just a year after *1984* was published, *Time* cited it in an article about a new type of miniaturized video camera tube called the Vidicon, which the magazine predicted "would just suit Big Brother's purposes." A couple of years later, the invention of the radar detector to catch speeding automobiles sparked the headline "Big Brother

Is Driving." A subsequent summary of developments in surveillance camera technology led *Time* to caution about a dangerous future: "Televisionaries confidently forecast the day when every home will have its private network (so mother can keep track of the kids) and telephones will come equipped with TV screens. But there is a chill in the air: in that event, would Big Brother and his thought-controlling telescreens be far behind? Active as peeping TV is today, Big Brother is still a kid brother."

Some argued that the "kid brother" was growing up faster than people realized. Following the discovery in early 1955 of a major wiretapping operation that covered much of the Upper East Side in New York, the *Washington Post* took the opportunity to invoke Orwell and editorialize against both illegal and legal electronic surveillance:

> There is something repellant and fearful about a situation where unknown people can listen in on conversations not for their ears. No message can be confidential, however innocent; no spoken word private, however intimate, when a telephone can be tapped or an electronic device can pick up talk, without even a contact on the line, from some distance away.
>
> [The Constitutional guarantee against unreasonable searches and seizures] is a warranty of a right most of us hold precious: the right to privacy when we, and not other people, think circumstances warrant privacy. It is a travesty of law enforcement when this right can be invaded by illegal eavesdroppers. It is unthinkable that the Government would ever strip the people of their privacy by legalizing Listening Toms.

As eloquent as the *Post* was in its condemnation of yet more illegal wiretapping, it conceded that it could not match the compelling imagery of former burlesque queen Ann Corio, whose line was one of those tapped. She felt, Corio told reporters, like she had been "taking a bath in a glass bathtub."

As the 1960s opened, Corio's glass bathtub was getting crowded. Despite the turmoil over wiretapping during the preceding decades, the Justice Department and the FBI were still conducting electronic surveillance in an unknown number of cases. More ominously, private sector surveillance had become a billion-dollar industry, a sum that encompassed not only the private detectives and corporate gum-shoes but also the brave new world of eavesdropping tools: smaller and more common surveillance cameras, carefully hidden peepholes, two-way mirrors, tiny electronic "ears" and microphones, and so on.

By the middle of the decade, it was clear that thanks to advances in technology, *everyone* was at risk from electronic surveillance. A 1964 article in the *Saturday Evening Post*, "Big Brother Is Listening," discussed not only the ongoing government surveillance efforts but also the tools and techniques available for purchase and use by the average citizen:

> Thanks to modern science, privacy is becoming more and more rare all over the world. Even a child can send away for a $15 device that picks up sounds in a room across the street. For $17.95 you can buy a machine that secretly tapes telephone conversations without touching a wire. And $150 buys a TV camera the size of a book that can spy on a room secretly while you watch on a distant monitor. Using these and other modern methods, American business has turned increasingly to espionage in recent years.

The anxieties and possibilities of private surveillance were amply demonstrated by an invasion-of-privacy lawsuit filed in 1964 in New Hampshire by Carl and Mae Hamberger against their landlord, Clifford Eastman. Over the course of several weeks, the Hambergers reportedly heard squeaking noises coming from a heating duct near the headboard of their bed. Upon investigation, Carl Hamberger discovered a three-inch radio speaker attached to wires that ran seven hundred feet to Eastman's home. The Hambergers promptly moved to a new apartment and filed suit for invasion of privacy. The landlord tried to get the case dismissed, but in December 1964, the New Hampshire Supreme Court ruled that the suit could go forward because of the seriousness of the alleged invasion. "It should not be necessary—by way of understatement—to observe that this is the type of intrusion that would be offensive to any person of ordinary sensibilities," the court concluded. "What married people do in the privacy of their bedrooms is their own business so long as they are not hurting anyone else."

A month later, the Belknap County Superior Court began hearing testimony on the Hambergers' $125,000 claim against Eastman for invasion of privacy. One irony is that a suit for invasion of privacy often requires testimony that is itself highly invasive of privacy. During her time on the witness stand, Mae Hamberger was asked by her attorney whether the discovery of the electronic device had interfered with her sexual relations with her husband. Saying that she "had never been so embarrassed in her life," Mrs. Hamberger testified that "it has been curtailed. Yes. To quite an extent." She also testified that after learning of the presence of the listening device, she had suffered a variety of other ailments, including extreme nervousness, dizziness, and weight loss.

In the end, however, the jury sided with the landlord, accepting his explanation that he did not install the device "for vicarious thrills," as the Hambergers' attorney alleged, but instead to monitor the operation of a pump in the basement of the Hambergers' rental. (Testimony was offered to the effect that an ordinary speaker can act as a simple microphone.)

Although the bedroom surveillance case may have ended unhappily from the perspective of the Hambergers, it served to intensify the public's fear that even the most private moments might be under assault from electronic surveillance and eavesdropping. If the privacy of the bedroom could be invaded with little more than a two-dollar speaker and some wire, how great was the risk from corporations and governments with vastly more sophisticated resources at their disposal? As the decade progressed, that question was increasingly posed but unsatisfactorily answered.

BIG BROTHER GOES TO WASHINGTON?

"How do we know that this is always being used for the benefit of the individual? How can we be sure that this information will not be used against a person?"

Those were the somewhat plaintive questions raised in December 1962 by Dr. Richard W. Hamming, a scientist at the Bell Telephone Laboratories in Murray Hill, New Jersey, at a symposium called "Man and the Computer." The event was sponsored by the American Association for the Advancement of Science (AAAS), an organization founded in 1848 "to advance science and serve society."

Dr. Hamming's remarks—and the conference as a whole—were an acknowledgment that the combined forces of information gathering and computer processing were steadily changing the nature of personal privacy in the United States. Already, Dr. Hamming said, a growing number of federal agencies and private organizations were using computers to compile, track, and analyze data about individual citizens. As examples, he cited the Social Security Administration, the Selective Service System, the Internal Revenue Service, and numerous insurance companies, employers, hospitals, doctors' offices, and airline companies. He noted that data about individuals, whether collected by a single organization or several, could be pooled and put to uses other than those for which the data was originally collected. But since scientists were just beginning to recognize and research the possible effects of computerization, neither Dr. Hamming nor the AAAS offered any recommendations on how to limit the impact on individual privacy.

Dr. Hamming's concerns about governmental data collection were only slightly ahead of their time. In December 1965, a consultant for the U.S. Bureau of the Budget (the predecessor of today's Office of Management and Budget), Edgar S. Dunn Jr., accidentally set off a political firestorm when he authored a memo recommending that the federal government create a centralized data service center to store and more efficiently analyze all of the information collected by the government. Overall, Dunn said, there was too much duplication and wasted effort in the government's handling of information, and it interfered with the ability of various agencies to compare notes and plan efficiently. He suggested that as an initial matter, information could be collected and consolidated from the Census Bureau, the Bureau of Labor Statistics, the Internal Revenue Service, the Social Security Administration, and the Federal Reserve Board. The data center's information would be made available to a variety of outside agencies (research firms, businesses, state and local governments, and scholars) as well as the contributing agencies themselves.

The proposal drew immediate criticism from two of Congress's leading privacy proponents, Rep. Cornelius Gallagher (D-N.J.) and Senator Edward V. Long (D-Mo.), both of whom had pithy things to say about the dangers of excessive computerization. "Somewhere along the line toward government efficiency," Long said, "we must cease pushing our citizens into the computer." Gallagher was equally glib: "People worry about who has the button on nuclear weapons. We've got to start worrying about who has the button on the computer."

A month later, Gallagher was appointed chair of the House Special Subcommittee on Invasion of Privacy, which was charged, among other things, with investigating the proposed data center. One of the subcommittee's first witnesses was Vance Packard, author of the 1964 book *The Naked Society*, a groundbreaking look at the impact of technology on personal privacy. "My own hunch," Packard testified, "is that Big Brother, if he ever comes to the United States, may turn out to be not a greedy power seeker but rather a relentless bureaucrat obsessed with efficiency."

The following day, antagonistic committee members relentlessly grilled Dunn and Raymond T. Bowman, the budget bureau's assistant director for statistical standards. Dunn assured committee members that the data bank could be programmed to disguise identities, block the unauthorized disclosure of private information, and even distinguish between queries posed for valid statistical reasons and those posed out of mere curiosity. However, Gallagher dismissed those assertions and told Bowman that the bureau had spent too little time thinking about who might use the data center and how constitutional protections would be put in place to prevent abuse.

In the fall of 1966, at a meeting of the Federal Bar Association in Washington, a panel was convened to discuss the privacy implications of the proposed data center. Two of the panelists, Washington lawyer Marcus Cohn and computer expert Paul Baran from the Rand Corporation, offered particularly insightful comments on the potential risk of the federal data bank.

"We are losing freedom," Cohn said, "because institutions themselves are becoming so large, so mobile, and so communicating." Baran also touched on the communication theme, telling attendees that the privacy threat posed by the data center was dwarfed by an even greater threat: the growing exchange of personal data between private companies and government agencies.

Both were uniquely qualified to understand the privacy risks posed by network communications. Cohn was a former trial attorney for the Federal Communications Commission, which just a year earlier had looked into the possibility of regulating the computer mainframe business because leased telephone lines (which are within the FCC's jurisdiction) were used to distribute data to and from time-share computers. At the same time, the FCC said, it would look into what steps the computer companies and communications firms were taking to protect the privacy of personal information traveling across the phone lines. However, the FCC ultimately dropped the idea and decided to let the computer industry develop without its oversight.

That no doubt was a relief to Baran, who at the time was in the midst of designing a decentralized communications network that would, as he predicted, eventually have a far greater impact on personal privacy. In Baran's design, information would be digitized into a series of self-contained electronic envelopes called "packets." Individual packets would be sent from one node, or network host, to another on the way from a message's origin to its destination. Each node would temporarily store the packet, calculate the next node in the most efficient route to the destination, and then pass the packet along. This process would be repeated as often as necessary to deliver all of a message's packets to their destination, where the receiving computer would compile them in the correct order and deliver the message intact. Just three years later, Baran's "distributed node" concept was successfully tested, with funding from the Department of Defense's Advanced Research Projects Agency (ARPA), on seven nodes (six universities and Rand). The tiny network, dubbed ARPANET, would eventually grow into the globe-encircling Internet.

In the spring of 1967, the debate over a centralized government data center moved to the Senate Judiciary Subcommittee on Administrative Practice and Procedure, chaired by Senator Long. Witnesses told the subcommittee that already, the number of computers in use by the federal government had swelled to fifteen thousand, with another forty thousand deployed in private businesses around the country. Stored on miles of magnetic tape was a staggering array of personal information, including census data, tax returns, fingerprints, mortgage payments, bank balances, military records, driving records, and so on.

Some of the most critical testimony was offered by Arthur R. Miller, a renowned professor of civil procedure at the University of Michigan Law School. (He later joined the faculty at Harvard Law

School and reputedly was the model for Professor Rudolph Perini, the cantankerous but brilliant figure in Scott Turow's *One L*). Miller, who four years later would author a well-received book called *The Assault on Privacy*, told the committee that if the national data center was constructed, a person's entire life could be examined or even deleted with the push of a button. His testimony earned warm praise from Senator Long, who said that he was "the sort of man right after my own heart."

Another of the leading voices in opposition to the data center plan was Dr. Alan F. Westin, who headed up a four-year study, funded by the Carnegie Foundation, that culminated in the publication in 1967 of a detailed look at privacy in America, *Privacy and Freedom*. "The trend toward greatly increased collection of personal data, the exchange of information among collectors, and the consolidation of such personal information into central data banks," Westin said, "represents by far the most serious threat to privacy in the coming decade."

Both Westin and fellow privacy author Vance Packard pointed out that one of the major problems posed by the growing computerization of personal data was the "petrification" of even the most minor transgressions in computer files that lack any information of extenuating circumstances or context. As Packard succinctly put it, "The notion of the possibility of redemption is likely to be incomprehensible to a computer."

In August 1968, Gallagher's Special Subcommittee on Invasion of Privacy issued a highly critical report, "Privacy and the National Data Bank Concept." The committee alleged that the Bureau of the Budget had still not given enough thought as to how individual privacy would be protected. It also challenged the data center's impact on society in terms that Orwell would have cheered:

A suffocating sense of surveillance, represented by instantaneously retrievable, derogatory or non-contextual data, is not an atmosphere in which freedom can long survive.

Liberty under law is our foundation as a stable nation, and it is the conviction of the committee that any private or governmental action which would restrict the exercise of liberty would compromise respect for law.

Gallagher said that the subcommittee's staunch opposition stemmed from two main concerns: whether the government even had the right to collect increasingly large amounts of detailed information from American citizens, and whether the data center would hasten the trend toward the creation of a bureaucratic and depersonalized society.

It is worth noting, however, that while Gallagher waged a long and successful legislative battle against the centralized government data bank, neither he nor any other member of Congress actually addressed the root causes of the problem: the fact that so many federal agencies were now in the business of collecting data and shoveling it wholesale into government computers. It is an interesting question whether, even in the 1960s, the government could have cut back on its apparently insatiable desire for information. Unfortunately, that is not a question that was ever seriously asked at either end of Pennsylvania Avenue.

THE MARRIAGE OF CREDIT AND COMPUTERS

The federal government was hardly the only entity stepping up the pace of its data collection in the 1960s. With the enthusiastic help of consumers themselves, credit card companies and retail businesses were amassing staggering amounts of personal information. Every single dollar of the over $51 billion in consumer credit debt was associated with detailed information: who had made the purchase, when it was made and where, the amount remaining on the purchaser's credit line, and so on. And underlying the ability to make the credit purchase in the first place was a credit application and background check that added more data to corporate and credit bureau files.

Unhampered by federal and state regulations, credit card companies and retailers were increasingly intrusive in their collection and assessment of personal data. As credit executives conceded, part of the problem stemmed from the fact that in their push to expand their business, credit card companies were extending card offers to people in lower and lower income brackets. William J. Cheyney, executive vice president of the National Foundation for Consumer Credit, summarized the situation succinctly when he told the *Wall Street Journal* in April 1960: "The three all-purpose credit card companies already have every legitimate traveler. From here on they'll have to get ordinary people and these people may not be quite as good a credit risk."

The willingness and desire to expand the ranks of credit card purchasers was causing problems for credit card companies and retailers. Some financial experts estimated that in 1960 as many as 100,000 Americans qualified as "credit drunks," individuals with too much credit debt for their income. And as the number of "skips" increased, so did the intrusions on personal privacy.

In an effort to minimize their potential losses, credit card companies began demanding more and more detailed information as a condition of issuing cards, while at the same time keeping a closer eye on card activity. In the event of any significant deviation from past practice or expected activity, the account would be passed up to a supervisor for review and possible further action. At the time there was no system or network for merchants to automatically check the balance or validity of a credit card; thus, in the event that an account holder was abusing his or her charging privileges, the card company's only recourse was to physically retrieve the card. American Express, for instance, had a staff of fifty employees whose sole job was to visit profligate cardholders and request the return of their American Express cards.

It wasn't long, however, before the card repossessors would lose their jobs to the "big brains" crowding their way into the corporate hierarchy. At a 1965 gathering of the Financial Public Relations Association in New York, a Bankers Trust Company vice president named W. Putnam Livingston told his fellow bankers that they should program their computers to track their customers using Social Security numbers.

"It is the one number associated with us that stays constant during our lifetime," Livingston said during the conference. "Persuade the public that the number by which a computer can recognize an individual is more distinctive than a name." He also suggested that a single nationwide credit database should be created and maintained by the federal government, an idea that even some of his fellow bankers dismissed as a "Big Brother proposal."

In 1965, the merger of credit information and computer technology kicked into high gear when the Detroit-based Credit Data Corporation began opening computer processing centers around the country to collect, store, and redistribute credit information. Within a year, the first center in Los Angeles had credit information on nine million people, all of which was available to Credit Data subscribers over the telephone within ninety seconds. The company's president, Dr. Harry C. Jordan, said that it was Credit Data's goal to offer regional or even national credit information to service the now $86 billion consumer credit industry. The company predicted that within a few years, the regional computer credit centers would be linked to each other in a national credit reporting network.

Not everyone agreed. In May 1968, W. Lee Burge, president of the Atlanta-based Retail Credit Company, told Gallagher's House Special Subcommittee on Invasion of Privacy that there was little risk of high-speed privacy invasions, since it would be "economically unfeasible" to transfer all of his company's 45 million individual credit files to a computer. Less than two years later, however, Retail Credit saw the light and acquired an Oregon company called Credit Bureaus Inc., which was in the process of creating a computerized credit reporting system. It was a first step in a long computerization process that would eventually turn Retail Credit into Equifax, one of the world's largest credit reporting bureaus, with annual revenues of just under $2 billion.

The House subcommittee was merely the first to start examining the issue of whether the credit bureaus had grown too intrusive, too powerful, and too careless with the private information of Americans. That same year, the Senate Judiciary Committee's antitrust and monopoly subcommittee, headed by Philip A. Hart (D-Mich.), also began investigating the credit bureaus. The subcommittee's work focused on two key questions: whether the information being collected and maintained by the bureaus was accurate and who could get access to the information.

Numerous witnesses told the Senate panel that they had been unfairly denied credit, life insurance, or even employment because of erroneous information in their credit file. As the hearings progressed, it became evident that some organizations (particularly insurance companies) were collecting not only financial information but also more subjective data, including unverified reports of extramarital affairs, excessive drinking, and even suspicion of homosexuality—the theory being that any behavior deviating from so-called societal norms could make the individual an unsuitable credit risk or result in an insurance claim for injuries or death caused by accident or violence.

The sources for such information were typically the neighbors of the person being investigated. One enterprising credit bureau, however, took an approach first made famous in Troy: it provided financial support to "Welcome Neighbor"—a service in towns and cities around the Northeast that sent employees to welcome new residents with gifts from local merchants—in exchange for information about the apparent affluence, lifestyle, and other habits of the household. Such reports were often filled with hearsay and innuendo but were nonetheless passed on to purchasers of credit or insurance reports.

Even more disturbing was the testimony that the information files were essentially an open book to everyone except the subject of a given file. The credit bureaus freely acknowledged that they sold information to virtually any marginally credible customer, including potential employers, insurers, retailers, and private investigators. Senators were particularly disturbed to learn that government agencies, such as the FBI, the State Department, and the Internal Revenue Service, had essentially unfettered access to consumer credit and insurance files. Virtually all of the data collectors, however, admitted that they would not tell an individual exactly what was in his or her file, but instead would only discuss it in general terms.

In 1970, at the urging of Senator William Proxmire (D-Wis.) and Congressman Gallagher, Congress passed one of its few staunchly pro-privacy pieces of legislation, the Fair Credit Reporting Act. Under the provisions of the bill, credit bureaus were required for the first time to allow consumers to inspect the contents of their file (except medical information). If a consumer believed that the file contained inaccurate information, the bureau was required to investigate the claim. If the information could not be verified or was incorrect, the bureau was required to delete it. If the bureau felt that the information was accurate and the consumer disagreed, then the consumer was entitled to include a statement in the credit file with his or her explanation of the item in question. In addition, the bureau was required to provide the consumer with a list of everyone who had received a copy of the consumer's file for credit or insurance purposes within the previous six months, as well as every potential employer who had received it in the previous two years. Authority for enforcing the new law was given to the Federal Trade Commission, which promptly began the process of drafting regulations to govern the handling of personal credit information.

"The new law," Proxmire said in a statement at the time, "gives every user of credit, be he rich or poor, a chance to prevent the kind of heartaches and inconveniences that have plagued so many consumers in the past. From now on, if you are refused credit even though you have paid your bills on time in the past, you will be able to find out why. Unfounded rumors and innuendoes from neighbors that sometimes creep in can be weeded out."

Although the Fair Credit Reporting Act was an important recognition of the importance of consumer credit in modern American society and the potentially devastating consequences of erroneous or poorly guarded information, it addressed only one relatively narrow piece of the massive data accumulation taking place. Left unexamined in all of the debates over the act was the sheer quantity of data generated by each consumer—data which would increasingly take on a life of its own as more and more businesses deployed computers to handle record keeping and then linked those computers together in a growing web of mainframes. Not even the most garrulous snooping neighbor could match the cold and grinding efficiency of the silicon gossips.

THE SUPREME COURT RECOGNIZES THE RIGHT TO PRIVACY

Congress was not the only branch of government that was consumed with the issue of privacy during the 1960s. In the stunning neoclassical marble building across First Street from the Capitol, the U.S. Supreme Court was engaged in an ongoing discussion of privacy unmatched in its history. Numbers can scarcely tell the whole story of the Court's growing interest in privacy, but they do offer some useful insights as to just how important the issue had become. Consider, for instance, that in the 166 years between the creation of the Supreme Court and the start of Earl Warren's term as chief justice on October 5, 1953, the word "privacy" appears in just 88 high court opinions, only a handful of which discussed the concept to any substantive degree. By contrast, the term appears in 107 opinions during Warren's fifteen and a half years as chief justice, and many of those are among the most significant privacy cases in the Court's history. In ways both large and small, the Warren Court made privacy a central legal concept in American law, a development reflected in the fact that "privacy" has made an appearance in a remarkable 535 opinions in the forty years since Warren's retirement.

The Court's application of the concept of privacy was wide ranging. For instance, in 1958 the Court overturned a $100,000 fine against the National Association for the Advancement of Colored People (NAACP) by the state of Alabama. The NAACP had been found in contempt of court and fined because it refused to turn over its membership lists to the state as required by state law. The Court agreed that the forced disclosure of a membership list was a violation of the right of association in the First Amendment, a right the Court said was in large part based on privacy. "This Court has recognized the vital relationship between freedom to associate and privacy in one's associations," the opinion pointed out. "Inviolability of privacy in group association may in many circumstances be indispensable to preservation of freedom of association, particularly where a group espouses dissident beliefs." A similar result was reached in *Shelton v. Tucker* (1960), which upheld a teacher's right to refuse to list his personal group membership, and *Bates v. Little Rock* (1960) and *Gibson v. Florida Legislative Committee* (1963), both of which upheld the NAACP's refusal to list local members.

The bulk of the Court's privacy cases, however, came under the Fourth Amendment, the prohibition against unreasonable searches and seizures, and they touched on nearly every theme in this book. For instance, in *Elkins v. United States* (1960) the Court held, partly due to privacy concerns, that the Fourth Amendment prohibited the introduction in federal court of wiretap evidence that was improperly seized by state officials.

A year later, in *Silverman v. United States*, the Court prohibited the introduction of evidence obtained by a "spike microphone," a listening device with a foot-long metal rod that federal agents pushed through a wall and up against the side of a heating duct, which served as a perfect sounding board for conversations about an illegal gambling operation. "We need not here contemplate the Fourth Amendment implications of these and other frightening paraphernalia which the vaunted marvels of an electronic age may visit upon human society," associate justice Potter Stewart wrote. "For a fair reading of the record in this case shows that the eavesdropping was accomplished by means of an unauthorized physical penetration into the premises occupied by the petitioners." The intrusion by the microphone's metal spike meant that the Court was saved from considering whether eavesdropping by federal agents was in itself a violation of privacy under the Fourth Amendment.

That same year, in *Mapp v. Ohio*, the Court issued a bombshell decision that substantially altered police procedure. Three Cleveland police officers conducted a warrantless search of the home of Dollree Mapp, a woman who was suspected of harboring a bombing suspect. During the course of their extensive search, the officers came across a trunk containing "certain lewd and lascivious books, pictures, and photographs." Mapp was convicted for possession of obscene materials and challenged the introduction of the seized evidence. The state defended the conviction (and its actions) on the grounds that the exclusionary rule that prevented the use of such evidence by federal agents was not applicable to the states. Associate justice Tom Clark, writing for the Court, disagreed:

> We find that, as to the Federal Government, the Fourth and Fifth Amendments and, as to the States, the freedom from unconscionable invasions of privacy and the freedom from convictions based upon coerced confessions do enjoy an intimate relation in their perpetuation of principles of humanity and civil liberty . . . [secured] only after years of struggle. They express supplementing phases of the same constitutional purpose—to maintain inviolate large areas of personal privacy.

Accordingly, Justice Clark said, the exclusionary rule that prohibits the introduction of evidence obtained through unreasonable searches and seizures applies to state court proceedings as well as federal.

The Warren Court's most famous privacy case, *Griswold v. Connecticut* (1965), is often cited as the case in which the Court "established" the right to privacy. The case involved a challenge to the constitutionality of a Connecticut law that made it a crime to provide married persons with information on how to prevent conception. "We deal," wrote Justice Douglas, "with a right of privacy older than the Bill of Rights—older than our political parties, older than our school system. Marriage is a coming together for better or for worse, hopefully enduring, and intimate to the degree of being sacred."

Various amendments to the Constitution, Douglas said, "have penumbras formed by emanations from those guarantees that help give them life and substance." He then offered a quick catalog: the First Amendment protects the freedom of association; the Third Amendment prohibits the quartering of troops in one's home; the Fourth Amendment protects from unreasonable searches and seizures; the Fifth Amendment prevents government intrusion on the freedom from self-incrimination; and the Ninth Amendment provides that the enumeration of certain rights is not intended "to deny or disparage others retained by the people."

Citing *Mapp v. Ohio*, Douglas said that "the right of privacy which presses for recognition here is a legitimate one." Having concluded that Connecticut's law was unnecessarily broad and invaded the "zone of privacy" of married couples, the Court ruled that it was unconstitutional.

Two justices dissented with the majority's opinion: Potter Stewart and Hugo Black. Justice Black, of course, had his own run-in with the concept of privacy thirty years earlier, when the Senate Lobby Committee he chaired seized thousands of personal telegrams in Washington. Black—who was a strict constructionist when it came to constitutional interpretation—said that he felt it was unwise and unwarranted to replace the Fourth Amendment's text with a vague protection of a "right to privacy."

"I like my privacy as well as the next one," Black said, "but I am nevertheless compelled to admit that government has a right to invade it unless prohibited by some specific constitutional provision. For these reasons I cannot agree with the Court's judgment and the reasons it gives for holding this Connecticut law unconstitutional."

Over time, the extension of the right to privacy to the marital relationship in *Griswold* would prove to be the most far-reaching and controversial of the Warren Court's privacy decisions (particularly insofar as it helped form the basis of *Roe v. Wade*, the Court's 1973 decision on a woman's right to abortion). But in the short term, it was the Court's decisions regarding the legality of wiretapping and eavesdropping that generated the most controversy.

In the summer of 1967, the Court was presented with a challenge to New York's eavesdropping law, which permitted the physical installation of a recording device in a suspect's office to capture conversations with nothing more than an assertion that the eavesdropping was "in the public interest." After reviewing the history of eavesdropping, from actual listeners hiding under the eaves to recently developed electronic "bugs," the Court concluded, in *Berger v. New York*, that the New York statute amounted to the issuance of a "general warrant" and thus was unconstitutionally broad.

"This is no formality that we require today," associate justice Tom Clark wrote, "but a fundamental rule that has long been recognized as basic to the privacy of every home in America. Few threats to liberty exist which are greater than that posed by the use of eavesdropping devices. Some may claim that without the use of such devices crime detection in certain areas may suffer some delays since eavesdropping is quicker, easier, and more certain. However, techniques and practices may well be developed that will operate just as speedily and certainly and—what is more important—without attending illegality."

The *Berger* decision was the prelude to an even more politically significant wiretap case the following winter: *Katz v. United States*. At issue was whether the FBI had violated the Fourth Amendment by attaching a recording device, without a warrant, to the outside of a public phone booth. Charles Katz, who was charged with interstate gambling, objected to the introduction of the recordings as evidence against him. In an opinion written by associate justice Potter Stewart, the Court made it clear that the Fourth Amendment was not limited to protecting mere physical property (such as papers) or even specific locations (like the home), but instead was intended to protect an individual's reasonable *expectation* of privacy, regardless of where that individual might be.

"Wherever a man may be," Stewart wrote, "he is entitled to know that he will remain free from unreasonable searches and seizures. The government agents here ignored the procedure of antecedent justification . . . that is central to the Fourth Amendment, a procedure that we hold to be a constitutional precondition of the kind of electronic surveillance involved in this case."

Once again, Justice Black took strong issue with the Court's analysis of Fourth Amendment jurisprudence and its conclusion:

Since I see no way in which the words of the Fourth Amendment can be construed to apply to eavesdropping, that closes
the matter for me. In interpreting the Bill of Rights, I willingly
go as far as a liberal construction of the language takes me, but
I simply cannot in good conscience give a meaning to words
which they have never before been thought to have and which
they certainly do not have in common ordinary usage. I will
not distort the words of the Amendment in order to "keep the
Constitution up to date" or "to bring it into harmony with the
times." It was never meant that this Court have such power,
which in effect would make us a continuously functioning constitutional convention.

Black's staunch (and solo) opposition notwithstanding, the *Katz*
decision made it clear once and for all that warrantless eavesdropping
and wiretapping was unacceptable under the Fourth Amendment.

The elimination of a popular law enforcement tool that had been
in use for at least fifty years (and more likely seventy) by both state
and federal agents unavoidably drew the Warren Court into the thick
of a heated political debate over the proper parameters of the Fourth
Amendment and the right to privacy. Ironically, one of the most ve-
hement critics of the Court's Fourth Amendment rulings—former
vice president Richard M. Nixon—was also one of the first attorneys
to argue an appeal based on the Court's recently announced "right to
privacy."

Nixon's client was James Hill, the father of a family held hostage
by three escaped convicts in a home outside Philadelphia in 1952. The
ordeal inspired numerous works, including a novel, a Broadway play,
and a movie that starred Humphrey Bogart as one of the convicts. As
the actors prepared for their Broadway opening, *Life* photographed
the rehearsals for a photo spread.

Hill sued Time, Inc., the publisher of *Life*, alleging that the magazine's article falsely suggested that the play mirrored the family's
experience. Despite Time's assertion that the Hill family was a legitimate subject of public interest, Hill was awarded damages of $30,000
under the New York statute prohibiting the misappropriation of a
person's image. The Supreme Court accepted the case to address

whether the verdict unconstitutionally infringed on the magazine's First Amendment rights.

During the oral argument, Nixon favorably cited *Griswold v. Connecticut* and told the Court that the right to privacy announced in that case "is of paramount importance." "Without it," he asked, "how is an individual to remain an individual in our mass communication society?" He argued that the differences between the real-life event and the photo article of the play rehearsal were significant and constituted commercial exploitation of Hill and his family that merited compensation under the statute.

After reviewing the history of the New York statute, including the 1902 *Roberson* case that gave rise to it (discussed in chapter 4), the Court rejected Nixon's argument and overturned the verdict. According to the Court, in order for New York's commercial exploitation statute to be constitutional as applied to the press, there must be proof that the story was published with knowing falsehood or reckless disregard for the truth. Since the judge failed to give the necessary instructions, the verdict was unconstitutional.

There is little reason to think that Nixon's subsequent attacks on the Court stemmed from his loss in the *Hill* case; it was a relatively minor case and a relatively narrow defeat. But there is also little question that over the next eighteen months, as Nixon turned his attention to presidential politics, criticism of the Supreme Court became one of the major planks in his campaign platform.

MORE BATTLES OVER WIRETAPPING

In the spring of 1968, much of Congress's time and attention was devoted to debating a massive crime bill, which ultimately became known as the Omnibus Crime Control and Safe Streets Act. The origins of the bill lay in the "Safe Streets" initiative proposed the year before by the Johnson administration, a proposal sent to Congress to dramatically increase federal assistance to state and local law enforcement.

Despite his efforts to get in front on the crime control issue, however, President Johnson quickly lost control of the legislation as it moved through Congress. In the view of most members of Congress (and much of the American public), Johnson's proposal did not do enough to address the nation's rapidly rising crime rate and declining sense of safety. There was also widespread discontent on Capitol Hill over many of the criminal law decisions issued by the Warren Court during the previous two to three years, with many believing that the Court had simply gone too far in protecting the rights of criminals. And finally, the congressional response to Johnson's crime bill was driven by the fact that 1968 was an election year, and one in which the electorate was clearly focusing on conservative issues like law and order.

During the fall of 1967, the Senate Judiciary Committee reshaped and expanded Johnson's bill to the point where it was completely unrecognizable. It was, the *Washington Post* editorialized, "not a rational attack on crime so much as an expression of provincialism and hysteria." The *Post* criticized Senator John L. McClellan (D-Ark.) for his insistence on broad authorization for wiretapping, which the paper predicted would be disastrous for the Constitution: "In our judgment, it would result in virtually unrestrained eavesdropping at the pleasure of the police and in a general fear, hitherto confined to totalitarian societies, that Big Brother might be listening in on every confidence and every intimacy of the home or the office."

Even more remarkable, the *Post* said, was a proposal by the Judiciary Committee that would make "voluntariness" the only standard by which to judge a confession and would bar the U.S. Supreme Court from reviewing any state supreme court ruling on whether a confession was freely given. "At one stroke," the *Post* warned, "the bill would take away the supremacy of the United States and the capacity of the U.S. Supreme Court to hold the states to constitutional criteria."

The crime bill contained ample topics for debate, but few generated as much discussion as the wiretapping provisions. In his original proposal, President Johnson had asked Congress to ban all electronic eavesdropping, with a narrowly limited exception for national security investigations. But from the start, Congress was unreceptive to President Johnson's call for wiretap restrictions, arguing that such methods were necessary if federal and state law enforcement officials were going to have any ability to effectively fight crime.

As the crime bill moved toward passage in the spring of 1968, the intense debate spilled over to the campaign trail. In May, former vice

president Nixon, then running for the Republican presidential nomination, issued a six-thousand-word treatise titled "Toward Freedom
from Fear," which laid out how he would make the streets of America
safer by ending crime and "removing from this nation the stigma of
a lawless society." The phrase "lawless society" was one that Nixon
employed frequently in his stump speeches that year, typically generating raucous applause from audiences that agreed with him that the
administration of President Johnson had been "lame and ineffectual"
by failing to prevent an 88 percent increase in crime over the previous
seven years.

It is an indication of how the political winds were blowing that
year that the Democratic-controlled Senate not only agreed with
Nixon but went much further than even he suggested. The legislation
adopted by the Senate less than two weeks later was breathtaking in
its authorization of police eavesdropping. Under the provisions of the
bill, federal authorities would be allowed to conduct wiretapping to
investigate a wide range of crimes, including murder, kidnapping,
robbery, narcotics, national security, and ominously, "labor racketeering." The grant of authority to state and local police was even
broader: surveillance was authorized to investigate any crime that
was "dangerous to life, limb, or property, and punishable by impris-
onment for more than one year."

Despite the ill favor with which the Supreme Court was viewed by
many members of Congress, the bill did provide for court supervision
of wiretapping. A showing of probable cause was required in order to
get authorization for electronic surveillance, and each order would
have to be renewed every thirty days. In cases involving national security and organized crime, surveillance could be conducted for forty-
eight hours without a warrant in the event of an "emergency," but
then a court order would be required.

The wiretapping issue took a dramatic twist just three days later,
when noted *Washington Post* journalists Drew Pearson and Jack
Anderson broke the news that Democratic presidential candidate
Robert F. Kennedy, while serving as attorney general, had ordered the
FBI to wiretap the telephone of the Reverend Dr. Martin Luther King
Jr. The ostensible reason, Pearson and Anderson said, was that Ken-
nedy believed that King was communicating with Communists and
was being influenced by them. The FBI initially refused to place the

tap on King's phones, but eventually complied when Kennedy signed an order for the wiretap in October 1963. The information garnered from the King wiretaps was allegedly used to track his movements around the country and to prepare a list of people for the FBI to interview for possible Communist sympathies.

Kennedy forcefully denied the wiretapping charge, but Pearson and Anderson were not done. Their next article described various FBI memos that made it unequivocally clear that Kennedy had in fact ordered a wiretap on King and had received detailed information from FBI files about other wiretaps. "It is not pleasant to be in the position of challenging the word of a member of the Kennedy family," the reporters said. "In all deference to the former Attorney General, however, there exist some important memos in the Justice Department which show conclusively that he did have knowledge of eavesdropping and that he authorized at least part of it."

How much of an impact those revelations would have had on the crime bill or Kennedy's presidential campaign will never be known. Certainly, it did not prevent him from achieving a dramatic but narrow victory over rival Eugene McCarthy in the California primary on June 5. But as Senator Kennedy left the ballroom of the Ambassador Hotel, where he had been addressing his supporters, he was shot and killed by twenty-four-year-old Palestinian Sirhan Sirhan. Kennedy's assassination sent shock waves through the country and rapidly accelerated the passage of the crime bill. In the wake of the senator's tragic death, few were willing to oppose tough anticrime legislation, regardless of its impact on the Constitution.

"Stirred up by the shooting of Sen. Robert F. Kennedy," reporter George Lardner Jr. wrote, "the House hurled an angry challenge at the Supreme Court yesterday and set the stage for swift and final congressional action today of crime control legislation." One of the few voices in opposition, or at least moderation, was Emmanuel Celler, the chair of the House Judiciary Committee, who warned that the Supreme Court would declare much of the bill unconstitutional. His argument was fiercely rejected by Gerald Ford, then House minority leader, who said, "I refuse to concede that the elected representatives of the people cannot be the winner in a confrontation with the Supreme Court. Let this vote today be the battlefield."

There was some speculation that Johnson might yet veto the bill.

But on June 20, he signed the bill with reservations and issued a somewhat futile call for Congress to repeal the wiretapping provisions. He praised legislators for banning wiretapping and eavesdropping by private parties and prohibiting the sale of "listening-in" devices in interstate commerce. But Congress, Johnson said, took "an unwise and potentially dangerous step" by allowing law enforcement officers to conduct electronic surveillance "in an almost unlimited variety of situations":

> If we are not very careful and cautious in our planning, these legislative provisions could result in a nation of snoopers bending through the keyholes of the homes and offices of America, spying on our neighbors.
>
> No conversation in the sanctity of the bedroom or relayed over a copper telephone wire would be free of eavesdropping by those who say they want to ferret out crime.
>
> Thus, I believe this action goes far beyond the effective and legitimate needs of law enforcement. The right of privacy is a valued right. But in a technologically advanced society, it is a vulnerable right. That is why we must strive to protect it all the more against erosion. . . . We need not surrender our privacy to win the war on crime.

Johnson basically told Congress that he intended to ignore the wiretap provisions, saying that he would send attorney general Ramsey Clark to the Hill to explain the dangers of the law Congress had adopted. He also said that his administration would continue its three-year-old policy of limiting wiretapping and eavesdropping to cases involving national security, and even then only when expressly authorized by the attorney general. As events would soon make clear, Johnson's successor would not be so restrained when it came to listening to American conversations.

9

"TOWARD FREEDOM FROM FEAR"

The Privacy versus Security Debate Intensifies

Richard M. Nixon did not invent the phrase "strict constructionist," nor was he even the first presidential candidate to offer it as the standard for his Supreme Court nominations. But few presidential candidates have made the makeup of the Court as central to their campaigns as Nixon did in 1968. In speech after speech, Nixon linked the rise in the national crime rate to the decisions of the Warren Court. At first, his allegations were general: in a lengthy article in *Reader's Digest* in September 1967, he said that "the fault cannot be traced to any single decision of any one court. It is rather the cumulative effect of many decisions, each one of which has weakened the law and encouraged the criminal." But as the campaign heated up in 1968 and the debate over the Omnibus Crime Control and Safe Streets Act (including its wiretapping provisions) intensified, Nixon began offering more pointed criticism of the Warren Court's rulings. He particularly challenged two of the Court's decisions—*Escobedo v. Illinois* (1964) and *Miranda v. Arizona* (1966)—which imposed strict limits on police questioning and the use of confessions by suspects.

"From the point of view of the peace forces," Nixon said in May 1968, "the cumulative impact of these decisions has been to very nearly rule out the confession as an effective and major tool in prosecution and law enforcement." Later that month, in a speech in Dallas, Texas, Nixon went even further and charged that the Warren Court had given a "green light" to the "criminal elements" in the United States.

Many presidential candidates have campaigned at least in part by running against the presiding Supreme Court; but even when those campaigns were successful, few new presidents have been able to act immediately on their judicial nomination promises. But just a few days after Nixon's speech in Dallas, it became unusually clear that the next president would be making at least one particularly significant appointment to the Supreme Court. Shortly after the assassination of Robert Kennedy on June 6, 1968, the chief justice, Earl Warren, wrote to President Johnson and informed him of his "intention to retire as Chief Justice of the United States effective at your pleasure."

Warren's ostensible reason for doing so was his advancing age—he was seventy-seven—but most observers at the time agreed that Warren was motivated far more strongly by the desire to avoid any possibility that his successor would be picked by Richard Nixon. Thanks to a long-standing feud arising out of the 1952 Republican presidential campaign, Warren loathed and mistrusted Nixon. But in the wake of Robert Kennedy's assassination, Warren correctly anticipated that Nixon's already popular law-and-order campaign would win him the presidency.

However, the chief justice's efforts to frustrate Nixon and better preserve the legacy of his Supreme Court leadership were unsuccessful. In June, Johnson nominated associate justice Abe Fortas to replace Warren, but his nomination was strenuously opposed by Republicans and conservative Southern Democrats. Although the Senate Judiciary Committee approved Fortas's nomination by a vote of 11–6, conservatives organized an unprecedented filibuster to oppose it on the floor of the Senate. (It was the first, and still the only, filibuster against a Supreme Court nominee.) Following a failed attempt by the Senate Democratic leadership to end the filibuster, Fortas voluntarily withdrew his nomination. With just over a month to go before the national election, there was no time for Johnson to nominate someone else.

It must have been with somewhat gritted teeth that Chief Justice Warren swore Nixon in as president on January 20, 1969. Even before he did so, Warren agreed to Nixon's request that he remain as chief justice until the end of the Court's 1968–69 term, to give the new president time to select his successor.

At least one current justice was perhaps naively unconcerned about possible changes to the Court. A month before the election, associate justice William O. Douglas, the Court's most outspokenly liberal member, gave an unusually frank interview to the *New York Times*.

Douglas said that it was doubtful, in his view, that citizens would allow "some Stone Age guys" to reverse the important decisions of the Warren Court.

"A constitutional decision in the Court is always open to change," Douglas acknowledged. "Much of the things we do are controversial. I just don't know that the sober second thoughts Americans have will allow fundamental change."

That might have been true if President Nixon had been limited to a single appointment, even one as influential as the chief justice; but over the next six years, the new president had an almost unprecedented opportunity to reshape the Court. Even as he was weighing possible replacements for Chief Justice Warren, Nixon got an unexpected bonus. In early 1969, reports began to circulate that Justice Fortas had accepted a lifetime annual $20,000 stipend for unspecified services from a foundation established by a Wall Street financier who was under investigation (and later jailed) for securities fraud. Although there was no evidence that Fortas himself had done anything wrong, Chief Justice Warren persuaded him to resign to protect the reputation of the Court. His sudden departure left Nixon with two vacancies on the Court and an unusually rapid opportunity to shape its future direction.

Nixon's choice for chief justice was a fulfillment of his promise to rein in what he saw as the liberal excesses of the Warren Court. He nominated Warren E. Burger, a thirteen-year veteran of the U.S. Court of Appeals for the District of Columbia Circuit and an outspoken critic of the Warren Court's criminal law decisions. Burger was easily confirmed by the Senate on June 9, 1969, by a vote of 74–3.

Nixon's efforts to fill the seat of Justice Fortas, however, did not go as smoothly. Two successive nominees, Clement F. Haynsworth and G. Harrold Carswell, were both rejected by the Senate. Haynsworth was defeated 45–55 on November 21, 1969, chiefly due to allegations by Senate Democrats and liberal Republicans that his rulings on the U.S. Court of Appeals for the Fourth Circuit were pro-segregation and staunchly antilabor. Carswell, whose name was sent by Nixon to the Senate in January 1970, ran into the same roadblock: during a 1948 campaign for the Georgia legislature, Carswell openly supported racial segregation.

Questions were also raised about Carswell's capabilities as a judge, since nearly 60 percent of his rulings as a district court judge had been overturned on appeal. Senator Roman Hruska (R-Neb.) tried to defend Carswell with one of the more memorable lines from the nation's long history of nominations: "Even if he is mediocre, there are a lot of mediocre judges and people and lawyers. They are entitled to a little representation, aren't they, and a little chance?" It wouldn't be the last time that academic and professional mediocrity were touted as positive qualifications for high office, but in this instance, Hruska's comments did Carswell little good: he was rejected by the relatively narrow margin of 45–51.

For his third choice, Nixon settled on Harry Blackmun, a member of the U.S. Court of Appeals for the Eighth Circuit. He was a fellow Minnesotan to Chief Justice Burger and had even served as the best man at Burger's wedding. Nixon no doubt felt confident that he had finally succeeded in locating a nominee who would not only survive the nomination process but also bring a cautious, conservative judicial style to the high court. But there were warning signs that the president might not get quite the justice he expected: Blackmun wryly told *Time* that he didn't know what the phrase "strict constructionist" meant, and he was praised by colleagues on the Eighth Circuit for his open-mindedness. It is intriguing, too, that the weekly newsmagazine made a point of describing Blackmun, sixty-one, as "a reserved man who is protective of his privacy." That assessment would prove significant in the years to come.

Only a handful of presidents—Washington, Taft, Harding, Franklin Roosevelt—have had the opportunity to appoint as many as four justices in a single term. In September 1971, President Nixon joined that small club when two more Supreme Court justices, John M. Harlan II and Hugo Black, announced that they were retiring from the bench. Despite the fact that the Democrats held the majority in the Senate, Nixon continued his push to nominate justices that he felt would undo the damage of the Warren Court. In a nationally televised address on October 21, 1971, Nixon announced that he was nominating Lewis Powell—a sixty-four-year-old lawyer from Richmond, Virginia, and former president of the American Bar Association—and William H. Rehnquist, a forty-seven-year-old constitutional expert who was currently serving as assistant attorney general in charge of the Office of Legal Counsel under attorney general John Mitchell.

Rehnquist was a particular proponent of tools to promote law and order, including wiretapping and other forms of electronic surveillance. As head of the Office of Legal Counsel, Rehnquist had frequently testified before Congress in support of legislation authorizing broader use of wiretaps and secret informants. During his nomination hearing, however, he told the Senate Judiciary Committee that he had worked behind the scenes to soften the Justice Department's argument, led by Attorney General Mitchell, that it had "inherent power" to wiretap alleged "subversives" without court oversight. He also backed away from earlier statements suggesting that police could conduct surveillance of peaceful political protests without violating the First Amendment. Rehnquist conceded that such surveillance might have a "chilling effect" on free speech and that judicial intervention might be required.

Despite some liberal qualms about whether Rehnquist was undergoing a "confirmation conversion" (a phrase coined a few years later by Senator Patrick Leahy (D-Vt.) during the nomination of Robert Bork), both Rehnquist and Powell were confirmed by comfortable margins, although it is fair to say that Powell's margin (89–1) was considerably more comfortable than Rehnquist's (68–26). With four successful appointments in just under three years, Nixon no doubt happily anticipated that the Court would forsake its wantonly liberal ways and embrace a more rational, law-and-order view of the world.

POLITICAL PARANOIA AND PRIVACY

A more tractable and pro-surveillance Court was an important goal for Nixon and his advisers. During the course of the 1968 campaign, Nixon left no doubt that he would be a more enthusiastic wiretapper than President Johnson. In addition to his policy statement on criminal law, he had urged the Republican National Convention's Committee on Resolutions to take a strong stand in the Republican Party's platform in favor of wiretapping:

Yet, as the profits of organized crime grow prodigiously into untold billions of dollars—the Attorney General of the United States expresses his public distaste for penetrating the secrecy of this organized conspiracy. He has publicly refused to use the strictly limited and publicly safeguarded wiretapping, authorized by Congress and approved by the courts, which is considered by many criminal justice officials as law enforcement's most effective tool against crime.

A new Attorney General, with a new attitude and a new awareness and a new determination, could make a world of difference in the quality of American life by making decisive inroads on the security of organized crime.

Nixon's pick for attorney general was John N. Mitchell, a Wall Street attorney who was a partner with Nixon in the New York firm of Nixon Mudge Rose Guthrie & Alexander, and who served as Nixon's campaign manager in both 1968 and 1972. During his confirmation hearings in January 1969, Mitchell bluntly told the Senate Judiciary Committee that he intended to expand the government's use of electronic surveillance in the battle against crime, "not only in national security cases, but against organized crime and other major crimes."

The new attorney general wasted little time carrying out his promise. During the first month of the Nixon administration, he expanded the use of wiretaps to include investigations of suspected racketeers. The attorney general also asserted that he had the authority under "national security" to conduct surveillance of domestic organizations, ranging from the extreme right to the far left. However, despite the fact that the Omnibus Crime Control and Safe Streets Act required the administration to give Congress a yearly report of its wiretapping activities, there was no clear indication of just how much domestic political surveillance was occurring.

Soon after Mitchell's appointment, the nation's attention was focused on the issue of surveillance by the renewed allegations that the FBI had wiretapped the telephone conversations of slain civil-rights leader Martin Luther King Jr. The reports of such surveillance had first surfaced during the nascent presidential campaign of former attorney general and New York senator Robert F. Kennedy, but the issue had subsided following his assassination in June 1968. A year later, however, during a hearing on boxer Cassius Clay's motion to vacate a five-year prison sentence for refusing induction into the U.S. Army, an FBI agent testified that the bureau had tapped King's wires for a number of years.

During the subsequent outcry, former attorney general Ramsey Clark called on J. Edgar Hoover, then in his forty-fifth year as director of the FBI, to step down. Hoover angrily refused, pointing out that the request for the King wiretaps had originated with Attorney General Kennedy and not the FBI. Nixon came to the defense of his embattled FBI director, saying during a press conference that he had checked with the FBI and "found that [the wiretapping] had always been approved by the attorney general, as Mr. Hoover testified in 1964 and 1965."

Regardless of who actually initiated the surveillance on Dr. King, confirmation of the widely rumored wiretapping intensified public concern about governmental surveillance. A week later, the American Civil Liberties Union filed suit in Chicago, charging that the Justice Department's policy of wiretapping domestic groups on "national security" grounds was unconstitutional. The ACLU suit was filed after the Justice Department refused to release transcripts of intercepted phone conversations of various antiwar and black power groups, as well as of eight individuals indicted on charges of inciting riots during the disastrous 1968 Democratic National Convention in Chicago. There was no need to release the transcripts, the Justice Department told the court, because the "national security" exemption provided by the Omnibus Crime Control and Safe Streets Act was broad enough to encompass domestic groups. It was not the intent of Congress, the department continued, to prevent the investigation of groups that "use unlawful means to attack and subvert the existing structure of government."

What startled many people, however, was the fact that the Justice Department went even further and argued that the federal courts had "no competence" to determine whether electronic surveillance of domestic subversives was necessary to protect national security. The implication was that only the president and the executive branch could make that decision. As one federal judge anonymously said to *New York Times* reporter Sidney Zion, the Justice Department was mounting an almost direct assault on the underlying principle of *Marbury v. Madison* (1803), the case in which the Supreme Court declared that it alone has the ability to decide whether acts of Congress and the executive branch are constitutional. "The department's position is as arrogant as hell," the judge said. "Among other things they seem to be urging an end to *Marbury v. Madison,* which would be a joke, son, if it weren't so shocking."

Sensing a rising tide of public concern about surveillance, Attorney General Mitchell told reporters in July 1969 that the Justice Department's use of electronic surveillance had decreased since the start of the Nixon administration. But any lull was merely temporary; a year later, in a speech to the International Association of Chiefs of Police in Atlanta, Mitchell described wiretapping as the best weapon to defeat organized crime and urged Congress to expand wiretapping authorization to include cases involving bombings or threats of bombing. "I believe that its use by federal authorities is not only a right but a duty," Mitchell said. "And I believe the same is true for other authorities in those states where wiretap is not outlawed."

A few months later in Detroit, however, U.S. district court judge Damon J. Keith ruled in the ACLU lawsuit that the Justice Department did not have the right to conduct surveillance on radical domestic groups without a warrant. "An idea which seems to permeate much of the Government's argument," Judge Keith wrote, "is that a dissident domestic organization is akin to an unfriendly foreign power that must be dealt with in the same fashion. There is a great danger in an argument of this nature, for it strikes at the very constitutional privileges and immunities that are inherent in United States citizenship."

Four months later, the U.S. Court of Appeals for the Sixth Circuit upheld Judge Keith's order, agreeing that neither Attorney General Mitchell nor President Nixon had an "inherent power" to conduct electronic surveillance of domestic groups. Writing for the 2–1 majority, Judge George C. Edwards Jr. said that the Fourth Amendment ban against unreasonable searches and seizures imposes a requirement on government agents to obtain a warrant for domestic surveillance. After a thorough review of the nation's history, the wiretap decisions of the Supreme Court, and congressional legislation on the topic, Judge Edwards sternly rejected the Justice Department's argument:

> The government has not pointed to, and we do not find, one written phrase in the Constitution, in the statutory law, or in the case law of the United States, which exempts the President, the Attorney General, or federal law enforcement from the re-

strictions of the Fourth Amendment in the case at hand. It is clear to us that Congress in the Omnibus Crime Control and Safe Streets Act of 1968 refrained from attempting to convey to the President any power which he did not already possess.

Essentially, the government rests its case upon the inherent powers of the President as Chief of State to defend the existence of the State. We have already shown that this very claim was rejected by the Supreme Court in *Youngstown Sheet & Tube Co. v. Sawyer* (1952), and we shall not repeat its holding here.

An additional difficulty with the inherent power argument in the context of this case is that the Fourth Amendment was adopted in the immediate aftermath of abusive searches and seizures directed against American colonists under the sovereign and inherent powers of King George III. The United States Constitution was adopted to provide a check upon "sovereign" power. The creation of three coordinate branches of government by that Constitution was designed to require sharing in the administration of that awesome power.

It is strange, indeed, that in this case the traditional power of sovereigns like King George III should be invoked on behalf of an American president to defeat one of the fundamental freedoms for which the founders of this country overthrew King George's reign.

U.S. solicitor general Erwin N. Griswold filed a petition for certiorari (a formal request for review) with the Supreme Court on behalf of the Justice Department, asking the Court to overturn the lower court rulings and uphold the warrantless wiretaps. Griswold apparently did not fully agree with Mitchell's rather imperial view of the Constitution; he dropped the "inherent power" argument on appeal, and instead suggested to the Supreme Court that surveillance of domestic radicals should be recognized as a narrow exception to the Fourth Amendment. Mitchell, however, clearly was unfazed by the Sixth Circuit's ruling. In June 1971 he gave a lengthy speech on the case to the Virginia Bar Association, in which he continued his full-throated defense of the administration's surveillance of radical groups. Mitchell even went so far as to describe domestic radicals as more dangerous than foreign forces. "Were the president to permit the overthrow of the government by unconstitutional means," Mitchell said, "he would be violating his constitutional oath. The Constitution of the United States cannot possibly be construed as containing provisions inconsistent with its own survival. It is a charter for a viable government system, not a suicide pact."

THE UNPREDICTABILITY OF THE NIXON COURT

Because of the fact that in just under three years in office, President Nixon had chosen nearly half of the members of the Supreme Court, many commentators fell into the habit of referring to the new bench as the "Nixon Court" rather than the traditional "Burger Court." Much of that had to do with Nixon's successful appointment of four justices—Burger, Blackmun, Powell, and Rehnquist—who seemed to fit his oft-declared requirement of "judicial conservatives" who would merely interpret the law and not make it.

The unusual moniker was also a reflection of the fact that Burger was a much less dynamic and effective chief justice than his predecessor. A number of books, including *The Brethren: Inside the Supreme Court* (1979), a contemporaneous insider account by Bob Woodward and Scott Armstrong, depicted Burger as a difficult and aloof chief justice whose handling of court conferences and assignment of opinions was frequently manipulative and often petty. Granted, it would have been challenging for any chief justice to preside over the Court during such a dramatic and rapid ideological shift; the splintered and occasionally antagonistic relationships among the justices at the time is amply reflected in the sheer number of individual opinions written in difficult cases. But without question, Burger's indifferent management style and preference for administrative improvements over substantive legal debates limited his ability to put a firm stamp on the Court.

Predictably, as Nixon's various appointees took their seats, the Court grew slowly more sympathetic to the federal and state governments, more forgiving of possibly unconstitutional procedural errors, and—particularly after Powell and Rehnquist were sworn in—much more pro-business. But it is also true that the pendulum did not swing nearly as far to the right as Nixon had hoped: not only was the new

Court respectful of the precedents the Warren Court had established, it actually expanded on several of them, especially in the privacy realm.

For example, in June 1971, with two Nixon appointees on board (Burger and Blackmun), the Court ruled for the first time that an individual whose Fourth Amendment right had been violated by federal agents could file a civil suit against the agents for damages. The opinion in *Bivens v. Six Unknown Federal Narcotics Agents*, written by associate justice William Brennan, a Warren Court stalwart, was enough to make a strict constructionist despair. "Of course, the Fourth Amendment does not in so many words provide for its enforcement by an award of money damages for the consequences of its violation," Brennan wrote. "But it is well settled that where legal rights have been invaded, and a federal statute provides for a general right to sue for such invasion, federal courts may use any available remedy to make good the wrong done." As might be expected, both Chief Justice Burger and Justice Blackmun dissented.

The following spring, in *Eisenstadt v. Baird*, the Supreme Court extended the "right of privacy" announced in *Griswold v. Connecticut* to unmarried individuals. The case involved a lecturer named William Baird, who was convicted under Massachusetts law for giving a sample of Emko vaginal foam, a contraceptive, to a young woman at the end of his lecture. Under Massachusetts law at the time, only doctors and pharmacists could distribute contraceptives, and only to married couples. Once again, Justice Brennan wrote the majority opinion. "The question for our determination," he said, "is whether there is some ground of difference that rationally explains the different treatment accorded married and unmarried persons" under Massachusetts law. The Court concluded that there was no rational basis for allowing married couples access to contraceptives and denying them to the unmarried.

"If the right of privacy means anything," the Court said, "it is the right of the individual, married or single, to be free from unwarranted governmental intrusion into matters so fundamentally affecting a person as the decision whether to bear or beget a child."

When *Eisenstadt* was argued, neither Justice Powell nor Justice Rehnquist had joined the Court, so they did not participate in the decision. However, three of four Nixon appointees were present for oral argument in the ACLU domestic wiretapping case, *United States v. U.S. District Court*. (Justice Rehnquist recused himself.) Although few thought that the Justice Department had made a very compelling case for the broad discretionary power it sought, there was still active curiosity about how Nixon's "judicial conservatives" would vote. Justice Powell, for instance, had caused a stir during his nomination process by releasing an article he wrote for the *Richmond Times-Dispatch*. In the article, Powell said that while he had not undertaken a "full analysis" of whether national security concerns merited the wiretapping of radical groups, he did think that "it is now extremely difficult to distinguish between foreign and domestic threats to our democratic institutions."

When the Court issued its ruling in *United States v. U.S. District Court* on June 19, 1972, the Nixon administration received three unpleasant blows. First, and perhaps least unexpectedly, it lost the case. Second, the decision was unanimous; not a single Nixon appointee supported the administration's position. And third, one of those appointees, Lewis Powell, not only drafted the opinion of the Court but did so in broad and unequivocal terms.

Justice Powell and the other members of the Court candidly acknowledged that "the covertness and complexity of potential unlawful conduct against the Government and the necessary dependency of many conspirators upon the telephone make electronic surveillance an effective investigatory instrument in certain circumstances." But while it is a fact that such surveillance can help maintain an orderly society, Powell said, that does not mean that government surveillance is a welcome development. "There is, understandably, a deep-seated uneasiness and apprehension," he wrote, "that this capability will be used to intrude upon cherished privacy of law-abiding citizens." He went on to spell out the danger in no uncertain terms:

> History abundantly documents the tendency of Government—however benevolent and benign its motives—to view with suspicion those who most fervently dispute its policies. Fourth Amendment protections become the more necessary when the targets of official surveillance may be those suspected of un-

orthodoxy in their political beliefs. The danger to political dissent is acute where the Government attempts to act under so vague a concept as the power to protect "domestic security."

The crux of the issue, Powell said, is that under the Fourth Amendment, an independent magistrate is required to determine the legitimacy of a proposed search. "The historical judgment," he wrote, "which the Fourth Amendment accepts, is that unreviewed executive discretion may yield too readily to pressures to obtain incriminating evidence and overlook potential invasions of privacy and protected speech."

Powell acknowledged a certain "pragmatic force" to the Justice Department's arguments for warrantless domestic wiretaps to protect national security: that prior judicial review would impede the president's duty to protect domestic security; that the surveillance was intended to gather information, not evidence; that warrant procedures are intended to regulate criminal investigations, not counterintelligence; that the courts are not capable of understanding the security issues involved; and that the warrant procedure would risk the identity and even the lives of government agents and informants.

Nonetheless, Powell said, the Justice Department had failed to present compelling reasons to disregard the warrant requirements of the Fourth Amendment. "Official surveillance," he wrote, "whether its purpose be criminal investigation or ongoing intelligence gathering, risks infringement of constitutionally protected privacy of speech. Security surveillances are especially sensitive because of the inherent vagueness of the domestic security concept, the necessarily broad and continuing nature of intelligence gathering, and the temptation to utilize such surveillances to oversee political dissent."

Demonstrating once again that despite their apparent isolation, the members of the Court do take some notice of the environment in which their decisions are issued, Powell addressed the broader concerns of the public. "By no means of least importance," he said, "will be the reassurance of the public generally that indiscriminate wiretapping and bugging of law-abiding citizens cannot occur."

Just two days before the Court's decision in the domestic wiretapping case, five men were arrested for breaking into Democratic National Committee headquarters at the Watergate office complex in Washington, D.C. The men were carrying burglary tools, cameras and film, tear gas guns, more than $2,000 in cash, and various outdated listening devices that nonetheless were capable of picking up both telephone calls and office conversations and broadcasting them to a hotel across the street.

SAM ERVIN TAKES ON THE WHITE HOUSE

When security guard Frank Wills noticed tape covering the locks on several doors in the Watergate complex and called the police in the early hours of June 17, 1972, he set in motion a train of events that would substantially reshape privacy law in the United States. The ramifications were not limited to federal and state law: thanks in large part to the reaction of the Nixon White House to the subsequent investigation, never again would a president enjoy the level of privacy and journalistic discretion that helped hide Franklin Roosevelt's disability or John F. Kennedy's serial infidelities. (Indeed, the culture of inquiry fueled by the Watergate scandal helped spur considerable postmortem prying into the private affairs of earlier presidents.)

One of the many ironies of the Watergate scandal was that it centered on a man who, despite his many years in the public eye (including eight years as vice president), may well have been the most protective of his own personal privacy.

"The Nixon Presidency is a private affair," Robert B. Semple Jr. wrote in a lengthy *New York Times* article on the first anniversary of Nixon's election, "because Nixon is an exceptionally private man. . . . The decision-making apparatus constructed by his chief of staff, H. R. Haldeman, has been designed to match this temperament and satisfy the President's twin passions for order and solitude."

But Nixon was also one of the nation's more intellectual presidents and a longtime student of history, with an eye toward posterity and his position in it. That aspect of his personality, combined with the healthy ego that is inevitable in any chief executive, led Nixon to install in the White House the instruments of his eventual downfall: an extensive recording system designed to capture both live discussions and telephone conversations.

It was an open secret in Washington that various presidents had recorded Oval Office discussions, as far back as Franklin Roosevelt, who hid a microphone in his desk lamp and taped conversations with reporters to make sure that he was not misquoted. As author William Doyle documents in detail in *Inside the Oval Office: The White House Tapes from FDR to Clinton*, nearly every president since FDR had done some amount of electronic recording.

But before the summer of 1973, the existence, and certainly the scope, of listening devices in the Nixon White House were largely unknown. In February of that year, the Senate established the Select Committee on Presidential Campaign Activities and appointed Senator Sam Ervin (D-N.C.) to chair it. A former member of North Carolina's supreme court, Ervin was a tall, bulky man with a bulldog face and fierce eyebrows that seemed to semaphore his mood, particularly when peering down at feckless administration officials who appeared as witnesses before his committee. Describing himself as a "strict constructionist," Ervin reportedly disapproved of the Warren Court's reading of the Constitution, particularly with respect to criminal procedure matters. At the same time, however, Ervin was uniquely qualified to lead an investigation into alleged privacy invasions on the part of the Committee to Re-elect the President and Nixon's White House staff. Despite his various policy disagreements with the Warren Court, Ervin was a staunch defender of personal privacy who was innately suspicious of government surveillance.

Three years earlier, in January 1970, *Washington Monthly* had run an explosive story on army surveillance of domestic groups. The magazine's main source was Christopher H. Pyle, a former army intelligence officer, who said that there were nearly a thousand army detectives charged with keeping track of civilian political groups. Pyle said that in some cases the detectives attended rallies and protest marches to gather information, but they got the bulk of their data from files created by the FBI, other government agencies, and state and local police.

"To assure prompt communications of these reports," Pyle told *Washington Monthly*, "the Army distributes them over a nationwide wire service. Completed in the fall of 1967, this Teletype network gives every major troop command in the United States daily and weekly reports on virtually all political protests occurring anywhere in the nation." Pyle also said that the army planned to link its Teletype system to computer data banks at Fort Holabird, which at the time housed the U.S. Army Intelligence School and Counter Intelligence Records Facility. The records facility was, among other things, a storage unit and clearinghouse for domestic radical data collected by the army and shared with government agencies such as the CIA, the FBI, and the Secret Service.

At the time Pyle went public with his bombshell accusations, Ervin was chair of the Senate Judiciary Subcommittee on Constitutional Rights. Following the publication of the *Washington Monthly* article, he asked Pyle to prepare a report on military surveillance for his subcommittee. In the meantime, Ervin and his committee launched their own investigation into the compilation of private data by federal agencies. In March 1970, the committee learned that the Internal Revenue Service had somewhere between 40 million and 100 million individual files on its computer tapes. Both the Secret Service and the CIA maintained lists of people potentially dangerous to elected officials, and the number of similar army files was allegedly in the millions. Vast amounts of additional information were stored in the computer files of the Social Security Administration, the Department of Health and Human Services, and the Census Bureau (which once again was gearing up for its decennial national tally).

Ervin was particularly incensed to learn during his inquiry that investigators for the federal government's Alcohol, Tobacco, and Firearms division (ATF) had been visiting public libraries in the spring of 1970 in an effort to track down the names of people who checked out books on explosives. "Throughout history," Ervin wrote in a letter to treasury secretary David M. Kennedy, "official surveillance of the reading habits of citizens has been a litmus test of tyranny." Kennedy denied that ATF agents were conducting such inquiries, but numerous library officials contradicted his response to Ervin.

Following the delivery of Pyle's detailed, seventy-six-page report to Ervin in February 1971, in which Pyle made it clear that the army "had created the apparatus of a police state," Ervin announced that the Subcommittee on Constitutional Rights would hold a series of hearings on government surveillance and data collection, with an eye toward crafting legislation to protect against government abuses of personal information.

On the morning of February 23, 1971, Ervin strode into Room 325 of the Russell Senate Office Building, the famous Caucus Room, and delivered his opening remarks. "These hearings were called," Ervin said, "because Americans in every walk of life are concerned about the growth of government and private records on individuals. . . . They are concerned that they are constantly being intimidated, coerced, or pressured into revealing information to the wrong people, for the wrong purpose, at the wrong time."

Senator Ervin illustrated his point in typically dramatic fashion: he dropped a 1,245-page Bible (weighing eleven pounds) in front of him on the committee table and then held up a two-square-inch piece of microfilm that, he said, could hold the entire text of the Good Book. Ervin then related an earlier conversation he had about miniaturization: "Someone remarked that this meant the Constitution could be reduced to the size of a pinhead. I said I thought maybe that was what they had done with it in the executive branch because some of those officials could not see it with their naked eyes."

The lead witness was Harvard law professor Arthur R. Miller, who had previously testified before Congress about the privacy implications of a central federal data center. He told the committee that in his view, much of Orwell's vision from the book *1984* had come to pass. "Nineteen eighty-four," Miller said, "is not a year, but a state of mind." He urged the committee to propose strict regulations on the sharing of data by federal agencies and to advocate for an enforcement agency to monitor federal privacy practices.

One of the highlights of the hearings, which continued through the spring of 1971, occurred when the Nixon administration sent assistant attorney general William H. Rehnquist to testify before the subcommittee. Rehnquist argued to Ervin and the other senators that no congressional oversight was necessary, on the grounds that the executive branch could police itself. "I think it is quite likely that self-discipline on the part of the executive branch," Rehnquist said, "will provide an answer to virtually all of the legitimate complaints against excesses of information gathering."

For a constitutional scholar, Rehnquist gave an answer that seemed remarkably dismissive of the concept of checks and balances. None of the senators were particularly satisfied with his testimony, and Rehnquist was invited back a week later to answer additional and increasingly hostile questions. But the assistant attorney general did not back down, telling the committee that the government had a right to gather whatever information it wants on its citizens so long as an individual is not compelled to provide it and the information was not used in court. Senator Ervin's rejoinder was stern: "There is not a syllable in [the Constitution] that gives the federal government the right to spy on civilians," he said.

The Subcommittee on Constitutional Rights hearings adjourned not long after Rehnquist's testimony, and Ervin's repeated efforts to reopen them with testimony from additional military witnesses were frustrated by both the army and the White House. Although no one realized it at the time, the Nixon administration had a vested interest in blocking any more inquiries into the army's domestic surveillance program. One of the graduates of the Army Intelligence School at Fort Holabird was Tom Charles Huston, an aide in the Nixon White House responsible for drafting a comprehensive plan of domestic surveillance.

It was against the vivid backdrop of the army surveillance hearings that Ervin opened the proceedings of the Senate Select Committee on Presidential Campaign Activities. Beginning in May 1973, Ervin's committee began holding a series of widely watched televised hearings as it attempted to unravel the Watergate scandal. By some estimates, as many as 85 percent of the nation's households watched at least some of the hearings that summer.

As compelling as they were, the hearings of the Senate Select Committee took on a whole new level of significance on July 16, when a surprise witness was called: Alexander P. Butterfield, a former White House deputy who was then serving as head of the Federal Aviation Administration. Minority staff counsel Fred Thompson, who later served in the Senate himself before a long run playing the district attorney on NBC's *Law & Order* (and a much briefer run as a 2008 Republican presidential candidate), asked Butterfield a simple but dramatic question:

Thompson: Mr. Butterfield, are you aware of the installation of any listening devices in the Oval Office?
Butterfield: I was aware of listening devices, yes sir.

Butterfield went on to tell the committee that he had supervised the installation of voice-activated recording devices in a number of different West Wing locations, including the Oval Office, various staff offices, the Cabinet Room, and a small office used by Nixon in the Executive Office Building across the street from the White House. In addition, telephone wiretaps were installed on phones in the Oval Office, the Lincoln Sitting Room (which is adjacent to the famous Lincoln Bedroom), the Executive Office Building, and even Camp David. Essentially, as so many incredulously noted at the time, the president had bugged himself.

The month before, John Dean, Nixon's former White House counsel, had testified to the committee that several senior White House officials, including Nixon himself, were involved in a conspiracy to cover up the Watergate break-in. Dean's charges were vehemently denied by the White House, but Butterfield's revelation raised the tantalizing possibility that there might be tape recordings of the conversations Dean described. "We now know there's a complete record of all these meetings," said Sam Dash, the attorney (and coauthor of *The Eavesdroppers*) who served as chief counsel for the committee. "I don't think you have to draw a line and add it up."

It would be hard to overstate the dramatic tension inherent in the constitutional struggles that followed among the various branches of the government. Nixon had previously promised that he would not invoke executive privilege with respect to any materials requested by the Senate committee, but when Senator Ervin wrote to the president requesting that he turn over five tapes and some related documents, Nixon refused. In a historic moment, the Senate committee voted unanimously on July 24 to subpoena the tapes from the president; a similar subpoena was issued at the same time by Watergate special prosecutor Archibald Cox. Two days later, Nixon sent a letter to John J. Sirica, chief judge of the U.S. District Court for the District of Columbia, saying that he would not comply with either subpoena.

"I cannot and will not consent to giving any investigatory body private Presidential papers," Nixon wrote. The Senate committee shortly thereafter voted unanimously to sue the president to compel him to release the requested documents. On August 29, 1973, Judge Sirica ordered Nixon to turn over the requested materials. Two months later, the Court of Appeals for the District of Columbia refused to overturn Judge Sirica's order, but sent the case back down to the district court for further proceedings.

In March 1974, a District of Columbia grand jury indicted seven administration officials for Watergate-related crimes and unanimously voted to list President Nixon (and others) as unindicted co-conspirators. Special prosecutor Leon Jaworski then issued a new subpoena that asked the president to release tapes of specific meetings for use in the criminal proceedings against the Watergate defendants. Again Nixon moved to have the subpoena quashed. Judge Sirica denied the motion, and both the White House and the special prosecutor asked the Supreme Court to hear the case on an expedited basis. The Court agreed, and oral arguments were held on July 8, 1974, before eight members of the Court. As with the domestic wiretapping case, Justice Rehnquist recused himself, on the grounds that he had worked under former attorney general John Mitchell, now one of the indicted Watergate conspirators.

Arguing before a standing-room-only audience, Jaworski laid out the crux of the constitutional dilemma facing the Court:

> Now, the president may be right in how he reads the Constitution. But he may also be wrong. And if he is wrong, who is there to tell him so? And if there is no one, then the president, of course, is free to pursue his course of erroneous interpretation.
>
> In our view, this nation's constitutional form of government is in serious jeopardy if the president—any president—is to say that the Constitution means what he says it does, and that there is no one, not even the Supreme Court, to tell him otherwise.

If Nixon held any hope that the members of the so-called Nixon Court would side with him, he was sorely disappointed. Less than three weeks later, the Court unanimously reaffirmed the central holding of *Marbury v. Madison* (1803): that the Supreme Court, not the other branches of government, has the final say on the meaning of the Constitution. In a carefully worded, restrained, but still firm opinion, Chief Justice Burger categorically rejected every argument put forward by the president and his lawyers for retention of the tapes.

Chief Justice Burger acknowledged that the president does have an expectation of privacy as to his conversations, an expectation that is heightened by "the necessity for protection of the public interest in candid, objective, and even blunt or harsh opinions in Presidential decision-making." However, he went on, that expectation must be balanced against "the right to production of all evidence at a criminal trial," a right that has "constitutional dimensions" similar to those of the president's privacy and confidentiality.

There had been some speculation, and even hints from the White House, that Nixon would choose to defy an adverse ruling by the Court, a move that would have precipitated an unprecedented and profoundly perilous crisis. But no doubt as the Court intended, the unanimous ruling made it politically untenable for Nixon to do anything but accede. As *New York Times* vice president and informal dean of American journalism James Reston put it, "Now we know there is no 'Nixon Court,' for he appointed three of the eight men who voted against him. There is only 'The Court,' and it reaffirmed the principle that the judicial branch, and not the President, will decide what the law is."

INVASION OF PRIVACY BECOMES AN IMPEACHABLE OFFENSE

In *Nixon in the White House: The Frustration of Power*, a perceptively titled book published halfway through President Nixon's first term, conservative columnists Rowland Evans Jr. and Robert Novak had described Nixon as "a man with an infinite capacity for keeping a permanent ledger of the ills done to him over the years." It was an attitude aptly reflected by Nixon's bitter, supposed farewell to the press after losing the 1962 California gubernatorial race: "I leave you gentleman now and you will write it. You will interpret it. That's your right. But as I leave you I want you to know—just think how much you're going to be missing. You won't have Nixon to kick around any more, because, gentlemen, this is my last press conference and it will be one in which I have welcomed the opportunity to test wits with you."

During Nixon's years in the political wilderness, between his 1962 loss and his 1968 triumph, such rancor and bitterness were essentially harmless. But following his election as president, he found himself with powerful tools to indulge his personal and political paranoia. The sheer variety of those tools, and the willingness of Nixon and his aides to use them for political purposes, offer a chilling overview of the ability of the government to invade a citizen's privacy in the late 1960s.

Almost exactly a year after the bungled break-in at the Watergate complex, the public began learning about the scope of the Nixon administration's privacy invasions. On May 5, 1973, John Dean turned over a number of documents to Judge Sirica, suggesting that they might "have a bearing on the subject under investigation" by the Senate Select Committee. Dean said that prior to being fired by the president, he had removed the documents from his office in the White House to prevent their destruction. Twelve days later, in a lengthy page 1 story, *Washington Post* reporters Carl Bernstein and Bob Woodward said that according to their sources, the materials provided by Dean to Sirica showed that the Watergate break-in was not a one-off event, but instead was "part of an elaborate, continuous campaign of illegal and quasi-illegal undercover operations conducted by the Nixon administration since 1969."

On June 7, the *New York Times* published a number of the documents that Dean had given Sirica. The contents were incendiary: a recommendation by Dean's predecessor in the White House, Tom Charles Huston, for increased domestic surveillance; an "Analysis and Strategy" prepared by Huston for H. R. Haldeman on domestic surveillance discussions conducted by representatives of the FBI, the CIA, the Defense Intelligence Agency, the National Security Agency, and each branch of the military; and a "Decision Memorandum" that began by stating that "The President has carefully studied the special report of the Interagency Committee on Intelligence (ad hoc) and made the following decisions. . . ." Among the measures endorsed by Nixon were electronic surveillance and penetrations, mail coverage (the opening of letters to or from targeted individuals), and surreptitious entry against "high priority internal security targets."

Initially, it was reported that the "Huston plan" had never been implemented, due to the objections of FBI director J. Edgar Hoover (whose reasons for blocking the plan were unclear). Huston himself had left the White House in the spring of 1971, reportedly frustrated by the rejection of his proposal, and moved back to Indianapolis to practice law.

His departure was only a few months too soon. In June of that year, former Defense Department analyst Daniel Ellsberg leaked the Pentagon Papers, a detailed and top secret analysis of the war in Vietnam, to the *New York Times*. After the Supreme Court ruled 6–3 on June 30 that the First Amendment protected the right of the *Times* to publish the papers, the White House decided to take matters into its own hands. Nixon authorized the formation of a White House Special Investigations Unit to investigate and stop the unauthorized leak of information to the news media. The group quickly became known as the White House Plumbers. Although the Plumbers probably carried out only one "operation"—a break-in of the office of Ellsberg's psychiatrist, Lewis J. Fielding, in an effort to discredit Ellsberg—the group embodied a spirit of lawlessness and vindictiveness that eventually consumed the entire White House.

That vindictiveness became evident when Dean testified before the Senate Judiciary Committee on June 26, 1973. During his lengthy appearance, he provided additional materials that suggested not only that various aspects of the Huston plan had been executed, but that other illegal activities had taken place. One of the more damning pieces of evidence was a memorandum that Dean himself sent on August 16, 1971, (just one month after the formation of the Plumbers) to one of Haldeman's assistants, Larry Higby, in which he outlined ways "we can maximize the fact of our incumbency in dealing with persons known to be active in their opposition to our Administration. Stated a bit more bluntly—how we can use the available federal machinery to screw our political enemies."

For instance, Dean suggested in the memo that key staff members, such as White House chief counsel Charles Colson and Pat Buchanan, a Nixon adviser and speechwriter, should list individuals that the administration "should be giving a hard time." Once it was determined what interaction those individuals had with the federal government, then the most effective harassment tactics could be chosen, including "grant availability, federal contracts, litigation prosecution, etc." And finally, Dean wrote, "the project coordinator then should have access to and the full support of the top officials of the agency or departments in proceeding to deal with the individual."

Together, Dean and Colson, with input from various other White House officials, compiled the infamous "Enemies List," a collection of the twenty most hated opponents of the Nixon administration. Recipients of the dubious honor included Alexander E. Barkan, national director of the AFL-CIO's Committee on Political Education; Ed Guthman, national editor of the *Los Angeles Times*; Rep. John Conyers (D-Mich.); Samuel M. Lambert, president of the National Educa-

tion Association; Daniel Schorr, a widely respected CBS reporter who was highly critical of Nixon; Paul Newman, a notoriously outspoken liberal actor; and Mary McGrory, columnist for the *Washington Star*, whom Dean accused of writing "daily hate Nixon articles."

The select group was later joined by a much larger enemies list, one that included a number of Democratic senators and representatives, numerous media and liberal action groups, and assorted business executives, labor leaders, and entertainers. Dean told the Senate Select Committee that federal agents were ordered to do background checks and tax audits of political enemies and that the IRS had been instructed to target left-wing groups for investigation and detailed audits.

For at least three years, left-wing and campus radical groups had been calling for Nixon's impeachment based on his conduct of the war in Vietnam. Those suggestions had largely been dismissed, even by Democrats, as impractical and excessive. But in the wake of Dean's testimony and the subsequent disclosure of the White House tapes by Butterfield, the I-word was heard a lot more frequently in Washington. Given the content of the tapes, it is unlikely that Nixon could have remained in office under any circumstances, but his eventual departure was undoubtedly sealed by the events of October 20, 1973.

Angered by the persistent efforts of special prosecutor Archibald Cox to subpoena the tapes, Nixon ordered his attorney general, Elliot Richardson, to fire Cox. Richardson refused to do so and resigned, as did his chief deputy, William Ruckelshaus. The order was finally carried out by solicitor general Robert Bork, who at that point was the most senior official remaining in the Justice Department.

The "Saturday Night Massacre" turned what had been a mere trickle of calls for the president's impeachment into a full-blown flood. Article I, Section 2 of the Constitution provides that the House of Representatives has "the sole Power of Impeachment," and on October 30, the House Judiciary Committee, under the leadership of Rep. Peter Rodino (D-N.J.), began meeting to determine whether it should exercise that power.

Over the course of the next ten months, the committee sifted through the mountains of Watergate-related information, held additional hearings beginning on May 9, 1974, and slowly built a case for what would be just the second impeachment of a president in the

nation's history. In the wake of Nixon's categorical refusal to comply with the subpoenas issued in April 1974, it became increasingly likely that the House Judiciary Committee would approve two or more articles of impeachment. On July 19, ten days after oral arguments in *United States v. Nixon*, the Judiciary Committee issued a report containing "selected evidence" of "White House Surveillance Activities and Campaign Activities." The report, which took up twelve pages of the *Washington Post* that morning, covered unauthorized wiretaps and other illegal activities stretching back to May 1969, just four months after Nixon was first sworn in as president.

Events proceeded rapidly thereafter. The Supreme Court's unanimous ruling on the withheld tapes was issued on July 24; just three days later, in a rare Saturday session, the House Judiciary Committee voted 27–11 to impeach President Nixon for attempting to obstruct the investigation of the Watergate break-in and conspiracy. The following Monday, by a vote of 28–10, a second article of impeachment was approved on the grounds that Nixon abused the power of the presidency to harass his political enemies. A third, alleging contempt of Congress, was adopted that Tuesday.

The abuse of power article adopted by the committee lays out the Nixon administration's utter disregard for the privacy of American citizens, in language and tone strikingly similar to the Declaration of Independence:

1. He has, acting personally and through his subordinates and agents, endeavored to obtain from the Internal Revenue Service, in violation of the constitutional rights of citizens, confidential information contained in income tax returns for purposes not authorized by law, and to cause, in violation of the constitutional rights of citizens, income tax audits or other income tax investigations to be initiated or conducted in a discriminatory manner.

2. He misused the Federal Bureau of Investigation, the Secret Service, and other executive personnel, in violation or disregard of the constitutional rights of citizens, by directing or authorizing such agencies or personnel to conduct or continue electronic surveillance or other investigations for purposes unrelated to national security, the enforcement of

laws, or any other lawful function of his office; he did direct, authorize, or permit the use of information obtained thereby for purposes unrelated to national security, the enforcement of laws, or any other lawful function of his office; and he did direct the concealment of certain records made by the Federal Bureau of Investigation of electronic surveillance.

3. He has, acting personally and through his subordinates and agents, in violation or disregard of the constitutional rights of citizens, authorized and permitted to be maintained a secret investigative unit within the office of the President, financed in part with money derived from campaign contributions, which unlawfully utilized the resources of the Central Intelligence Agency, engaged in covert and unlawful activities, and attempted to prejudice the constitutional right of an accused to a fair trial.

Even in the wake of the approval of the impeachment articles, Nixon vowed to persevere. But in early August, it was discovered that one of the tapes turned over by the White House had been recorded on June 23, 1972, just a few days after the Watergate break-in. On the tape, President Nixon and H. R. Haldeman could be heard discussing ways to use the CIA to interfere with the FBI's investigation. Virtually all of Nixon's remaining political support vanished, and a delegation of senior Republicans—Senator Barry Goldwater, Senator Hugh Scott, and Rep. John Rhodes—went to the White House to tell him that the House would unquestionably impeach him and that only twelve to fifteen senators, at most, would vote to acquit him. Faced with inevitable defeat in Congress, Nixon resigned at noon on Friday, August 9, 1974.

The rampant civil rights and privacy abuses of the Nixon administration profoundly altered the way most Americans viewed their government. The lingering question, as the Ford administration got underway, was what, if anything, Congress would do to prevent such egregious invasions of personal privacy from happening in the future. The answer, it turned out, was not much.

10

THE PHANTOM DELETE KEY

The Incredible Durability of Data

On August 13, 1974, in an evening address to a joint session of Congress just three days after taking office, President Gerald R. Ford promised his former colleagues and the American people that his administration would not be guilty of the abuses of power and rampant privacy invasions that had helped to chase Richard Nixon from office. "As vice president, I addressed myself to the individual rights of Americans in the area of privacy," he said. "There will be no illegal tappings, eavesdropping, bugging, or break-ins in my administration. There will be hot pursuit of tough laws to prevent illegal invasions of privacy in both government and private activities."

But despite the best of intentions, neither the Ford administration nor Congress delivered on the promise to adopt more effective safeguards against invasions of privacy from either a rogue government or overly inquisitive corporations. The wide gaps between what was needed, what was proposed, and what was finally adopted by Congress offer useful insights into the ongoing challenges to effective protection of personal privacy.

Ford's remarks on privacy were a reference to his leadership of the Domestic Council Committee on the Right of Privacy (DCCRP), a cabinet-level group established by President Nixon to study the growth of federal and private data banks and to propose ways to prevent invasions of privacy resulting from the misuse of stored information. In a fifteen-minute national radio address on February 24, 1974, Nixon said that he was giving Ford and his group four months to come up with specific recommendations that would ensure, as Nixon put it, that "man remains the master and never becomes the victim of the computer." The irony was not lost on Senator Philip A. Hart

(D-Mich.), who gave the Democratic response. "With or without so-phisticated technology," Hart said, "unprincipled men can find ways to invade our privacy. A crowbar, after all, is a rather simple ma-chine."

Notwithstanding Nixon's effort to divert attention from his own privacy invasions, the DCCRP, by all accounts, worked diligently on the issue of personal privacy, and Ford himself became a strong proponent of greater privacy protections. At a meeting of the Georgia Bar Association in June 1974, for instance, Ford warned of the poten-tial privacy invasions of new two-way communication systems that were just coming on the market.

"The administration," Ford said, "is considering draft legislation that would prohibit snooping and monitoring of communications en-tering and leaving a citizen's home via cable television." The goal, he suggested, would be to prevent cable companies from compiling records of the viewing habits of their subscribers, which he considered an "essential safeguard" to protect people in "a wired society."

Three weeks later, Ford told the American Medical Association that the privacy of both doctors and their patients was increasingly at risk. "We are all too painfully aware," he said, "of wiretapping, bug-ging, and even allegations that records in a doctor's office are no lon-ger safe from intruders." Ford's remarks were widely interpreted as an offhand reference to the 1972 break-in of the office of psychiatrist Dr. Lewis Fielding, perpetrated by the White House Plumbers during their campaign to discredit Daniel Ellsberg.

At the same time, in keeping with his generally conservative views, Ford used concerns over personal privacy as an argument against a national health care system, arguing that such a system would re-quire a "vast medical information network" capable of causing "all-out hazards to traditional freedom." Such a system, he predicted, would result in doctors working for the government rather than their patients, a warning that was warmly received by the assembled doctors.

As Ford repeatedly pointed out, the DCCRP's most notable suc-cess that spring was the partial derailment of a new federal computer network known as FEDNET. The network was the brainstorm of the General Services Administration (GSA), which quietly planned to build a $100 million network of advanced data-crunching computers without any oversight or input from Congress. As news of the plan emerged in the spring of 1974, it sparked widespread criticism, much to the astonishment of the GSA. During testimony before the Senate Special Subcommittee on Privacy, Information Systems, and Constitutional Rights, GSA chief Arthur Sampson denied suggestions that his agency was trying to keep FEDNET a secret and assured senators that the only objective was to reduce administrative costs.

Sampson's assurances apparently were not convincing. Legislators expressed particular concerns about the data communications capabilities of the proposed system, as well as the fact that its modular design would allow rapid expansion throughout the government. Staff members for the Senate committee conceded that just 1 percent of the government's thousands of computers would be part of the initial FEDNET hookup, but argued that advances in computer technology would make it easy to connect other computers to the system in the future. Moreover, security was nearly entirely lacking: the information on FEDNET, the GSA admitted, would be available to anyone with access to a terminal connected to the system.

The outcry over the system led the GSA to drop the data communications part of the proposal, but not the purchase of newer and more powerful computers. While privacy advocates hailed the "victory" over creeping federal intrusions, the reality was that the interconnection of federal computers was merely slowed, not stopped. With no reliable, long-term oversight of privacy issues by Congress or the executive branch, the electronic exchange of data between federal computers and the resulting diminution of privacy crept in, like the fog, on little cat feet.

However well-intentioned Ford's leadership on privacy may have been, the DCCRP's efforts were overwhelmed by the ongoing governmental crisis. Ford himself recognized the problem, telling a conference of broadcast editorial writers at the end of June 1974 that "one of the most serious problems that we face today," privacy, is being drowned out by the "flow of news on the Watergate matter." By that time it was evident that the DCCRP would not meet Nixon's four-month deadline for policy proposals, either because the subject of governmental privacy was simply too vast or because, as Ford suggested, everything was subsumed by Watergate.

PRESIDENT NIXON: "THE PATRON SAINT OF PRIVACY LEGISLATION"

Even though the DCCRP petered out, Congress had not been entirely idle on the privacy front. In the wake of the outrages of Watergate, Washington was under intense pressure to take some action to improve protections for personal privacy. Dr. Alan F. Westin, a professor at Columbia University and a longtime privacy researcher, jokingly told Sam Ervin's Senate Judiciary Subcommittee on Constitutional Rights that "in a certain way, I suppose that Richard Nixon may go down in history as the patron saint of privacy legislation." One of the House's more enthusiastic privacy advocates, Rep. Barry Goldwater Jr. (R-Calif.), even went so far as to boast that the Ninety-third Congress would earn the title "the Privacy Congress."

The reality, however, was something different, not just in Congress but in the Ford White House as well. During the emotional events of the summer of 1974, two privacy bills began working their way through Congress, one from each side of the Capitol building. Both proposals contained a number of similar elements: full disclosure of all federal record-keeping systems, a requirement that any personal information collected by federal agencies be kept up to date, authorization for individuals to review and correct information about them held by the government, limitations on the sharing of personal information among government agencies, and security requirements.

But the House and Senate disagreed on two important points. First, the House wanted to provide the CIA and the Secret Service with blanket exemptions to any federal privacy rules, while the Senate proposed much narrower exemptions—based on specific need—to law enforcement, foreign policy, and national security agencies. And second, at Senator Ervin's urging, the Senate legislation proposed the creation of a federal Privacy Protection Commission to help enforce the law. According to the accompanying Senate legislative report, the commission would be "composed of five experts in law, social science, computer technology, and civil liberties, business, and State and local government and supported by a professional staff." Among other things, the commission would have the power to:

Monitor and inspect Federal systems and data banks containing information about individuals;

Investigate and hold hearings on violations of the Act, and

recommend corrective action to the agencies, Congress, the President, the General Accounting Office, and the Office of Management and Budget;

Investigate and hold hearings on proposals by Federal agencies to create new personal information systems or modify existing systems for the purpose of assisting the agencies, Congress, and the President in their effort to assure that the values of privacy, confidentiality, and due process are adequately safeguarded; and

Make a study of the state of the law governing privacy-invading practices in private data banks and in State and local and multistate data systems.

Even as proposed, the Senate's Privacy Protection Commission would have been something of a paper tiger, since the legislation did not provide for any enforcement mechanisms and did not apply to the private sector at all. Nonetheless, both the House of Representatives and President Ford opposed the creation of a federal privacy commission, arguing that each individual federal agency should be responsible for establishing and monitoring its own policies. During conference negotiations over the bill, the Senate agreed to drop the idea of a federal privacy agency, and the two chambers compromised by agreeing to set up a commission to study issues of privacy instead.

In their award-winning and journalism-altering book *All the President's Men*, Bob Woodward and Carl Bernstein described how the *Washington Post* for months was virtually alone in its investigation and coverage of the Watergate affair and a frequent target of harsh denunciations by Nixon press secretary Ron Zeigler. Perhaps that explains why the *Post* was particularly disappointed in the Privacy Act of 1974, the sole piece of privacy legislation to emerge from the Watergate Congress. The *Post* found the final product to be at most a tepid improvement:

> The prevailing attitude on the Hill seems to be that Mr. Nixon's resignation removed the danger, and an institutional approach is not required. So legislation to end warrantless wiretaps went nowhere; the internal security operations of the FBI have not been closely scrutinized; no real curbs on intelligence gathering

have been pushed through. The 93d Congress, in other words, has left a long agenda of unfinished business in this connection—and has left us wondering what further offenses must be committed and revealed before enough legislators decide to act.

President Ford was more enthusiastic. When he signed the legislation on January 1, 1975, he issued a statement that described the new law as "an initial advance in protecting a right precious to every American—the right of individual privacy." He referenced once again his interest in the subject and his former role as head of the DCCRP, and expressed his satisfaction that the commission created by the Privacy Act "has been limited to purely advisory functions." The goal, Ford said, was "to set the Federal house in order before prescribing remedies for State and local government and the private sector."

When the Privacy Act took effect on September 27, 1975, it became illegal for the first time for federal agencies to disclose information about someone without that person's written permission. There were exceptions, the biggest of which was the interdepartmental exchange of information within a federal agency for "routine purposes," a term that was not specifically defined within the law. And although citizens now had the ability to examine and correct federal information about themselves, there were exceptions to that right as well, most notably for files held by federal law enforcement and national security agencies.

One of the more useful aspects of the law was a requirement that federal agencies create lists of the various types of information already in the hands of the government. By the effective date of the Privacy Act, nearly eighty different federal agencies had listed more than eight thousand different systems for storing personal information, ranging from the routine (various federal payroll accounts) to the serious (possible federal criminal suspects) to the trivial (a list of people who applied for a government parking spot).

During a speech at the dedication ceremony for a new building at Stanford Law School on September 21, President Ford promised to vigorously enforce the new law. Stating the obvious, he told the law students that American privacy was under relentless assault and that "one of the worst offenders is the federal government itself."

"We must protect every individual from excessive and unnecessary intrusions by a Big Brother bureaucracy," Ford said.

Ford put much of the blame for government privacy invasions on social service programs "enacted by Congress often for laudable purposes." He pointed out that in order to carry out the goals of programs like Social Security, welfare, student loans, unemployment benefits, and so on, it is necessary for the government to collect increasingly detailed information about the people it is serving. The combination of large amounts of personal data and computerization, he argued, increases the danger of unwarranted invasions of each person's privacy.

The president's conclusion was insightful. "I see the great challenge of our next hundred years," Ford said, referencing the Bicentennial, "as the advancement of individual independence, of specific steps to safeguard the identity of each and every American from the pressures of conformity. The pressures close in upon us from many quarters—massive government, massive management, massive labor, massive education, massive communication, and massive acquisition of information. To meet this challenge, we still need a positive and passionate commitment to law, to learning, and to liberty."

THE PPSC, FISA, AND THE RIGHT TO FINANCIAL PRIVACY ACT

Thanks in part to Ford's own objection to effective privacy oversight, the Privacy Protection Study Committee (PPSC) that was established by the Privacy Act of 1974 had no tools with which to demonstrate a positive commitment to effective privacy law. Under the leadership of New York management consultant David F. Linowes, the PPSC held hearings around the country, beginning in August 1975, on a variety of information-gathering industries, including mail-order companies, banks, insurance companies, employers, hospitals, and credit card companies. Despite the often disturbing testimony it heard, the PPSC ultimately could do little more than try to stir public consciousness before issuing a quickly shelved report, similar to the one that had marked the end of the DCCRP's labors.

The most provocative testimony given to the PPSC cast an unflattering light on the Internal Revenue Service and its often overly close relationship with the private sector. Over the course of several days, the PPSC heard testimony from a parade of executives from airlines, credit card companies, hotels, and car rental agencies. All told the same story: that they regularly received requests from various federal agencies, but primarily from the IRS, for information about consumers and cardholders. Most said that they turned over the information without requiring a warrant and without notifying the person whose information was sought. There was certainly a staggering amount of information available to federal investigators; with the growing national computer network for credit checks and purchase processing, credit card companies were processing more than five billion transactions each year.

Part of the problem, the PPSC learned, was that the relationship between the private sector and federal law enforcement agencies bordered on the incestuous. According to Rep. Bella Abzug (D-N.Y.), few federal agencies needed to bother obtaining a court order before requesting (and receiving) consumer data. "Every major credit card company and credit reporting company has a special unit, usually staffed by former FBI or police officers, to handle requests from governmental authorities."

Concerns about the IRS were not limited to its data collection procedures. In a report issued in June 1976, the PPSC strongly recommended that the revenue agency be restricted from using taxpayer data for any purpose other than that for which it was collected. The confidentiality of tax returns, the PPSC said, was an "essential element in preserving the effectiveness of the tax system."

Two years later, Congress followed up on the revelations of the PPSC by adopting the Right to Financial Privacy Act of 1978, which created a statutory Fourth Amendment protection for a consumer's personal records held by financial institutions, including credit card companies. Henceforth, consumer data could not be released without a valid search warrant or express permission from the consumer. Naturally, there were a number of exceptions, including those that fell into what was described as "Class 6": "emergency disclosures and disclosure to federal agencies charged with foreign intelligence or counter intelligence or other national security protective functions."

The threat of foreign intelligence and the danger to domestic privacy from federal efforts to combat it remained hot topics well after Watergate. Two independent commissions, one led by former senator Sam Ervin and the other by Senator Frank Church (D-Idaho), conducted extensive investigations into domestic surveillance by the Nixon administration. Based on their work, in 1978 Congress adopted the Foreign Intelligence Surveillance Act (FISA) to establish oversight of executive branch surveillance.

Under the original terms of the law, the president (acting through the attorney general) could authorize electronic surveillance without a court order for up to a year, so long as the sole target was foreign intelligence information from foreign powers or agents and there was "no substantial likelihood" that the communications of any U.S. citizen would be intercepted by the surveillance. Alternatively, the attorney general or his designee could seek a warrant from a special court created by the act, the United States Foreign Intelligence Surveillance Court.

For much of its existence, this eleven-member secret court was located conveniently in the headquarters of the U.S. Department of Justice. (In March 2009, it moved to a concrete-reinforced courtroom and offices in the D.C. federal courthouse.) It is charged with reviewing warrant requests for electronic surveillance of people within the United States who are believed to be foreign agents. The proceedings are ex parte—which means that only Department of Justice officials present evidence—and no public record of the court's proceedings is kept. Reportedly, in the thirty years since the formation of the Foreign Intelligence Surveillance Court, fewer than two hundred warrant requests out of nearly twenty thousand have been denied.

In general, the passage of FISA was well received, since it seemed to strike a reasonable balance between the competing concerns of domestic security and constitutional rights. Certainly, there were very few challenges to the law over the years, and even less media attention. Three decades later, that would change.

OF APPLES AND ACORNS:
THE ORIGINS OF THE PERSONAL COMPUTER

The unwitting combination of the Social Security number and mainframe computers in the 1950s may have blown the first significant hole in the wall of personal privacy by making government and corporate databases such powerful and threatening tools, but it was the invention of the personal computer that truly reduced the idea that a "man's house is his castle" to rubble. To the extent that privacy is defined as control of one's own information, the arrival of the personal computer made such control vastly more difficult to maintain. As we'll see, much of that had to do with the relatively obscure design choices of mostly anonymous hardware engineers and software programmers (although a few went on to gain a certain notoriety). More importantly, the combination of the personal computer and the Internet would later take the concept of electronic exhibitionism to unprecedented heights (or lows, depending on one's perspective). While it is impossible to capture in a few hundred words the many twists and turns of the early personal computer industry, the following vignettes offer some instructive insights into the birth of what has become such a powerfully omnipresent device.

For a few years, at least, the rise of personal computing emulated the rapid development of photography, the chief difference being that there was no single grand unveiling of home computer technology the way there was when the French Academy of Sciences released Daguerre's invention to the world in 1839. But as with photography, it was hobbyists who brought passion and curiosity and more than a little obsession to the early days of home computing. The personal computer industry has many apocryphal stories of its origins, but the reality is entertaining enough; its roots lie in small and unassuming notices that began appearing in community calendars in the mid-1970s, advertising the formation and meetings of amateur computer clubs.

Club members (who were overwhelmingly male) attended workshops and lectures with titles like "How to Put Together a Microcomputer," traded tips and spare parts, and swapped copies of programs (typically written in Beginner's All-purpose Symbolic Instruction Code, or BASIC) for playing simple games, balancing checkbooks, storing lists of their eight-track tapes, and so on. They avidly read the computer club newsletters and early computer journals, such as *Dr. Dobb's Journal of Computer Calisthenics & Orthodontia* and *Creative Computing*. As membership in the clubs steadily grew and awareness of computers began creeping into the mainstream media, public interest in microcomputers grew rapidly. When one of the first computer conferences, the West Coast Computer Faire, was organized in San Francisco in April 1977, it attracted nearly thirteen thousand visitors, nearly twice what was expected. By August 1977, the nation's largest computer club, the Southern California Computer Society, had an estimated five thousand members.

To modern ears, the capabilities of those hobbyist electronic computers seem remarkably archaic. One typical home computer setup, available in 1977 from a store called Computer Shack, came with an Intel 8080 processor operating at 2 megahertz, 16 kilobytes of random-access memory (RAM), a keyboard, and a single 5¼-inch floppy disk drive capable of holding 256 kilobytes of data. There was no display included in the kit; instead, the system was designed to be attached to a television, which would display the output from the computer. Altogether, the components cost $2,500 (roughly the equivalent of $8,500 in today's dollars), which helps explain why the do-it-yourself approach was so popular. (With a little soldering expertise, the same basic computer could be built for a quarter to a third of the price.) To illustrate how far the computer industry has come, in 2009 Dell advertised a laptop computer with a 2.13-gigahertz processor (more than a thousand times faster), 2 gigabytes of RAM (a million times as much memory), and a 120-gigabyte hard drive (nearly 500,000 times larger than the floppy). And of course, the contemporary laptop comes equipped with its own color screen, a DVD drive, speakers, a wireless connection, and so on. The cost: $499, or the equivalent of just $147 in 1977.

Notwithstanding their limited capabilities and relatively high cost, early computers sold briskly, thanks to the allure of having a device in the home that was roughly as powerful, at least in terms of processor speed, as the million-dollar mainframe computers delivered to government agencies like the Census Bureau and Social Security Administration in the early 1950s. In 1977, estimates of the number of home computers sold ranged from 20,000 to 100,000; two years later, a quarter of a million home computers were sold, and analysts predicted that figure would double the following year. Even more remarkably, the $385 million spent on computers was expected to rise to as high as $3.5 billion by 1982.

As befits a young and largely entrepreneurial industry, most of the early computer companies were small and somewhat eclectic, with names ranging from the obscure to the descriptive to the humorous: MTS, Computer Warehouse Store, Osborne, Umtech, Commodore, Kentucky Fried Computers, and Apple. Most vanished almost as quickly as they appeared, but two companies—Apple and IBM—helped turn what had been an entertaining hobby into first a full-blown industry and soon thereafter an entire sector of the U.S. economy.

Of all the entrepreneurial start-up stories that litter personal computer history, Apple's is easily the most iconic. In early 1975, two buddies in northern California, Steve Jobs and Steve Wozniak, began attending meetings of the Homebrew Computer Club in Menlo Park. That's in the heart of what is now known as Silicon Valley, but then it was an area better known for its peach orchards than its microprocessors. According to Wozniak, one of the purposes of the group was to show off ideas for building a home computer.

"The Apple I and II were designed strictly on a hobby, for-fun basis, not to be a product for a company," Wozniak reminisced in an article for AtariArchives.org. "There was a lot of showing off to other members of the club. Schematics of the Apple I were passed around freely, and I'd even go over to people's houses and help them build their own."

Encouraged by the feedback from their fellow Homebrew members, Jobs and Wozniak founded Apple Computer on April 1, 1976, complete with a groovy hand-drawn logo of Isaac Newton sitting under a tree. That summer, Jobs approached Paul Terrell, the owner of a local computer store called the Byte Shop, who told him that he would buy fifty of the Apple I machines at $500 each, provided that they came preassembled. Jobs took Terrell's purchase order and used it to establish the credit they needed to order the parts to build the machines. It was a dicey start-up, but together with some friends, Wozniak and Jobs set up shop in the Jobs family garage in Los Altos and managed to build enough computers to collect from Terrell, pay the parts distributor, and have some left over.

A year later, this time with considerably more financial backing and a small but growing staff, the two young computer manufacturers introduced the Apple II to the general public at the West Coast Computer Faire on April 16, 1977. The goal of the company's design—as Apple's vice president of marketing, Mike Markkula, told David H. Ahl, a reporter for *The Best of Creative Computing*—was to simplify the personal computer for the consumer. Apart from the technical specifications, Markkula's comments could just as easily have been issued by Apple today.

"We really want to be *the* computer company," Markkula said, standing beside Apple's booth at the 1977 West Coast Computer Faire, "not the small-business computer company or something else—just the personal computer company! So that's the reason you see a molded plastic case, BASIC in ROM [read-only memory], and so on. In fact, we want to extend the whole concept to make it even easier to use."

The Apple II went on sale six weeks after the Faire, with two different models available: one with 4 kilobytes of RAM for $1,298 and one with the maximum 48 kilobytes of RAM for $2,638. Despite the relatively high price, consumers appreciated the machine's graceful appearance and ease of use, and the Apple II quickly became the first major commercial success of the personal computer industry.

The success of the Apple II and the rising enthusiasm for home computers did not go unnoticed by IBM, the computer industry's leading manufacturer of "big iron," the nickname given to the company's large, often steel-encased mainframes. At first it looked like IBM would be institutionally incapable of competing with the more agile and consumer-friendly start-up companies. Its first microcomputer—the IBM 5100, introduced in 1975—was actually quite innovative: it was portable (although it weighed a back-breaking fifty-five pounds), it could access 64 kilobytes of memory, it had a tiny five-inch screen with a port for an external monitor, and it had an internal tape drive capable of storing 204 kilobytes of data. Such innovation, however, came at a remarkably steep cost: up to $20,000 per machine. With that kind of price tag, the primary market for the 5100 was a fairly small pool of well-funded scientists and researchers.

Recognizing that its long-established procedures for computer development were not well suited to the personal computer market, IBM decided to create what was essentially an entrepreneurial start-up within its corporate structure. In July 1980, the company put together a task force of twelve engineers, sent them to the Entry Level Systems Division (ELSD) research facility in Boca Raton, and told them to develop a personal computer.

The task force, code-named "Project Chess" but colloquially referred to as the "Dirty Dozen," put together a prototype of a home computer in less than a month and presented it to IBM management for approval. The design, code-named "Acorn," got the go-ahead from Big Blue's brass, and Project Chess was given a year to bring Acorn to market.

Under the leadership of chief scientist Larry Potter and ELSD head Don Estridge, the Project Chess team met its deadline, but only by making some very un-IBM-like decisions. For instance, rather than use only components designed and manufactured by IBM (a long-standing corporate practice), the team decided to use parts built by other manufacturers, a design decision it described as "open architecture."

The team also decided that rather than using its existing sales force, IBM would sell its personal computer to consumers through department stores and chains like Sears and ComputerLand. And most importantly, the Project Chess team decided that it did not have time to develop its own software. Instead, in August 1980 it contacted a small but growing software company named Microsoft and paid its lead programmer, Bill Gates, a $15,000 consulting fee to work with Project Chess to develop the software specifications for Acorn. Later that year, IBM agreed to license an operating system for the Acorn, dubbed PC-DOS, from Microsoft. In one of the most profoundly lucrative deals in the history of commerce, Microsoft bargained for and received the ability to market its own version of the operating system, known as MS-DOS.

As befits a sober, business-oriented product, the IBM PC, formerly known as Acorn, officially made its debut not at some earthy-crunchy computer faire but at simultaneous events at the ELSD facility in Boca Raton and the ballroom of the Waldorf-Astoria Hotel in New York City on April 12, 1981. A bare-bones IBM PC system was priced at $1,565, while a fully loaded system with color graphics and 256 kilobytes of RAM could be had for just under $6,000. In addition to PC-DOS, the IBM PC came with a variety of software programs, including the popular spreadsheet VisiCalc; a word processor called EasyWrite; Microsoft's first game, Adventure; some simple accounting software from Peachtree; and, in a hint of the future, software to link to commercial databases maintained by Source Telecomputing Corporation and Dow Jones.

Reaction from the more established players in the personal computer field was mixed. Apple's Markkula told the *Wall Street Journal* at the time that he thought the IBM PC would be good for the personal computer industry as a whole because it would expand interest in the new devices. At the same time, however, he predicted that the mainframe manufacturer might have a hard time adjusting to the market. "IBM knows as well as anyone the power of an established base," he said. "Now the shoe's on the other foot." John Roach, the president of Tandy Corporation, which manufactured the TRS-80 (lovingly known to many as the "Trash-80"), was even more dismissive of IBM's announcement: "I don't think it's significant."

In a remarkable show of corporate bravado, Apple bought a full-page ad in the *Wall Street Journal* on August 24, 1981, that began "Welcome, IBM. Seriously." The ad went on to congratulate IBM on its first personal computer and to predict that in 1982 as many as a million people would decide to purchase a new computer.

"We look forward to responsible competition in the massive effort to distribute this American technology to the world," Apple continued. "And we appreciate the magnitude of your commitment. Because what we are doing is increasing social capital by enhancing individual productivity. Welcome to the task."

It was a task that IBM undertook with not only massive commitment but considerable success. By Christmas, just four months after the PC's introduction, IBM had orders for over 100,000 units, more than Apple had sold during the entire year. Big Blue was well on its way to redefining the personal computer industry in the image of the IBM PC and in the process consigning Apple (at least for the next couple of decades) to the increasingly tiny market niche of aging hippies and graphic designers.

THE PHANTOM DELETE KEY

From the perspective of personal privacy, it didn't matter at all whether the logo on the outside of a personal computer was Apple, IBM, Tandy, Atari, or one of the dozens of other small computer companies that flickered in and out of existence over the next several years. What did matter were two separate developments: first, that hundreds and thousands of computer programs were being written to store a staggering array of personal information on the new devices, and second, that unbeknownst to all but a few software-savvy individuals, that information was rapidly taking on a life of its own.

What made the Apple II computer so revolutionary was that it was designed, built, and marketed as a general-purpose consumer appliance, one that could run not only programs written by the consumer but a growing number of commercial software packages. (By 1984, *VanLoves Apple Software Directory* contained a list of over fifteen hundred programs that would run on the Apple II.) The possibilities, as Apple stressed in its early ads, were limitless: "Apple II can also manage household finances, chart the stock market or index recipes, record collections, even control your home environment."

Apple's promises notwithstanding, the real potential of the personal computer to move beyond home video arcade and list maker was demonstrated by the 1979 release of VisiCalc, a relatively simple but innovative spreadsheet that became the first software "killer app." The software, designed by MIT graduates Dan Bricklin and Bob Frankston and distributed by Personal Software, was unlike anything else available for the microcomputer market. For the first time, personal computer users could do their own analysis of financial information and test different business scenarios by simply changing the figure or formula contained in various cells of the spreadsheet. As computer industry chronicler Robert X. Cringely later wrote in *Accidental Empires: How the Boys of Silicon Valley Make Their Millions, Battle Foreign Competition, and Still Can't Get a Date*, "VisiCalc was a compelling application—an application so important that it alone justified the computer purchase. Such an application was the last element required to turn the microcomputer from a hobbyist's toy into a business machine."

In a lengthy interview published in *Byte* in December 1984 and January 1985, Apple's Steve Wozniak agreed. "There were two main factors that led to our success—our floppy disk and VisiCalc," he said. "Out of the original home computers, which included the TRS-80 and the Commodore PET, ours was the only one that had enough memory to run VisiCalc. VisiCalc and the floppy disk sent this company into the number-one position."

The ability to work out business financing, maintain a check register, and do other spreadsheet tasks on one's own computer was impressive enough. But the potent combination of the Apple II's floppy disk and software like VisiCalc was the start of something much more profound. As vast as the information was that the government and businesses had collected and stored over the years (both legally and illegally), it rapidly paled in comparison to the amount of information that first hundreds of thousands, then tens of millions, of personal computer users created and stored each day. Even the relatively small storage capacity of the Apple II floppy drive (known as "Disk II") was impressive: one single-sided disk could hold 114 kilobytes of data, the equivalent of just over two thousand of the punch cards designed by Herman Hollerith for the 1890 census.

Moreover, Apple's Disk II made it easier to transport, replicate, and share personal information. Initially, such sharing was done via "sneakernet"—hand-to-hand delivery of floppies—but the popularity of the program helped spur interest in the transfer of files over greater distances. The power of VisiCalc and its relative ease of use also marked the beginning of the end of the "roll your own" software era. At $49.95, it made far more sense for most people to buy a copy of VisiCalc than to try to write their own software, and educators soon stopped predicting that every school child would need to learn a computer language like BASIC in order to get a job.

The downside of electronic storage, however, was that any data saved to a disk immediately became significantly more durable than most people realized. If someone were to write out a spreadsheet calculating their profits from insider trading, for instance, or from some other illegal activity, complete and total destruction of the evidence was no further away than the nearest book of matches or lighter. Most people assumed that the same was true for electronic files; after all, the Apple II's operating system, called DOS 3.1, came with a handy "delete" function to get rid of unwanted files.

The only problem was that the delete function of DOS 3.1, like virtually every other disk operating system to hit the market, did not actually erase the data contained in an unwanted file. At the time the disk operating systems were being written, it was simply too time-consuming for the operating system to overwrite every bit of information in a file when it was deleted. So instead, programmers used a couple of shortcuts. First, the delete function instructed the operating system to replace the first character of the file name with a special symbol (typically a $ or a ~) to indicate that the file should not be including in directory or file listings. And second, it told the operating system to wipe out the unwanted file's information in the file allocation table (the operating system's map of where the various chunks of the file were stored).

It wasn't merely expediency that led early programmers to use those shortcuts. By leaving the actual data from a "deleted" file on the disk, there was at least the chance that it could be recovered if the user decided that he or she had made a mistake. And it didn't take long for other programmers to write software that would try to undelete files (a feature that was one of the major selling points of the popular Norton Utilities software package). Just how successful the undeletion was, however, depended on whether any of the old file's data had been overwritten by new files in the often painful interval between "oops" and "can I get it back?"

When Bill Gates and Paul Allen wrote their version of DOS— one flavor of which became IBM's PC-DOS and another their house brand, MS-DOS—they made the same programming decision about unwanted data. In their case, however, that decision had much more far-reaching consequences. Because IBM had adopted open architecture for its PCs, competitors could reverse engineer the design of the IBM PC and produce "clones" that operated in a similar fashion. Whether Gates and Allen anticipated that development at the time of their negotiations with IBM is unclear; but in any case, since they retained the right to market MS-DOS to other computer manufacturers, they were perfectly positioned to provide an operating system to Big Blue's competitors that made it possible for their machines to run the same software as the IBM PC.

Thanks to IBM's powerful market position and sales acumen, along with the availability of low-priced clones, the IBM PC rapidly became the standard business computer, and in the process Microsoft became the world's leading computer software company. But remarkably, despite incredible advances in the speed and capacity of personal computers over the last thirty years, the delete key still remains more phantom than functional. Despite the increasing sophistication of today's operating systems, the handling of deleted data has remained essentially the same since MS-DOS.

When it released Windows 95 in August 1995, Microsoft introduced a new feature: a special directory called the Recycle Bin. When a user "deleted" a file, it was transferred to the Recycle Bin, where it would stay until the user emptied the directory. Although that made it even easier to recover files that were "deleted" by mistake, it also increased the unintentional durability of electronic data, since many people often forget to empty the Recycle Bin. And because Microsoft left unaltered the operating system's ineffectual elimination of deleted data, even those who do remember to empty the Recycle Bin still have much, if not most, of their deleted data on the hard drive.

The fact that file data lingers after a file is "deleted" has given rise to somewhat reciprocal, and often competing, industries. A variety of software manufacturers offer products that purport to truly delete electronic information, primarily by writing over every sector of a computer file with random data. Since the physical nature of magnetic storage makes it almost impossible to completely erase data, there is a lively debate over whether a particular bit of data needs to be rewritten three, seven, or even thirty-five times to be unrecoverable. The more salient point is that few people go to such lengths, with the result that nearly every hard drive is an unintentional diary of computer activity.

That fact has given rise to the practice of "computer forensics," or the recovery of accidentally or purposefully deleted files from computers and other types of electronic devices. Thanks to the ubiquity of personal computers, the vast amount of information that people store on them each day, and the durability of data, computer forensics has become one of the leading tools of law enforcement during criminal investigations and is well on its way to becoming a multibillion-dollar industry. Computers, cell phones, and handheld devices like the BlackBerry and the iPhone have become the latest battleground for constitutional battles over searches and seizures.

The 1970s began with the stunning revelation that a U.S. president was willing to use whatever legal and illegal means he felt necessary to harass his political enemies by invading their personal privacy. The disclosures of political spying horrified many in Washington and spawned dozens, if not hundreds, of hearings. But in the end, it was a sadly missed opportunity. The failure to address the competing concerns of efficiency, security, and privacy in a systematic fashion was all the more significant in light of the technological innovations that occurred in the latter half of the decade. With every file that is created, and every ineffectual effort to delete unwanted data, Americans essentially are bugging, tapping, and recording their personal activities in ways that Nixon could have only imagined.

11

NO PC IS AN ISLAND

The Rise of Online Communities

While perpetuation of the species may be the dominant evolutionary force in humanity, the desire to communicate with each other runs a close second. Few things better illustrate that drive to communicate than the evolution of the personal computer, which over the course of thirty years went from being an awkward and solitary hobbyist's toy to a pocket-sized combination computer and telephone capable of sending and retrieving information around the world.

Personal computers began talking to each other in no small part because of that most isolating of weather events: a massive blizzard that moved across the country in late January and early February 1978. When the blizzard hit Chicago, it brought the city to a standstill, and people suddenly found themselves with some unexpected free time on their hands. For Randy Suess and Ward Christensen, two members of the Chicago Area Computer Hobbyists' Exchange (CACHE), it was a great opportunity to work on a project that they had been discussing: the creation of an electronic bulletin board system that would allow CACHE members to post messages and newsletter articles to each other. Christensen had already written a program to transfer computer files across telephone lines from one computer to another, and he adapted that software so that it could answer incoming calls, store messages, and offer a menu of other options to people who dialed in. Suess handled the hardware, building a computer with a single floppy drive and a modem card to answer incoming calls. By the beginning of February, the system was operational, and the first computer bulletin board system (BBS) was born.

The idea of using the computer to communicate with other computer users proved phenomenally popular. Within ten years, according to now-defunct *Boardwatch* magazine, there were 6,000 BBSes in operation; at the industry's height in 1992–93 (just prior to the introduction of the World Wide Web) the number of BBSes in the United States had climbed to more than 45,000. Although the majority of BBSes were general in nature, serving as a convenient online meeting place for people to chat, exchange messages, and swap files, many were specialized, catering to communities of computer users with specific interests such as flying, horses, law, coin collecting, and so on.

Most of the BBSes were operated as a hobby (neither the software nor the hardware was particularly expensive), and the only cost to use them was a long-distance phone charge if the BBS was located outside the user's local dialing area. In a preview of what would eventually happen with the Internet, however, a number of BBSes were established as for-profit enterprises that charged a fee for access (on top of whatever phone charges the user might pay). Particularly successful BBS companies, such as Exec-PC in Wisconsin and Event Horizon in Oregon, easily grossed several million dollars per year in hourly access fees and annual subscription rates.

In an effort to capitalize on the potential for lucrative revenues from computer users, a handful of national BBSes were started in the late 1970s and early 1980s. Over time, three dominated the market: CompuServe (which eventually became a subsidiary of America Online), the Source (which was bought up by CompuServe in 1989), and the Dow Jones News/Retrieval System (which eventually was folded into Factiva, a division of Dow Jones). The chief advantage of the national BBS services was that they established multiple access points around the country, which meant that more and more people could access the system without paying long-distance toll charges. That substantially increased consumer and corporate interest in both computer bulletin boards and computers generally and helped lay the groundwork for the future growth of the largest and most successful online service, America Online.

At the same time that the national computer bulletin board systems were growing in popularity, many of the country's independent bulletin board systems began talking to each other as well. Tom Jennings, a California programmer, developed a form of BBS software called Fido that could be used to communicate with other BBSes running the same software. Over time, as more and more BBSes began using Jennings's software, the resulting network became known as FidoNet.

One of the most popular features of both FidoNet and the commercial national BBSes like CompuServe was the ability of users to send messages to each other. Direct user-to-user e-mails were less common on FidoNet, because there was usually a time delay in the transfer of messages from one BBS to another. (The transfers tended to happen in the wee hours of the morning, when long distance rates were lowest.) However, a related function called EchoMail, which took batches of messages dealing with a particular topic and redistributed them to other bulletin board systems, was particularly popular.

With respect to user-to-user communications, the national BBSes had a huge advantage, since all files were stored on the same central servers. That meant that if one CompuServe user sent a message to another CompuServe user, it was delivered almost instantaneously. But even more compelling was the fact that users could "talk" to each other in real time in electronic chat rooms. In an interview with the *Washington Post* in 1985, former U.S. Army officer David Hughes predicted that "personal computers will be used as naturally for communication and free assembly as the telephone and meeting places are now." Among frequent BBS users, Hughes was regarded as the informal president of the Network Nation (a contemporary nickname for the growing online communities), and he offered a suitably political assessment of the impact of the new technology: "Tom Paine would have first published his *Common Sense* on a local computer bulletin board."

One topic that received remarkably little attention at the time was the impact of these new communications networks on personal privacy. There may well have been a common-sense understanding that anything posted to a bulletin board, computer or otherwise, was hardly private. After all, the very point was to enable computer users to share information with each other, and most people intuitively associate bulletin boards with the posting of public information. But there was a metalevel of observation and supervision that largely went unexamined: the fact that everything that occurred on a BBS, whether in a hobbyist's basement or the servers of CompuServe, was open to the system operator, or "sysop." When the first BBS was launched in Chicago, for instance, Ward Christensen would sometimes watch what users were typing onto the system as they were doing it. The BBS users would have no idea that someone was electronically watching over their shoulder as they typed.

Even if a system operator was not sitting at a screen watching BBS activity in real time, the potential for surveillance of electronic information grew exponentially with the invention and growth of online communities. At any given time, a sysop could simply scroll through the stored messages or files on his or her system, a capability that quickly came to the attention of law enforcement. Moreover, communication from one personal computer to another greatly enhanced the durability of electronic data. It was hard enough to delete a file when it was created and stored on a single computer; it was another thing altogether to try to track down and successfully delete a computer file or electronic message that had been uploaded to a BBS and then perhaps distributed around the country across FidoNet. Each iteration of a file or message might itself be copied multiple times during system backups, and each would be just as difficult to permanently delete as the original file on the user's own computer.

While there may not have been much privacy with respect to what was posted to a BBS, there was at least the potential for somewhat more privacy with respect to who was doing the posting. Many BBSes at the time allowed users to log in anonymously; the systems were essentially open to anyone who found the BBS's phone number and dialed in. Once logged in to a BBS, callers typically did not use their real names but instead adopted nicknames, or user IDs, which might be as straightforward as their own initials or as obscure as a favorite comic book hero or literary figure. For the numerous BBSes that specialized in particularly dodgy subjects—pornography, hacking, white supremacy—the ability to remain anonymous was a feature, not an accident.

The farther one moved up the BBS food chain, the more difficult it was to maintain one's anonymity. Many free BBSes required user information before allowing access, and subscription BBSes and commercial networks required both personal data and sufficient financial information to be able to collect payment. The implications were profound: the same credit card information that could be used to track real-world purchases and other activities could now be used to track online behavior as well. The information collected about purchases was significant enough—likes, dislikes, favorite stores, family information, and so on—but the ability to collect online information was much more worrisome. Typically, even in the days of the wide-open BBS, the information posted online by users was highly personal, covering every possible topic from sexual preferences to political opinions. While it was unquestionably true that the reasonable expectation of privacy was low, the popularity of BBSes marked the beginning of a new era of data mining and law enforcement investigations.

BEDTIME FOR PRIVACY

It was an unfortunate coincidence that at the same time that computer users were unwittingly (or at least unreflectively) baring their souls electronically, the federal government came under the control of an administration that so strongly advocated personal data collection, data mining, and government surveillance. Ronald Reagan based much of his 1980 presidential campaign on his opposition to what he considered to be the two most destructive threats to the lives of the average American: the Soviet Union and the federal government. A good argument can be made, given his acceptance speech at the Republican National Convention that summer, that he believed Washington was a greater threat than Moscow:

> I will not accept the excuse that the federal government has grown so big and powerful that it is beyond the control of any president, any administration or Congress. We are going to put an end to the notion that the American taxpayer exists to fund the federal government. The federal government exists to serve the American people. On January twentieth, we are going to reestablish that truth.

Reagan promised that when he became president, he would eliminate waste and shift federal programs to state and local governments. One of his most frequent applause lines during the campaign was "I want to get government off of your backs and out of your private lives."

As it turned out, personal privacy is at risk not only when the government wants to do more for its citizens (such as provide Social Security benefits) but also when it allegedly wants to do less. What few people anticipated was just how willing the Reagan administration would be to invade personal privacy in the aggressive pursuit of its economic goals. It didn't take long for the Reagan administration to demonstrate its willingness to push the envelope of personal privacy in its campaign against welfare and other federal programs.

One of the chief obstacles to a more efficient government, administration officials argued, was the Tax Reform Act of 1976. Congress had passed the law in response to the blatant privacy abuses of the Nixon administration, but the law, the Reagan White House said, was overly restrictive and unnecessarily interfered with investigations of nontax crimes and other administrative goals. And the Tax Reform Act was not the only problem: Reagan administration officials felt the same way about the provisions of the Privacy Act of 1974, which among other things restricted the ability of federal agencies to share information and release it for nonagency purposes. Particularly during Reagan's first term (which coincidentally ended in 1984), the White House devoted considerable time and effort to proposals intended to roll back or even eliminate the minimal federal privacy protections that were in place.

Less than a month after Reagan was sworn in, budget director David Stockman proposed "Project Intercept," which would require the Internal Revenue Service to withhold tax refunds from anyone failing to make court-ordered child support payments. While few disagreed with the ultimate goal of increasing child support payments (which the Reagan administration also hoped would lower welfare payments), civil libertarians were leery of using IRS information for any purpose other than the enforcement of income tax collection.

Project Intercept was just the tip of the iceberg. In July 1981, the White House threw its support behind legislation that would authorize the IRS to give private bill collectors the names and addresses of people who owed money to the federal government. Senator Charles Percy (R-Ill.) said that as of September 30, 1979, the U.S. government was owed $25 billion, a situation he described as "the most shocking example of waste and mismanagement of public funds I have encountered in my fifteen years as a United States senator."

John Shattuck, the director of the Washington office for the American Civil Liberties Union, warned that release of addresses by the

IRS could undercut the agency's central mission. "Once the doors to the vast personal data within the IRS are opened, even if only a crack," Shattuck said, "taxpayers' fears for their privacy can begin to overcome their duty to reveal essential details of their lives for purposes of tax payment."

But the push for broader use of IRS data continued. In November 1981, deputy attorney general Edward C. Schmults testified on behalf of the administration in support of legislation designed to substantially broaden the ability of federal law enforcement agencies to tap into IRS databases when investigating nontax crimes. In some cases federal investigators were required to obtain warrants before receiving the information, but in nearly half the cases a simple request from the agency head was all that was required.

Two other proposals floated by the Reagan administration in its hectic first year stirred stronger opposition both in Congress and in the public at large. In early April, the White House suggested the idea of creating a massive computerized data bank of every federal welfare recipient. Administration officials said that the data bank, dubbed the National Recipient Information System, would serve as a "strong deterrent to fraud and abuse." Under the proposal, recipients of aid to families with dependent children would be cross-matched against other federal databases, in particular that of the IRS.

With cries of "Big Brother" resounding through the Capitol and the threat of a lawsuit by the ACLU, the White House backed off the idea. Instead, the administration gave the program a new name—the Intergovernmental Recipient Information System—and said that state aid programs would not be given access to federal tax information. However, states would be allowed to access a variety of other federal data to look for fraud or overpayments, including files compiled by the Social Security Administration, the Veterans Administration, and the Office of Personnel Management.

At the same time that administration officials were floating the welfare data bank idea, a host of federal agencies were quietly implementing their own computer matching programs. One of the most aggressive agencies was the Department of Health and Human Services (HHS), which demonstrated the potential for computer matching with its "Project Missing Kids." The program was intended to ferret out families that claimed welfare checks for nonexistent children.

First, programmers at HHS compared welfare payment records to Medicaid files to find the names of children who had never received medical care. Those names were then matched against public school enrollment records to see whether the children actually existed. HHS officials told reporters that for every dollar of administrative costs, the program successfully recovered seven dollars in fraudulent payments.

The Reagan administration was so impressed with the results of Project Missing Kids that it established the Orwellian-sounding Long-Term Computer Matching Committee (an offshoot of the administration's Council on Integrity and Efficiency) to explore ways in which computer matching could be used by other agencies in the government. As with the Tax Reform Act, some computer-matching zealots argued that the provisions of the 1974 Privacy Act, which regulates the exchange of information among agencies, unnecessarily complicated the sharing of information and the search for fraud.

Civil libertarians in turn questioned whether the proposed savings and efficiencies outweighed the potential privacy abuses. As Shattuck pointed out, the government's matching program gave it the ability to conduct broad general searches and then identify specific people for potentially abusive investigations. Evincing a clear skepticism that the government had deleted its earlier domestic surveillance records as ordered by Congress, Shattuck asked, "What happens if the government decides to match its list of federal employees against domestic security files compiled by the FBI in the 1960s when it was investigating antiwar and civil rights activists?"

HHS's director of advanced computing techniques, James E. Foster, dismissed Shattuck's concerns, albeit in somewhat chilling terms. "No one is talking about creating one huge, *1984*-style data bank of information about all Americans," Foster said. "Law-abiding citizens will have nothing to fear." His comment anticipated the campaign slogan of British Conservative Party leader John Major, who campaigned for prime minister in 1992 on a platform of increased surveillance cameras and the accompanying slogan, "If you've got nothing to hide, you've got nothing to fear." One wonders: sixteen years later, Britons have become the most-watched citizens of any Western nation, with literally thousands of closed-circuit television cameras trained on public spaces across the country.

Although they were few and far between, there were some ideas that even the Reagan administration felt were too threatening to personal privacy. One good example was legislation proposed in 1982 by Senator Alan K. Simpson (R-Wyo.) to fight illegal immigration. A key feature of Simpson's plan was a requirement that within three years, the administration "establish a secure system to determine employment eligibility in the United States."

In an interview with the *New York Times*, Annelise G. Anderson, associate director of the Office of Management and Budget, said that a comprehensive employment eligibility system was a feature of totalitarianism and could easily be misused. "One of the things that a totalitarian society can't abide is not being able to control the movement of people," Anderson argued. "If you want to maintain a free society, you have to tolerate a little bit of slack in your ability to fully enforce the law. If you have everybody identified, you can stop people on the street to see if they have registered for the draft. If you have no ID, you have no way to find these people." She also had a practical objection: implementing a system that would "reliably determine," as the legislation required, whether a person was who he or she claimed to be and was eligible to work would cost at least $1.5 billion to implement.

Her comments were echoed by longtime *New York Times* columnist and self-described "libertarian conservative" William Safire, who wrote, "One of the great differences between free and enslaved societies is the right of the individual to live and work without the government knowing his every move. There can sometimes be privacy without freedom, as those in solitary confinement know, but there can be no freedom without privacy." He praised Anderson and her husband, Martin Anderson, as "what is left of the conservative conscience of the Reagan administration" and criticized attorney general William French Smith for failing to oppose the legislation. The prospects for individual liberty, he concluded, were grim: "We are entering the computer age. Combined with a national identity card [an idea being debated by the House of Representatives at the time] . . . government computers and data banks pose a threat to personal liberty. Though aimed at 'undocumented workers,' the computer tattoo will be pressed on you and me."

Safire's apocalyptic predictions of digital branding were entertaining, but he missed one of the overarching consequences of the Reagan administration's data collection efforts: the rapidly growing "privacy divide" in American society. People at the lower end of the economic scale or in need of help were forced to make their lives an open book, but for those with sufficient economic resources, privacy was a privilege that could more easily be maintained. One example arose in late 1980, when the incoming Reagan administration concluded that the $2 million allocated by the federal government for the presidential transition was insufficient to cover the actual cost involved. Reagan's campaign set up the Presidential Transition Trust and the Presidential Transition Foundation to solicit private donations. The following summer, the General Accounting Office asked to examine the financial records of the two organizations, but the Reagan administration refused, arguing that revealing the names of the donors who had contributed more than $500,000 to the cost of his transition would be an unwarranted invasion of their privacy.

"We do not intend to release the names of the donors, and never did—the only reason being that they get on lists for other people," said Verne Orr, the transition's budget director. "Charities love to get lists of people who give big sums."

The Reagan administration's reluctance to reveal the names of its transition donors was not unique; various other presidents and ex-presidents have been reluctant to name the people who have contributed to transitions, inaugurations, presidential libraries, and charitable foundations. Nonetheless, it does suggest that there is often a double standard when it comes to privacy: yes to well-heeled donors, no to welfare recipients and others in need. The operative question, all too often, is "How much privacy can you afford?"

THE YEAR THAT ORWELL MADE FAMOUS

Attempts to use IRS information for nonrevenue purposes and the compilation of huge databases of information about private citizens were not the only Nixonian flashbacks inspired by the Reagan administration. In April 1981, reports surfaced that an interagency working group led by CIA director William J. Casey was proposing to ease restrictions on domestic surveillance of American citizens. The restrictions were first put in place by President Ford in 1976 (one of the few by-products of the Domestic Council Commission on the

Right of Privacy) and then expanded by President Carter in Executive Order 12036, which established formal guidelines for all intelligence-gathering activities.

President Carter's order stated flatly that "the CIA may not engage in any electronic surveillance within the United States." Casey proposed language that was considerably more permissive: "The CIA may engage in electronic surveillance activity within the United States only for the purpose of assisting, and in coordination with, another agency." In addition, Casey proposed giving the CIA and other intelligence agencies much greater freedom to conduct "surreptitious searches" and proposed limiting the amount of oversight that the attorney general could exercise over the agency's activities.

Public and congressional reaction to the idea of domestic surveillance by the CIA was both swift and negative, and the White House scrambled to downplay concerns. White House counsel Edwin Meese III told reporters that the controversy was a "tempest in a teapot," adding that "the White House is absolutely opposed to the CIA getting into domestic spying." But although Casey did not get everything he wanted, he did succeed in eliminating President Carter's categorical prohibition. On December 4, 1981, President Reagan issued Executive Order 12333, which repealed and superseded President Carter's earlier order. One of the provisions of Reagan's order was that the CIA shall "collect, produce and disseminate foreign intelligence and counterintelligence, including information not otherwise obtainable. The collection of foreign intelligence or counterintelligence within the United States shall be coordinated with the FBI as required by procedures agreed upon by the Director of Central Intelligence and the Attorney General."

Thanks in part to the well-publicized proposal for expanded domestic surveillance by the CIA and the steady drumbeat of stories about how the Reagan administration was attempting to scour every federal computer chip for personal information, "Big Brother" was a frequently referenced concept as the fateful year 1984 approached. Literally hundreds of newspaper and magazine articles in 1983 and 1984 referenced Orwell's character, and the concept was a veritable mantra for civil libertarians who were trying to stem the creeping computerization and data mining of federal information.

While the full impact of personal computer technology on privacy would not be realized until some years after 1984, civil liberties advocates were increasingly concerned with Congress's failure to protect privacy rights from long-standing technological threats. On October 24, 1985, a report by the Office of Technology Assessment (OTA) was delivered to Rep. Robert W. Kastenmeier (D-Wis.), who at the time was serving as chair of the House Judiciary Subcommittee on Courts, Civil Liberties, and the Administration of Justice. The report stated in unequivocal terms that federal privacy laws had completely failed to keep pace with the enormous advances in technology, with the result that individual privacy was far more threatened than it had ever been before.

"The existing statutory framework and judicial interpretation thereof do not adequately cover new electronic surveillance applications," the OTA said. "The Fourth Amendment—which protects 'the right of the people to be secure in their persons, houses, papers and effects against unreasonable searches and seizures'—was written at a time when people conducted their affairs in a simple, direct and personalized fashion. Telephones, credit cards, computers and cameras did not exist. Although the application of the Fourth Amendment is timeless, its application has not kept abreast of current technologies."

The OTA report made it clear that a number of federal agencies were busy establishing their own permissive rules regarding new forms of electronic communications. As many as a quarter of the 142 agencies surveyed—including the Drug Enforcement Administration, the FBI, the U.S. Customs Service, the IRS, and the Criminal Division of the Justice Department—admitted that they were either currently conducting surveillance or actively planning to track computer usage and intercept electronic communications ranging from electronic mail to cellular phone conversations. One of OTA's policy analysts, Priscilla M. Regan, acknowledged that her agency had not examined the activities of the nation's intelligence agencies; had it done so, the OTA's own report would have been classified. "God only knows what these agencies are doing," Regan said. "It's fair to say that we would certainly have found much higher amounts of surveillance of computer systems if we produced a classified study and examined these agencies closely."

CONGRESS LOCKS THE BARN DOOR

In an effort to remedy the problems identified by the OTA, Kastenmeier and Senator Patrick Leahy introduced the Electronic Communications Privacy Act (ECPA), which was designed to extend the protections of Title III of the 1968 Omnibus Crime Control and Safe Streets Act (which limited the use of wiretapping by federal investigators). Under the terms of the ECPA, antiwiretapping provisions would expand the "protection against interception from voice transmissions to virtually all electronic communications . . . the digitized portion of telephone calls, the transmission of data over telephone lines, the transmission of video images by microwave or by any other conceivable mix of medium and message." The legislation, which became law on October 21, 1986, contained two sections: Title I, which prohibited the interception of wire, oral, and electronic communications while in transit, and Title II (also known as the Stored Communications Act), which provided protection for communications stored electronically.

In addition to making it a crime to intercept various types of electronic communications, the ECPA also established standards for the issuance of warrants to law enforcement officers seeking access to various types of electronic communications and stored records. It was the first comprehensive update of the original wiretapping law in two decades. Prior to the adoption of the ECPA, Leahy said, a federal agent would have needed a warrant in order to listen to a phone conversation but not to rifle through a suspect's e-mail account.

"This is a comprehensive piece of legislation in an area that you simply cannot approach piecemeal the way we have up until now," Senator Leahy said during the debate over its passage. "If the law is not passed, we may as well tell corporations that we've outlawed locks and security alarms on their doors." The senator's "piecemeal" remark was a reference to the fact that there had been several high-profile interceptions of banking and corporate data but no clear laws under which the perpetrators could be charged. Thanks to growing corporate concerns about electronic intrusions and persistent consumer worries about privacy, the legislation was supported by an unusually broad coalition of advocacy groups, ranging from the ACLU to the National Association of Manufacturers.

When it comes to privacy, however, Congress often takes one step forward and two steps back. That same year, Congress adopted the Money Laundering Control Act of 1986, which added two new sections to the Bank Secrecy Act. The latter was a 1970 law that had remarkably little to do with secrecy and a great deal to do with imposing anti-money-laundering reporting requirements on financial institutions. One of the new provisions made it a crime to use banks or other financial institutions in an attempt to disguise the proceeds of a crime. The other made it a federal offense to structure bank transactions in an attempt to avoid the requirement that banks report cash transactions in excess of $10,000. (This provision would cause problems some years later for New York governor Elliot Spitzer when he attempted to disguise payments made to a call-girl service.)

The Reagan administration had pushed for a version of the bill that would have been even more invasive of privacy than the adoption of additional reporting requirements. Treasury officials asked Congress to order banks to turn over customer account information to law enforcement (without notifying the customer) anytime the bank "had reason to believe" that the account information might have something to do with criminal activity. The proposal would have effectively repealed the Right to Financial Privacy Act of 1978. Fortunately, Congress (thanks in large part to the efforts of then senator Joe Biden) declined to do so.

With the Reagan administration coming to an end, Congress took one final stab at limiting the damage that had been done to personal privacy. It passed the Computer Matching and Privacy Protection Act of 1988, which was intended to bring the practice of interagency computer database matching under some type of regulatory control. The ACLU told Congress that between 1980 and 1984, the Reagan administration had set up 110 separate computer matching programs and had compared approximately two billion separate federal files. The new law required agencies to negotiate written agreements before sharing records for matching, to notify people whose records were being matched, and to obtain at least two pieces of proof before cutting off federal benefits as a result of an adverse match. In the end, however, the act was something well short of either a complete ban on computer matching or an effective regulatory scheme. The most significant accomplishment of the Computer Matching and Privacy Protection Act was to institutionalize the routine sharing of information among federal agencies, thereby eviscerating one of the key goals of the Privacy Act of 1974.

PERSONAL COMPUTERS AND THE ILLUSION OF PRIVACY

Humanity has a long history, from rock carving forward, of finding new ways to express fantasies about sex, solicit sexual partners, and even enhance sexual experiences. As soon as two human beings could use a computer to communicate, the odds were good that at least some of that communication would be about sex.

The likelihood that sex, in some form or other, would wind up on personal computers was greatly increased by the fact that personal computers offer a powerful illusion of privacy. Consider the evolution that occurred in adult films: for years, the most anonymous viewing occurred when someone paid cash to watch a "blue movie" in an adult theater—there was no paper trail and little likelihood, if one was careful, of being recognized. The arrival of the videotape player and videocassettes drove adult theaters out of business, in part because of convenience—no more visits to typically sketchy parts of a city—but also because they heightened an individual's sense of privacy. Now one could watch an adult movie in one's own home, where there was even less risk that one's cinematic tastes would be discovered.

But the video revolution is also a perfect example of how technology both giveth privacy and taketh it away. For consumers with the money to buy adult videocassettes outright, it was still possible to be anonymous (unless one bought them from a mail order company). But since the earliest adult videos retailed for as much as $300 a copy, the practice of renting videos quickly became popular. Any store that rents items needs a certain amount of personal information about its customers so that, if necessary, it can track down the renter and get its property back. Moreover, video rental stores typically keep track of what particular customers rent, in part for inventory control and in part as a service to customers ("I can't remember, did I see *Sorority Debutantes 13* or *14*?").

Most people did not give much thought to the embarrassment potential of their video rental records until the summer of 1987, when the rental histories of two high-profile figures, Lt. Col. Oliver North and Robert Bork, were publicly disclosed. At the time, North was testifying before Congress about his role in the Iran-Contra scandal, and Bork was under consideration by the Senate for a seat on the Supreme Court.

Neither video rental list contained anything particularly salacious, but the disclosures outraged members of Congress. Senator Alan Simpson offered the most pungent assessment, describing the *Washington City Paper*'s publication of Bork's video rentals as "arrogant, smart-aleck, super-sarcastic, puerile, sorry, and pathetic." Fellow Senate Judiciary Committee member Patrick Leahy, one of the Senate's leading privacy advocates, sponsored a bill called the Video Privacy Protection Act of 1988, and Congress acted with unusual speed to adopt it. Signed into law by President Reagan on November 5, 1988, it prohibited the release of video rental information to anyone other than the customer absent a search warrant or other court order.

While the videocassette player unquestionably reshaped the concept of privacy with respect to movie viewing, the personal computer had one profound advantage: it was both an entertainment device and a communication tool. Once set up in the living room or bedroom, a personal computer could be used to access online materials without even leaving the home. Even more compelling was the fact that a computer user could create a new, anonymous identity while online (a phenomenon neatly captured by cartoonist Peter Steiner in a July 1993 *New Yorker* drawing of two dogs at a computer with the caption "On the Internet, nobody knows you're a dog").

Almost immediately, the perceived privacy and anonymity of the personal computer began altering social mores. People who might never have purchased a copy of *Playboy* began subscribing to BBSes, such as "Micro-Smut," that were entirely devoted to pornography. Even on more mainstream and general-interest bulletin boards like ExecPC, subscribers began exchanging sexually explicit stories, jokes, and images. Proving once again the old adage that "sex sells," the practice of uploading and downloading scanned centerfolds, mostly from *Playboy*, became so popular that Playboy Enterprises eventually filed a successful copyright infringement suit against ExecPC and its system operator, Jim Maxey.

Electronic dating services also flourished, not merely on small local BBSes but also on national networks like CompuServe and the

Source. In a graphic demonstration of the social and legal challenges that computer communications would cause, the ads quickly became far more explicit than those printed in local newspapers. When the Reader's Digest Association purchased the Source in 1982, reporter Rudy Maxa wrote a column about the classified data desires of the Source's 22,000 subscribers. The self-described "gorgeous and adventurous" Ginger from Houston listed her interests as "intimate apparel, sex, and romance." A Maryland couple said that they were looking for "couples, sex" and playmates to join them at Plato's Retreat, a world-famous sex club (now defunct) on Manhattan's Upper West Side. And three women from Florida, Maxa said, "expressed an interest in drugs and sex in language not suitable for reprinting in a family newspaper, or *Reader's Digest*, for that matter."

In form, if not in content, online dating ads were not significantly different from their paper equivalent. But online chat rooms were something new altogether: a forum where people could converse electronically, in real time, with complete strangers from around the world on an endless array of subjects. Thanks to the powerful illusion of privacy and anonymity, computer users demonstrated a willingness to talk in the most explicit terms about topics that they would never discuss with their neighbors, their family, or even their spouses. For the online services, the chat rooms were a huge boon: not only did they help to attract new subscribers, but they also kept existing subscribers interested and online, despite the often staggering per-minute connection charges required to access the services.

In the pursuit of electronic titillation, people completely lost sight of the fact that actual privacy was nonexistent. Each online service could match even the most masking or arcane user name to a real person and could track when that person logged on to the service, what areas he or she visited, and how long the session lasted. Message boards and chat rooms were monitored (albeit loosely), and particularly obscene or offensive messages could be deleted. Users who violated an online service's code of conduct could be blocked for an evening or kicked off altogether. Nor were records of online activity limited to the service itself. If a long-distance call was required to log on, the phone company would have a record of that as well. If a credit card was used to pay the subscription or usage fees, that information was stored by the credit card company. And to varying degrees, traces of the online information lingered on the hard drive of the personal computer itself. It did not take federal and state law enforcement officers long to realize that every online service and every personal computer was a potential treasure trove of investigative leads or criminal evidence.

Many people, particularly social conservatives, found the rising online licentiousness disturbing enough, but the illusion of personal computer privacy had an even darker side: the use of computers and online services to facilitate sexual assaults on children and to exchange child pornography. There has always been an uneasy tension between the concept of privacy and criminal behavior, particularly for crimes, like domestic or child abuse, that typically take place within the confines of the home. For far too long, law enforcement used the privacy of the home as an excuse to avoid investigating domestic crimes. But by the early 1980s, attitudes had changed, and police were generally more responsive to complaints of spousal or parental assault.

The possibility that personal computers might actually be instruments of abuse raised significant new privacy issues. In 1985, for instance, Senator Paul Trible (R-Va.) proposed one of the first pieces of legislation to criminalize the transmission of certain types of electronic data. Under his bill, the Computer Pornography and Child Exploitation Prevention Act of 1985, the use of a computer bulletin board to send messages relating to child pornography would become a federal felony.

Trible's bill was referred to the Senate Judiciary Subcommittee on Juvenile Justice, and although hearings were held, it was never sent to the floor of the Senate for a vote. However, the Juvenile Justice hearings helped spur the Reagan administration to create the Attorney General's Commission on Pornography, better known as the Meese Commission. After holding a series of hearings across the country, in July 1986 the Meese Commission issued a detailed and ironically graphic report (including explicit plot summaries and transcripts for various adult films then available). Most of the Meese Commission's recommendations centered around better enforcement of existing laws, but a couple in particular raised privacy red flags: that the Justice Department create an "obscenity law enforcement data base," the contents of which were unspecified but which would be available to federal, state, and local law enforcement, and that the IRS "aggressively investigate violations of the tax laws committed by producers and distributors of obscene material."

Most of the Meese Commission's recommendations went unfulfilled, but the controversial proposals helped underscore one significant point: computers were rapidly becoming so central to the daily affairs of Americans that any criminal investigation involving a computer was essentially an investigation of a suspect's entire life. Few people could face the prospect of such an inquiry with complete equanimity.

But personal computers, BBSes, and national services such as America Online and CompuServe were just the beginning. Over the course of the next decade, the World Wide Web would weave its way into every corner of American society. All of the problems and perils of the 1980s—increasing reliance on computer technology, ineffective deletion of data, pervasive federal and corporate data mining, overly aggressive search and seizure techniques, ill-conceived and reactionary legislation—would combine to make the growing global network of personal and mainframe computers a staggeringly vulnerable repository of our most private information.

12

ELECTRONIC EXHIBITIONISM
AND VOYEURISM

Privacy in a Webbed World

The impulse to publicize the milestones of our lives to family, friends, and neighbors is not a new phenomenon. For more than two centuries, newspapers have routinely carried announcements of such personal life-altering events as births, marriages, and deaths. For many years, cost limited such announcements to the wealthy or nobility. But the tremendous increase in newspapers during the Industrial Revolution democratized both the number of people who could afford to announce their good news and the range of events reported (community awards of various types, graduations and honor rolls, the accomplishments of local athletes, and so on).

The first mention of Englishman Timothy Berners-Lee in the mainstream U.S. press fell squarely into that decidedly old-fashioned tradition: on May 6, 1990, the *New York Times* ran a brief notice of his engagement to Nancy Carlson, a programmer/analyst at the World Health Organization in Geneva, Switzerland. "Mr. Berners-Lee," the paper noted, "is a software engineer at the European Particle Physics Laboratory in Geneva." The couple, the *Times* later reported, was married in July 1990 at a church in Fairfield, Connecticut.

Not only would it be the last time that Berners-Lee was mentioned in such a matter-of-fact manner, but the young researcher was about to fundamentally change the concept of personal publicity for everyone else as well. In March 1989, while working as a contractor at the European Organization for Nuclear Research (best known as CERN, the acronym for its original French name) in Geneva, Berners-Lee had the inspiration that shook the world and earned him a knighthood from Queen Elizabeth: combining the concept of hyperlinks (a method of electronically linking two pieces of information) with the rapidly growing communications network known as the Internet. (At the time, CERN was the largest Internet node in Europe.) With the help of fellow CERN computer scientist Robert Caillou, Berners-Lee drafted a proposal for the creation of a new information-sharing system called the World Wide Web. After receiving approval to pursue the project (his supervisor described the proposal as "vague, but exciting"), Berners-Lee spent the better part of a year developing the first Web server, the first rudimentary browser, and the first Web editor. Berners-Lee then launched the world's first Web site on a server at CERN on August 6, 1991.

The brilliance of Berners-Lee's invention lay in the fact that a hyperlink can serve as an electronic connection between any two types of information: words to other words, words to photos, photos to other photos, headlines to full stories. The concept and the implementation are simple, but the potential applications are essentially endless. Like the process of photography a century and a half earlier, Berners-Lee's innovation was released to the world without license or royalty. As a result, anyone with the necessary technical skills and access to a Web server could set up a Web site and begin publishing whatever material interested them. The true age of electronic exhibitionism was about to dawn.

One more piece, however, was needed: a relatively simple and effective browser for viewing the various types of content on the Internet, including the files available using Berners-Lee's World Wide Web. In 1992, at the National Center for Supercomputing Applications at the University of Illinois at Urbana-Champaign, programmers Marc Andreessen and Eric Bina wrote a browser called Mosaic. The software was notable for its ease of use, its simple and clean interface, and its relatively smooth handling of multiple types of content on a single Web page. Versions of Mosaic for the Macintosh and Windows operating systems were released in December 1993; at the time there were just 623 Web sites in the entire world. One year later the number of Web sites had risen to 10,022, and by January 1996 the best estimate was that 100,000 sites were in operation. In an article for *Wired* in October 1994, Gary Wolf (coauthor of *Aether Madness: An Offbeat Guide to the Online World*) argued that the most profound aspect of

Mosaic was that it encouraged every computer user to add content to the Web.

Wolfe's observation about the Mosaic-induced impulse to publish was particularly perceptive. The remarkable rise of the World Wide Web was fueled in large part by an apparently insatiable desire on the part of the average person to publicize information about himself or herself and share information on a seemingly endless number of subjects. Rather quickly, the Web became a pulsing, ever-shifting Rorschach inkblot of human interests and desires. In the process, the concept of personal privacy underwent some profound changes.

Pleasure was one of the driving factors behind the posting of personal information online. Even before the World Wide Web became a global phenomenon, people were posting profiles of themselves on electronic dating services, job search BBSes, and other online communities. By the early 1990s, online dating was a cultural phenomenon, and reports were already surfacing of couples who met online and later got married. At the time, one of the most popular services for cyberdating was BITNET ("Because It's There Network"), a system that at its peak linked together over five hundred educational institutions around the world. Users could exchange e-mail and topical messages, but the real action lay in the system's interactive chat feature, known as BITNET Relay.

As a *Washington Post* article noted at the time, the chief drawback to BBS romance was the cost of phone calls and connection charges. The World Wide Web had an enormous advantage in that regard: the decentralized nature of the network and its open accessibility made it possible for virtually unlimited numbers of organizations and networks to connect to the Web at very low cost. In a short period of time, huge numbers of local access points to the Web were established around the United States (as well as many other nations), which eliminated the long-distance phone charges typically associated with many BBSes. Now computer users could get access to an entire universe of Web sites through a single dial-up connection. That one development completely reshaped the economics of online access and essentially wiped out a once-thriving BBS community.

One thing it didn't do was wipe out the active online dating scene. To the contrary, as the World Wide Web took off in 1996 and 1997 (with the number of Web sites growing at well over 100 percent per year), dating sites quickly became among the most popular of the early destinations. General sites like Yahoo! Personals and Match .com were among the early leaders, but as with so much else on the Web, specialization quickly set in. "Surfers" could soon post profiles on a huge range of dating sites that catered to specific ethnicities, jobs, colleges, or fetishes.

Given that the cost of publishing on the Web is so much lower than printing a comparable announcement in the newspaper (a major part of the economic problems that newspapers face today), many people now choose to broadcast information about themselves online that would be far too trivial or expensive to put in a newspaper. The motivating factor behind the success of the current Internet rage—the social networking sites like MySpace, Facebook, LinkedIn, Twitter, and so on—is that people crave a sense of community, and one of the ways to build community is to share a certain amount of personal information. Online social networks thrive because they enable us to share personal information more quickly and easily than ever before, creating the impression that we are all newsworthy now.

Facebook in particular has co-opted the language of the news industry, with its "live feed" and "full stories." In the process, services like Facebook encourage us to reveal increasingly large amounts of information about ourselves, from the banal ("I'm standing in line at the post office") to the embarrassing (photos of ourselves and friends in compromising positions and conditions) to the profound ("It's a boy!"). Only the last might have at one time merited the cost of a printed announcement in a community newspaper, but the Internet is a great leveler of both people and information.

Even in the days when publication of significant events was limited to the newspaper, there was always the risk that the information would be put to unintended uses. Across the country, for instance, real estate agents and apartment hunters regularly read the obituaries looking for properties that might be available for sale or rent. Insurance sellers and home furnishing stores used birth announcements to target their advertisements. A 2004 book by Rhonda Adams, *Six-Week Start-Up*, specifically recommends the personal announcements in newspapers as "one of the very best sources of information about your community, and thus potential customers."

The growth of the World Wide Web, and in particular the rise of social networking sites, has greatly exacerbated the commercial use of personal information, for several reasons. First, the geographic scope of publication has dramatically expanded. Most personal announcements were placed in local newspapers, and the spread of the information was correspondingly limited. But publication on the World Wide Web by definition implies a global audience. Second, as noted above, the amount of information that people publish about themselves has steadily increased. Third, the nature of the Web and of computers in general makes it easier to collect and correlate personal information. The ability to compile increasingly detailed dossiers about Web surfers increases the intrinsic value of each piece of information, regardless of how inconsequential it might be on its own.

But the fourth factor is by far the most significant: the value of the information to the publisher itself. When a local newspaper publishes an obituary or wedding announcement, its economic interest in the information contained in the announcement is limited to whatever it charged for publication and for the diffuse additional benefit of providing interesting content to its readers. But the social networking sites that make publication of personal information so easy have substantial economic interest in the information that their users publish online. For them, user information is the very medium in which they trade (and in fact, most sites explicitly state that they own the information posted to their sites). As a result, such services are highly motivated to find ways to monetize the virtually unlimited personal information that Web users are quite voluntarily publishing about themselves.

It can be difficult to strike a reasonable balance between effective monetization of information and user privacy. For instance, Facebook caused a considerable controversy in late 2007 when it announced its new information-sharing program called "Beacon." In its original form, Beacon was intended to allow Facebook's business partners to send "social ads" to a Facebook user's friends, announcing that the user had taken some action on the partner's site. For instance, if a Facebook user rented the movie *Psycho* from Blockbuster.com, the Beacon program would allow Blockbuster to put an item in the user's news feed that announced what he or she would be watching that night.

Facebook users reacted angrily to the idea that their non-Facebook activity might involuntarily wind up in their news feed. Much of the controversy had to do with the ability to control the distribution of information; although Facebook launched the program with pop-up dialog boxes that gave users the chance to say no to the social ad, the boxes tended to disappear quickly or not work at all. Unless the user quickly checked "no," Facebook assumed permission to publish the social ad. After numerous protest groups formed on Facebook itself, the company revamped Beacon to require permission from users before distributing social ads (an approach known as "opt-in," as opposed to the original "   quirement). While the company's decision to alter its soc   m muted the controversy, it did not resolve the much b   on of who should control the information that people p   online.

"INFORMATION WANTS TO BE FREE"

Any individual can make what seems to be a rational decision to post personal information to a Web site in the hope of obtaining some perceived benefit (a sizzling romance, the perfect job offer, his or her fifteen nanoseconds of fame). But truly rational decisions (at least in the economic sense) require complete information. The reality is that most people don't realize how little control they retain over the information they post on the Web, whether on a social networking site or their personal Web site. As many, many people have discovered, it is far too easy for information to be copied from one location on the Web to another or to be spread around the globe in a seemingly endless string of forwarded e-mails.

Not only is it essentially impossible for someone to control the information that he or she posts to the Web, it is increasingly difficult to track, let alone control, the information that others post. As those who have Googled their name know, information tends to pop up from the most unexpected sources: 5K race results, high school reunion lists, church newsletters, local newspaper articles, the Web sites and blogs of relatives, and so on. Even more challenging is the fact that in a wired and Web-crazed world, the durability of information extends far beyond individual hard drives. Once on the Web, any given piece of information enjoys a metaphysical existence that raises some interesting philosophical questions about concepts of knowledge, repentance, remorse, forgiveness, and rehabilitation.

Seven years before Timothy Berners-Lee launched the first Web site, author Stewart Brand (best known for his publication of the 1970s lifestyle bible, *The Whole Earth Catalog*) identified the fundamental force driving the computer age while speaking at the first Hackers' Conference in 1984: "On the one hand information wants to be expensive, because it's so valuable. The right information in the right place just changes your life. On the other hand, information wants to be free, because the cost of getting it out is getting lower and lower all the time. So you have these two fighting against each other."

In his remarks, Brand used the word "free" in the sense of "without cost," a reflection of the remarkable drop in the cost of getting bytes of information from one side of the planet to the other. The powerful truth of his observation can be seen in the diminution or outright demise of physical content delivery systems, from music CDs to newspapers to books. But over the intervening quarter century, a secondary meaning—that information wants to be free of control, or by its nature is uncontrollable—has largely supplanted Brand's original meaning.

Brand's insight, in both its senses, has been proven true time and again on the World Wide Web. Part of what was happening during the 1990s was simply a continuation of the illusion of privacy associated with personal computers; Internet surfers sitting in the privacy of their home had no difficulty persuading themselves that their activities were both unknown and unknowable. But thanks to both the design of the Internet and the behavior of Web browsers themselves, that is far less true than it was in the era of electronic BBSes.

To begin with, every personal computer essentially maintains a second-by-second diary of Internet activity. For a long time, until the gradual introduction of broadband connections, accessing the Internet could be a tedious process, measured in trickles of 14.4, 28.8, or 57.6 kilobits per second. Much like the handling of file deletion in the early days of DOS, programmers looked for shortcuts that could help speed up online activity. Realizing that most Web pages don't change much from hour to hour or even day to day, programmers designed browsers to download an entire Web page the first time it is visited. If a Web surfer later returns to that page (and most do), the browser first checks to see whether the version of the page stored on the hard drive (in what is known as the Internet cache) matches the current version of the Web page. If it does, then the browser uses those bits to display the Web page, since pulling the data off the hard drive is much faster than downloading it again, particularly if a slow modem is being used. However, the Internet cache approach means that with a little bit of poking, one can fairly easily reconstruct what Web sites the computer has visited recently. And thanks to the fact that the actual process of deleting files has not changed significantly in the last thirty years, the contents of the files in the Internet cache still lurk on the hard drive even if the files have been deleted. It takes concerted effort (and special software) to render them irrecoverable.

In late 2008 and early 2009, in an effort to address consumer concerns over the lingering traces of Internet activity, several major browsers (Firefox, Internet Explorer, Opera, and Google Chrome) introduced a privacy mode. (Apple's Safari browser had done so in early 2005.) The feature works slightly differently in each browser, but the general idea is that in privacy mode, the browser will not put any information about online activity on the hard drive whatsoever.

While this new feature may protect individuals from prying bosses, spouses, or parents on company and home computers, it is still the perpetuation of an illusion. Privacy mode does not cloak a computer user's identity, so it does not prevent an Internet service provider (ISP), Web server, or Web site from recording information about the user's online activity. One of the constants of Internet software design is that electronic logs are kept to measure performance, track usage for billing, identify problems, and resolve disputes. An Internet surfer's activity online can be (and probably is) tracked by his or her ISP, some or all of the intermediary servers that carry traffic from the browser to Web sites and back, and by the sites themselves. It used to be true that such records were not kept very long due to storage constraints, but thanks to dramatic decreases in the cost of hard drives (and increasingly forceful suggestions from law enforcement agencies), such activity records may be kept for months or even years at a time.

In the award-winning film *All the President's Men*, Bob Woodward's anonymous government source, Deep Throat (played inimitably by Hal Holbrook), growls, "Follow the money." On the Internet, information may want to be free, but it is money that truly trashes privacy. At about the same time that Mosaic was being developed, programmers began writing software to explore (or "crawl") as many Web sites as possible and index the materials that people put online. By making those indexes publicly available, search engines made it possible to find content on the Web.

It takes money to create and operate a search engine, and many of the companies that offer them have struggled with how to profit from their work. By far the most successful has been Google, the company that has become virtually synonymous with the concept of Internet searching. Founded in 1998 by Stanford University students Larry Page and Sergey Brin, the company has ridden its proprietary search engine technology to an enviable position as one of the foremost software companies in the world. In the process, Google has dedicated itself to making more and more of the world's information accessible from any Internet-enabled device; for instance, the company recently undertook an effort to scan as many books as possible and index them for search. The book-scanning program led to high-profile litigation with some of the country's largest publishers, but the lawsuit was settled after the parties agreed to share revenues from ads displayed alongside the books and payments for downloads of copyright-protected works.

Over the years, the Google Web crawler, or spider, has indexed billions of pages, and each day tens of millions of people use the Google index to search for information on those pages. Like virtually all other search engines, Google is freely available to anyone and does not require signing in before using the service. But even relatively anonymous searching is still a two-way street: Google not only provides a list of possible answers to each search query but also collects, stores, and analyzes information about the person doing the searching (his or her query, IP address, operating system, browser, language, ISP, and so on). Google uses the information it collects both to hone the operation of its search engine and to generate a huge percentage (roughly 99 percent) of its massive revenues. On every page of search results, Google provides a number of sponsored results and textual ads (short text-only ads). Google auctions off various search terms to advertisers, who pay to have their offers appear on the results pages associated with those terms. The more precisely Google can help advertisers target their ads, the more it can charge for its advertising space, so it is certainly in Google's interest to know as much as possible about the people who use its search engine.

Compounding the privacy concerns about Google was its March 2008 purchase of DoubleClick, the Internet's largest server of online advertising. Since its creation in 1996, DoubleClick has developed a wide range of tools for compiling dossiers about Internet surfers, and it makes those dossiers available to advertisers and marketing agencies. It is most notorious for its use of "cookies," small bits of data that are stored on a Web surfer's hard drive and can be used to track various types of online activity, including the sites a person visits, the ads he or she clicks on, and so forth. The news that Google was buying the infamous ad server raised concerns that Google would combine an individual's search activity with the commercial activity in DoubleClick's dossier on that person, thus permitting the delivery of even more specifically targeted information.

Both the Federal Trade Commission in the United States and privacy regulators in the European Union took a close look at the privacy and competitiveness implications of Google's acquisition of Double-Click. In the end, both regulatory groups agreed to allow the deal to go through, but concerns remain about Google's commitment to privacy and its staggering access to personal information (not only through its search engine but through additional services like Gmail, Google Docs, and Google Reader). Many worry that the company's unofficial motto, "Don't Be Evil," is not enough to ward off the temptations of selling ever more specific information about consumers to companies desperate to minimize the costs and increase the efficiency of advertising, both online and off. The more fundamental question is whether our own love of convenience and utility outweighs the loss of privacy that occurs every time we search the Web.

DATA MINING: YOU ARE WHO YOUR HABITS SAY YOU ARE

In many ways, the dark world of too much knowledge that Orwell foresaw for 1984 arrived a decade later than he predicted: 1994 was the year that interest in the practice of data mining, already enormously popular among federal agencies, began spreading like wildfire through corporate America. In the years since, massive computing power, vast electronic databases of consumer activity, and our own online exhibitionism have combined to push the practice of data mining beyond mere identification of consumers into the much more disconcerting realms of pattern recognition and behavioral modeling.

The concept behind data mining is simple and chilling. Over the last half century, credit card companies have compiled massive amounts of data about the spending habits of their cardholders. National retail businesses have smaller but still impressive amounts of information about the reading habits, clothing preferences, and even food choices of their customers, depending on the nature of their particular business. In the perpetual search for lower costs and higher profits, corporate management began asking their information technology staffs to conduct increasingly sophisticated analyses of the mountains of data in their computer files. By combining proprietary data with public (and perhaps not so public) sources of information, corporations discovered that it was possible to compile startlingly detailed, and therefore lucrative, profiles of neighborhoods, households, and even individual consumers.

Recognizing a new business opportunity, computer manufacturers like IBM, Unisys, and Thinking Machines (a now-defunct supercomputer company with the *Matrix*-like motto, "We're building a machine that will be proud of us") began manufacturing supercomputers specifically designed to sift through massive quantities of data (gigabytes in the early 1990s, petabytes today, exabytes tomorrow), searching for elusive patterns of consumer behavior and compiling increasingly detailed profiles of specific consumers based on the digital footprints that most people leave in the world. The quantity of data is truly astonishing: six months ago, Google said that it was processing twenty petabytes of data each day, which is very roughly equivalent to two-hundred billion photographs or one-tenth of the entire world's printed material. Any way you slice it, it is a lot of data.

Journalist and emerging technology guru Esther Dyson was one of the first to comment on the new trend:

Some people think privacy is an inalienable personal right that can't be sold; others think consumers, rather than TRW [the credit reporting company now known as Experian], should have the right to sell their personal information perhaps using firms such as TRW as an agent. Maybe both points of view are right:

Consumers do own their data and should control its use. However, publishing a "data image" of a person, just like improperly
publishing a photo image of a nonpublic figure, can be a violation of moral as opposed to personal rights. That is, the damage
is not financial, but it can result in a financial settlement.

Dyson's recognition of the concept of a "data image" was particularly apt and helps explain some of the concern that the practice
of data mining inspires. When Abigail Roberson's image was misappropriated at the beginning of the twentieth century (as described in
chapter 4), the experience was clearly upsetting to her but in the end,
not especially harmful. Moreover, Roberson had one advantage that
most people today lack: the misappropriation of her image was overt,
which gave her a chance to challenge it, albeit unsuccessfully, in court.
A century later, data mining helps corporations and the government
draw hidden digital images of individuals that are far more detailed
and potentially destructive than the discreet drawing that graced the
"Flour of the Family" sacks.

In theory, the more information that marketers or advertisers have
about a specific person, the more accurately they can target that individual with offers in which he or she is likely to be interested. The
Holy Grail of advertising, after all, is to offer a service or product to
people at the moment at which they are most likely to actually purchase it, without wasting advertising on people who have no interest.
The information provided by consumer activity is coming ever closer
to achieving that goal; a shopping spree for running outfits can bring
an onslaught of running shoe catalogs or marathon brochures, while
the purchase of symphony tickets will produce a flood of fine arts
mailings.

But nothing matches the Internet for the immediacy of its feedback, that sense that advertisers and businesses essentially can see
what people are thinking when they are online. The data collected
by search engines alone is often enough to sketch the rough outlines
of particular surfers. For instance, in the summer of 2006, AOL (as
America Online was then officially known) released a database of
information that it had collected about searches performed on its site.
The identities of the individual searchers were hidden behind random

numbers, but as *New York Times* reporter Michael Barbaro easily demonstrated, there was more than enough information in the database to track down some of the searchers. Searcher number 4417749, it turned out, was Thelma Arnold, a resident of Lilburn, Georgia.

Over the course of several months, Arnold had searched for a wide variety of information, such as "numb fingers," "60 single men," "tea for good health," "termites," and "mature living." There was nothing particularly startling about her specific search history—which may help explain why she was willing to allow Barbaro to identify her in his article—but it is not difficult to imagine how her search history might cause problems. For instance, she frequently helped her friends by searching for information about various medical ailments, including "dry mouth," "nicotine effects on the body," and "hand tremors." It is not difficult to imagine that if Arnold needed to change insurance or was involved in medical litigation of some sort, those kinds of searches might cause problems—or at the very least raise questions about various aspects of her personal life that might not otherwise be asked.

In response to outcries over the release of the data, AOL pulled the information from the Internet and apologized for its release. There was no suggestion, however, that AOL would stop collecting such information or refuse to sell it to marketers and businesses. For businesses struggling to figure out how to survive online—like AOL or Yahoo! or even Google—the value of the information generated by consumers themselves is simply too great to throw away. And most of the time, consumers are happy to receive the kind of specialized attention that data collection makes possible. The desire to receive special treatment, to be greeted as a familiar and valued customer, runs deep. It is that impulse that makes Internet cookies tolerable; the most common use is to store a user's log-in name and password for a particular site (such as the *New York Times*) so that upon returning, the user does not have to reenter the information but can go straight to the content he or she desires. It is the electronic equivalent of a respectful and courteous greeting at a five-star hotel: "Good evening, sir. It's good to see you again. Welcome back to the Queen Elizabeth." The key difference is that with sufficient economic resources, one has a better chance of controlling the spread of one's information. Most five-star hotels do not resell the information they acquire about their guests, whereas many Internet sites (including many of the largest) have few qualms about doing so.

One of the biggest concerns about the practice of data mining is the possibility of making fallacious connections. The fact that someone buys Minnesota Twins tickets, for instance, is not a firm indicator of that person's baseball allegiance: is the purchaser merely passing through Minneapolis and taking the opportunity to see a new stadium, or perhaps buying the tickets for a friend? Are searches for the recipe for LSD part of a class on the history of the 1960s or the first step in a crime (or both, for that matter)? Additional searches and information from various databases may help answer those questions, but what motivates human behavior can rarely be discerned with perfect accuracy.

Difficult economic times, unfortunately, make it more likely that businesses will act on mere suppositions in the hope of somehow reducing risk or minimizing costs. One example of how that can go awry occurred in late December 2008, when reports surfaced that American Express was arbitrarily lowering credit limits for some customers based on data mining analysis of their purchasing patterns. One customer, according to the *Atlanta Journal-Constitution*, received a letter saying that his credit limit had been reduced. The problem was not his repayment history—which was excellent—but the repayment history of customers at stores at which he had shopped. A spokesperson for American Express said that the company was merely taking steps to manage risk and that it made sense to take into account the repayment practices of everyone who shops at a particular store. As many people pointed out at the time, a credit limit reduction by American Express can immediately cause other problems, not the least of which is a reduced credit score.

THE BRAVE NEW WORLD OF IDENTITY THEFT

It is largely impossible to function in the world without telling at least some people who you are, your occupation, your residence, and other information about you; in that sense, one's identity is probably the least private aspect of one's life. At the same time, one's identity is intensely personal and thus well within the zone that most of us describe as private. While we share some parts of our identity with the world at large, we reserve other aspects for select individuals: special friends, family, a partner or spouse. The key element is control: there are some aspects of our identity beyond our control (our public persona), others that are entirely within our control to share as we choose (our sense of self, our memories, our personal experiences), and some that fall in a gray area in between, where control might be desirable but is not always possible. Above all, it is our identity that reaffirms our sense of uniqueness in the sea of humanity. Even if a person shares every last molecule of DNA with a twin or triplet, there is still no exact match for that person's private thoughts and feelings, for his or her identity. As Descartes might have said on Facebook or Twitter, "I have privacy, therefore I am."

Perhaps that is why the crime of identity theft has made such an impression on the modern psyche. Not only does it underscore the growing sense that we are all little more than the sum of our numbers and database entries, it also raises difficult questions, both existential and practical: Who am I? And how can I prove it?

The modern-day epidemic of identity theft stems from the toxic combination of an intrinsically insecure Social Security number that has become a de facto national identification number, massive computer databases vulnerable to hacking, a rapidly growing global data and communications network, and lax security procedures that allow databases and data processing reports to be stored on laptops. Together these elements have helped the crime of identity theft become one of the fastest-growing problems for law enforcement.

Elements of the crime have been around since the Depression, when thieves would steal Social Security checks from mailboxes and cash them by pretending to be the recipient. But identity theft is a far more comprehensive form of theft: it means having enough information about a person to assume his or her entire financial identity. With the right information, an identity thief can empty bank accounts, max out credit cards, open new credit card accounts (and max those out as well), take out loans, and then simply disappear, leaving the victim to struggle for months or years to reestablish his or her true identity.

The HowStuffWorks Web site offers a discouragingly thorough (and somewhat bizarrely helpful) list of all the different places from which thieves can obtain the personal information necessary for identity theft. Among some of the more obvious sources of personal information are trash cans and dumpsters (in the practice known as "dumpster diving"), mailboxes, employer and business records, hospital records, rental forms and landlord records, online and offline databases, hacked merchant accounts, and cloned e-mail messages or Web sites. Increasingly, identity thieves also use a technique known as "phishing," in which a seemingly valid e-mail is sent requesting financial information (for example, a bank account number to help transfer a large sum of money out of a war-torn African nation).

Regardless of the source of private financial information, the key to identity theft is the Social Security number. Dozens of federal agencies use it as an identifier, often in records that are freely available to the public or obtainable through Freedom of Information Act requests. The Web has exacerbated this problem as well: the materials that government agencies and courts put online often contain Social Security numbers and other useful information for identity thieves. Even more problematic are the numerous commercial businesses—banks, credit card companies, health insurance companies, and so on—that request and use Social Security numbers to track customer files and conduct further research.

All this would not be quite so much of a problem if government and commercial computer databases were more secure. Long before the World Wide Web was developed and implemented, "phone phreaks" and hackers experimented with ways to access, manipulate, and retrieve information from telecommunications networks and rudimentary computer networks. In one of the earliest cases, a Fairfax City, Virginia, man was charged in 1983 with using a personal computer to illegally access credit card information from Credit Bureaus Inc. in Atlanta. He managed to charge over $50,000 worth of consumer goods on the credit cards before he was tracked down and arrested.

That is utter peanuts compared to more recent computer thefts of credit card information. In July 2005, a small team of hackers pulled up outside a Marshalls store in St. Paul, Minnesota, and used a Wi-Fi–equipped laptop to hack into the store's computer network. From there they were able to find the electronic path to the central servers of TJX, the parent company of Marshalls, T.J. Maxx, and other retail outlets. The hackers then proceeded to download database files from the TJX servers containing somewhere between 45 million and 200 million credit card numbers. Even more lucrative were the files containing detailed personal information—including driver's license numbers and Social Security numbers—for 450,000 unlucky TJX customers. By the time the hack was discovered a year later, the TJX credit card numbers had become a virtual cottage industry on the Internet. Industry analysts estimated that TJX might be liable for as much as $1 billion in fraudulent charges.

In the summer of 2006, the U.S. Department of Veterans Affairs (VA) suffered a particularly egregious loss of data when a laptop and external hard drive were stolen from an employee's home. Stored on the laptop and hard drive were the unencrypted names, birth dates, and Social Security numbers of millions of active-duty service members and U.S. veterans. The VA did not announce the data loss for three weeks, which substantially increased the risk of identity theft. The stolen equipment was eventually recovered, and the VA agreed to pay up to $20 million in damages to veterans who incurred expenses for data monitoring or who could demonstrate emotional distress from the data breach. Only after this incident did the VA institute a program for encrypting sensitive data.

Despite these high-profile incidents, the problem of credit-card data theft is growing steadily worse. According to a report from the Identity Theft Resource Center, a San Diego–based research group, 656 organizations—government agencies, businesses, and universities —reported a loss or theft of consumer data in 2008, a 47 percent increase over the 446 groups that reported losses the previous year. A significant number of cases involved lost or stolen laptops containing sensitive data, ranging from copies of consumer databases to classified government information. Even more remarkable is that fact that of the more than six hundred cases of data breach, only 2.4 percent involved data that had been encrypted and only 8.5 percent involved data that was even protected by a password.

The Web has unquestionably complicated computer security issues. After all, the entire point of the Web is the free and easy exchange of information from Point A to Point B. In that type of system, security is friction, and both users and systems tend to work around it. That helps explain, for instance, why passwords tend to be fairly easy to crack (particularly when the default password is never changed) and why the software patches intended to plug the security holes are so inconsistently installed. Moreover, the Web has made it much easier for communities of hackers to form and exchange information, ranging from password-cracking tools and the software needed to break into databases (there are complete kits available) to the stolen credit card numbers themselves.

While much of the blame can be laid at the feet of the governmental agencies and corporations that do not do a good enough job of protecting private information, it is also fair to say that consumers are often their own worst enemies. Given the advances that have taken place in the dark art of malware (malicious software such as viruses, worms, Trojan horses, zombie programs, and the like), consumers share the responsibility of practicing safe computing. But far too few consumers have effective passwords, install the necessary firewall software, or download security patches for their operating systems as frequently as they should. When it comes to identity theft, there is more than enough responsibility to go around.

Some effort has being made to address the issue on the federal level. On May 10, 2006, President George W. Bush issued Executive Order 13402, establishing the Identity Theft Task Force (ITTF). The goal of the ITTF, Bush said, was to prepare "a coordinated strategic plan to further improve the effectiveness and efficiency of the Federal Government's activities in the areas of identity theft awareness, prevention, detection, and prosecution."

After two years of study, the ITTF issued a report detailing how the federal government could better combat identity theft. Recommendation 1 was straightforward: "Decrease the unnecessary use of SSNs [Social Security numbers] in the public sector."

"One of the most practical and cost-effective ways to prevent breaches," the report said, "is to collect and maintain sensitive data only when it is necessary to do so." The task force recommended a complete review of how Social Security numbers are used, both by government agencies and the private sector, as well as appropriate guidelines from the Office of Personnel Management and a clearinghouse for agency "best practices" involving the use of the numbers.

In the report's conclusion, however, the task force offered a somewhat bleak outlook on the growing identity theft industry:

The fight against identity theft is an "end to end" challenge in which the security risks and responsibilities are spread from consumers, to enterprises, to information technology and tele-communication vendors, software providers, and others who facilitate the collection, use, maintenance, and eventual destruction of personal information. Newer areas of identity theft are growing fast, as thieves steal data in order to commit medical, immigration, employment, and mortgage fraud, for example. What identity theft will look like ten years from now is impossible to predict.

The task force issued thirty-one separate recommendations for combating identity theft, but there is good reason to be skeptical about how quickly and thoroughly those recommendations will be implemented. The chief impediment, at least for the time being, is that the Social Security number is such a useful tool for linking computer databases, and neither government nor the private sector is in any hurry to give up the potential benefits of data mining that it makes possible.

SHATTERED PRIVACY: THE USA PATRIOT ACT, THE TIA PROGRAM, AND ADVISE

In the wake of the terrorist attacks on September 11, 2001, the Bush Administration, Congress, and the American public were eager to take whatever measures they could to prevent similar attacks from occurring in the future. But what is surprising is that in their efforts to protect the nation, attorney general John Ashcroft, the Bush White House, and congressional conservatives took such precise and comprehensive aim at the laws designed to protect and defend our right to privacy.

The bill known as the USA PATRIOT Act (a "bacronym," or reverse acronym, that inspired the bill's full name, the Uniting and Strengthening America by Providing Appropriate Tools Required to Intercept and Obstruct Terrorism Act of 2001) was actually a hodge-podge of initiatives, many of which had been unsuccessfully bouncing from one congressional committee to another prior to 9/11. But in the wake of the attacks, Attorney General Ashcroft urged congressional leaders in both houses to act swiftly to give the Bush administration the power to effectively fight terrorism. On October 2, 2001, at the height of the negotiations between Congress and the administration,

Ashcroft told CNN's Larry King that he was disappointed at the pace of Congress's deliberations but was hopeful that the legislation would pass.

Despite the complexity of the PATRIOT Act (which contained more than 340 pages of often-dense text) and the sweeping nature of the powers requested, Congress passed the law with remarkable speed: President Bush signed the bill into law on October 26, 2001, just forty-five days after 9/11 and just three days after the final form of the bill was introduced in the House of Representatives. Congress spent little enough time debating the administration's proposals and their implications for liberty and privacy; the only way they could have acted as quickly as Ashcroft evidently wished would have been to close up shop and cede all legislative authority to the White House.

In the end, neither the American public nor most of its representatives had any idea just how aggressively the right to privacy was under attack. With the passage of PATRIOT Act, the Bush administration succeeded in undermining nearly all of the scant privacy protections adopted by Congress over the last forty years:

- the Wiretap Statute (Title III of the Omnibus Crime Control and Safe Streets Act of 1968)
- the Electronic Communications Privacy Act of 1986
- the Computer Fraud and Abuse Act of 1986
- the Foreign Intelligence Surveillance Act of 1978
- the Family Education Rights and Privacy Act of 1974
- the Pen Register and Trap and Trace Statute (part of the Electronic Communications Privacy Act)
- the Immigration and Nationality Act of 1952
- the Money Laundering Control Act of 1986
- the Bank Secrecy Act of 1970
- the Right to Financial Privacy Act of 1978
- the Fair Credit Reporting Act of 1970

For civil libertarians worried about the conservatism of the Bush administration, the PATRIOT Act was a target-rich environment. For instance, Section 201 of the act effectively reinstated the practice of wiretapping individuals suspected of domestic terrorism. Section 204 authorized law enforcement to obtain voice mail messages through a simple search warrant, which is easier to obtain than the previously required wiretap authorization. Section 206 amended the Foreign Intelligence Surveillance Act to allow the FBI to apply for roving wiretaps, a tool designed to let agents intercept suspect communications without having to specify what telephone line or computer system is being monitored. The rationale was that terrorists attempt to foil surveillance by frequently switching phone lines and e-mail systems, and a roving wiretap allows the FBI to keep track. At the same time, however, it also permits a level of surveillance reminiscent of the "general warrants" that gave rise to the Fourth Amendment in the first place.

Two provisions raised particular concerns. Section 216 expanded the types of information that could be captured using "pen registers" (devices used to list phone numbers dialed from a particular location) and "trap and trace" devices (which collect information about the source of incoming calls, similar to caller ID). Well before the attacks on 9/11, the FBI had begun monitoring Internet traffic through the use of a controversial surveillance program called Carnivore (which the public first learned of in 2000). The bureau argued that it was authorized to track information about the origin and destination of Internet traffic, including e-mails, on the theory that such information is analogous to phone numbers. Obviously, e-mail addresses and subject headers alone offer far more descriptive information than a simple phone number. The debate over the propriety of the FBI's interpretation was effectively shut down by the adoption of Section 216.

Even more disturbing was Section 215, which gave the FBI the ability to seek an order from the Foreign Intelligence Surveillance Court "requiring the production of any tangible things (including books, records, papers, documents, and other items)" from any business, medical organization, educational institution, or library if, in the opinion of the FBI, the information might be relevant to an investigation of international terrorism or clandestine intelligence activities. In a highly unusual step, Congress made it extremely difficult to monitor or protest the investigations of the FBI, since anyone receiving a search warrant issued by the Foreign Intelligence Surveillance Court is prohibited by law from disclosing receipt of the warrant or a description of the records produced.

Many saw this as an open-ended fishing license into some of the most private activities of Americans, particularly with respect to FBI searches of library borrowing records. In a letter to its members, the American Library Association said: "You remain entitled to legal counsel. Therefore, you may call your attorney and/or the [American] Booksellers Foundation [for Free Expression] or, if a librarian, the American Library Association, and simply tell us that you need to contact our legal counsel. Because of the gag order, however, you should not tell us that you have received a court order." Veteran *Village Voice* columnist Nat Hentoff offered a bleak summary of the impact of Section 215:

> This, mind you, is part of a law in the United States of America, not the People's Republic of China. Because of the chilling effect of this section of the U.S.A. Patriot Act, it's uncertain how many booksellers and librarians will even call a lawyer. And for those who do, it's difficult to predict how successful a court challenge will be in the present, and long-term, atmosphere of fear of shadowy terrorists among us.

Hentoff pointed to the fact that during World War II the Supreme Court upheld the internment of Japanese citizens on security grounds, and he grimly concluded that it would be much harder today to challenge FBI library searches: "This time, because of the [PATRIOT Act] gag order, there will be even less public criticism because we will not know how often these searches are made—and what specific books are under suspicion. You might have some of those books in your home."

Library record searches were just the start. A little more than a year later, the news broke that John Poindexter, President Reagan's former national security adviser and a key player in the Iran-Contra scandal, had been appointed to run a new federal operation called the Information Awareness Office (IAO). Poindexter, who had been working as a contractor for the Defense Advanced Research Projects Agency (DARPA) on systems designed to sort through large amounts of data, had approached the Pentagon with the idea of a "Total Information Awareness" (TIA) initiative, following the 9/11 attacks. The goal of the program was to use advanced data-mining techniques, combined with massive aggregation of private and government data, to create a "counterterrorism information architecture." DARPA (which ironically funded the initial research that led to the Internet) agreed to host the IAO, established a budget of $200 million, and selected Poindexter to run the program. It was an idea that made the old FEDNET concept look amusingly quaint.

In a speech in early 2002, Poindexter laid out the rationale for the TIA program: "We must become much more efficient and more clever in the ways we find new sources of data, mine information from the new and old, generate information, make it available for analysis, convert it to knowledge, and create actionable options." A specific goal of the program, he said, was to "break down the stovepipes" that blocked the sharing of information between government and commercial databases and interfered with effective data mining techniques. Ideally, Poindexter argued, the Information Awareness Office would be able to sift through enormous amounts of data and find a common thread of a terrorist threat in bank records, phone calls, airline tickets, restaurant charges, and so on. In many ways, Poindexter proved to be his own worst enemy in the perhaps inevitable battle with civil libertarians. In what can only be described as a blinding fit of arrogance, he chose *Scientia Est Potentia* as the motto for the IAO: "Knowledge Is Power." Few found that to be a comforting thought.

"You Are a Suspect" was the headline of a scathing column that week by *New York Times* columnist William Safire:

Every purchase you make with a credit card, every magazine subscription you buy and medical prescription you fill, every Web site you visit and e-mail you send or receive, every academic grade you receive, every bank deposit you make, every trip you book and every event you attend—all these transactions and communications will go into what the Defense Department describes as "a virtual, centralized grand database."

To this computerized dossier on your private life from commercial sources, add every piece of information that government has about you—passport application, driver's license and bridge toll records, judicial and divorce records, complaints from nosy neighbors to the F.B.I., your lifetime paper trail plus the latest hidden camera surveillance—and you have the super-snoop's dream: a "Total Information Awareness" about every U.S. citizen.

This is not some far-out Orwellian scenario. It is what will happen to your personal freedom in the next few weeks if John Poindexter gets the unprecedented power he seeks.

Thanks in large part to the public outcry that followed Safire's column, funding for the TIA program was put on hold in early 2003, and DARPA was ordered to report back to Congress on its work so far and its plans for further data mining. The Pentagon tried changing the name of the program to *Terrorist* Information Awareness, but Congress formally eliminated the TIA program's funding in the 2004 Department of Defense appropriation bill.

It is occasionally possible to truly kill off a federal program, but it is never easy. It is particularly difficult to do so when the program is enthusiastically supported by the administration and a significant portion of Congress. In February 2006, the *National Journal* reported that although the TIA program was halted and the Information Awareness Office shut down as an organizational structure, much of the research into data aggregation that the IAO was supervising was quietly transferred to other agencies within the Pentagon. For instance, the government's Advanced Research and Development Activity agency (ARDA) reportedly took over the core database and information analysis work of the TIA program and rechristened it with the seemingly benign code name "Basketball." ARDA also took over a TIA project called Genoa II (which it renamed "Topsail") that was designed "to develop decision-support aids for teams of intelligence analysts and policy personnel to assist in anticipating and pre-empting terrorist threats to U.S. interests." ARDA is housed at the National Security Agency at Fort Meade, Maryland, which helps explain why a veil of silence has largely descended over further efforts to learn more about the government's data mining technologies.

Several other data analysis programs have raised similar privacy concerns. In early 2007, Senator Patrick Leahy asked the Government Accountability Office (GAO) to review a Pentagon program known as Analysis, Dissemination, Visualization, Insight and Semantic Enhancement (ADVISE), a data mining initiative that bears an uncanny resemblance to the discredited TIA program. The GAO's report criticized the program for using private information without notifying citizens that it was doing so and for using private information for purposes other than originally intended. David M. Walker, the GAO comptroller, testified to Congress that the Bush administration was running at least three data mining programs and that there were likely others that remained classified.

Later that summer, the Justice Department admitted to Congress that the FBI had developed a program called the System to Assess Risk (STAR), which analyzed various databases for information about a potential terrorist suspect and assigned a threat value based on that information. Justice Department officials defended the program as simply a high-tech version of what analysts were already doing by hand, but some in Congress disagreed. Senator Leahy, one of the most senior members of the Senate Judiciary Committee, said that the program was another example of the administration's disregard for civil rights. "The Bush administration," he said, "has expanded the use of this technology, often in secret, to collect and sift through Americans' most sensitive personal information."

It is, needless to say, difficult to balance issues of personal privacy and national security. But given the vast electronic resources of the federal government and the enormous quantities of data available for mining, there is clearly enormous potential for abuse. Recent history demonstrates, sadly, that there is a potential for surveillance tools to be misused for political purposes, to harass and hound those who disagree with a particular administration's policies. In theory, Congress should serve as a check on the worst invasions of an administration, but too often is complicit in such invasions for its own purposes.

CONCLUSION

The Perilous State of Privacy

In light of how easily control of information is lost or actively destroyed in today's society, is it still possible to talk about a "right to privacy" or privacy at all? That depends, in large part, on who is looking for information and what they intend to do with it. The tremendous popularity of the Internet, the sophistication and thoroughness of search engines, our own evident fascination with publishing information about ourselves—all of these factors (and many others) raise genuine questions about not only whether it is possible to live a truly private life but whether privacy can or even should be constitutionally protected.

The one common thread in privacy debates over the course of our nation's history is the concept of control—that privacy at its core is the ability to determine what information will be shared with others and when it will be shared. The ability to control personal information has steadily declined for most Americans over the last several decades, and for the e-generation now coming of age it scarcely existed at all.

One particularly compelling example occurred during the course of my research on this book. While working in a coffee shop in New Haven, Connecticut, I was listening to some music using Apple's iTunes software. Apple included a new feature in a recent upgrade that allows the limited sharing of music between computers over a local network (if turned on, the sharing feature allows iTunes users to play each other's music, but not copy it). If your iTunes software finds another iTunes user on the network with sharing turned on, it displays the name of that shared library on your screen. In most cases, the name of the shared library is the name of the person who owns the computer; for instance, my library of music shows up as

"Frederick Lane's Library," along with my own genre preferences: classical, sixties folk, musicals and show tunes, and some classic rock.

This particular morning, my copy of iTunes detected another iTunes user on the coffee shop's Wi-Fi network. The individual's full name was displayed, and—given the first name and the makeup of the crowd around me—it seemed likely that the user was one of the women in the café. A brief exploration of her shared library provided a remarkable amount of information about her musical tastes: the songs she was listening to that morning, her favorite playlists (the names of which offered their own revealing insights), her most frequently played tracks, recently purchased albums, and so on.

Having spent several months researching privacy, the next logical question was whether I could figure out whose copy of iTunes was being shared. Since there were several young women in the coffee shop at the time, I wondered whether I could link the name of the iTunes user to a photograph. Thanks to Google, that took less than one minute: a photo from the *Yale Daily News* of the women's rugby team made it clear who in the café was sharing her library that morning. The same search also turned up the name of her hometown, the fact that she was an equestrian (including the name of her horse and the results of her last several events), the name of her house at Yale, her major, a high school term paper, and the fact that her grandfather had died a few months earlier (which in turn provided the names of her parents and siblings). It is a safe assumption that she had not personally posted any of the information that turned up so easily in Google.

Admittedly, the no-longer-anonymous iTunes user could have retained somewhat more control over her identity that morning by not sharing her iTunes library, but that does not change the underlying fact that the concept of personal privacy for her generation is vastly different than it once was for older Americans. College, high school, and even middle school students are increasingly accustomed to the idea of a life lived largely online, where remarkable amounts of personal information are freely shared with anyone possessing Internet access. And even if individual students choose not to broadcast their own information, proud schools, parents, and clubs will often do it for them; anyone with a blog or digital camera is a potential chronicler of his or her friends' private information. As some have discovered to their dismay, that's not always a good thing: there's a Facebook group called "*30 Reasons Girls Should Call It a Night*" that features photos of people (mostly women) in various states of inebriation, many labeled with the subject/victim's name. If that person is a Facebook user herself, the name helpfully links to her presumably more sober profile.

For civil libertarians, historians, and parents, such casual attitudes toward personal information and private behavior are profoundly worrisome. It was only a generation ago, after all, that the Nixon administration was aggressively using federal agencies to collect private information as part of its campaign to harass its political enemies and mute domestic discontent. Parents worry (as they should) that private information might make a child more vulnerable to stalking or attack; as the iTunes library example illustrates, it is far too easy to compile a potentially dangerous amount of information about someone using information that he or she is almost certainly unaware is being broadcast.

Even putting aside the issue of physical safety, there is a very real possibility that the information people put online will affect their professional well-being. Most of the major corporations in the United States, for instance, have employees in their human resources departments who spend much of their day searching the Web for information by and about job applicants. Needless to say, if the choice is between someone whose party exploits are chronicled in living color and someone whose online persona is more tempered, most businesses will pass on the overly publicized candidate.

PRIVACY BEGINS AT HOME, BUT THAT'S NOT ENOUGH

As with most social problems, it is ultimately each individual's responsibility to protect his or her privacy and to understand the implications of releasing information into the world. We each need to do a better job of understanding the implications of our actions, taking steps to limit the spread of information that can be misused, and voting for state and federal candidates who demonstrate an awareness and appreciation of the importance of this issue.

In particular, both parents and schools need to do a more thorough job of teaching young people the value of privacy in their own lives and for the nation as a whole. Better education about personal privacy should be an essential part of school curricula at every level. The need for such instruction is particularly acute in light of the fact that children and students are far more likely to use the types of electronic devices and Web services that routinely leak private information into the world.

At various times in our nation's history, our representatives have made the determination that certain issues or problems were simply too large for individuals or even the various states to handle effectively. For instance, in 1906 Congress created the Food and Drug Administration to inspect the nation's meat supply and prevent the sale of adulterated food. The Federal Trade Commission was established in 1914 to protect consumers and minimize unfair and anticompetitive business practices. In 1927 the Federal Radio Commission was established to bring order to the chaotic radio industry. The Federal Aviation Administration was created in 1958 to supervise the U.S. aeronautics industry, and in 1970 (under President Nixon, no less) the Environmental Protection Agency was created to protect American health by promoting a cleaner environment.

Each of those problems (and many others) required a coordinated national approach in order to be addressed effectively. And as recent experiences at the Securities and Exchange Commission have shown, an ongoing commitment to regulatory oversight is also necessary. Personal privacy has long since joined that category of issues that requires the macro-level expertise and continued oversight of a national regulatory body, a Federal Privacy Protection Agency that could monitor and enforce the privacy practices of both government and the private sector.

Back in 1974, in the wake of Watergate, Senator Sam Ervin proposed just such a commission, but it was strenuously opposed by the Ford administration and by congressional conservatives and was not included in the final version of the Privacy Act adopted that year. Even if Ervin's privacy commission had been adopted, however, it would have essentially been a well-funded federal suggestion box, empowered to do little more than study privacy issues and receive complaints. As the *Washington Post* said at the time:

Experience with other reforms such as civil rights law and the Environmental Policy Act has shown all too clearly that many agencies, left to themselves, are very slow to change their policies and attitudes. Nor is the existing White House committee [the Domestic Council Committee on the Right of Privacy] a reliable substitute for a permanent oversight agency with a clear, statutory mandate. If Congress really wants federal data bank policies to be reformed, a small but forceful agency, with that as its single mission, is required.

There is some irony in looking to the government to protect a social value that it has so frequently attacked. But as the Environmental Protection Agency and other federal agencies have demonstrated, it is possible for an organization of well-trained and dedicated professionals to play an effective enforcement role for both government and the private sector. And it is abundantly clear that thirty-five years after Ervin's proposal, the need for a federal privacy commission is more acute than ever before. Privacy issues abound in every aspect of our lives, and the consequences for abuse and misuse of personal information grow graver and more profound each day. It is difficult enough for the various independent privacy rights groups, such as the ACLU, the Electronic Privacy Information Center, and the Privacy Rights Clearinghouse, to keep pace with all the changes that are occurring, let alone for the average individual to do so. And yet all of us, to one degree or another, are affected by the business practices, technological tools, software innovations, and other developments that attack personal privacy from every direction. An agency with seasoned professionals could help strike the right balance among the numerous competing considerations that are currently weighed against privacy: national security, government efficiency, corporate profits, personal pleasure, and so on.

There are four general areas in which a Federal Privacy Protection Agency could play a particularly important role: the protection and enhancement of the Fourth Amendment, the monitoring and regulation of governmental data practices, the monitoring and regulation of corporate data practices, and the education of the public.

PROTECTING AND ENHANCING THE FOURTH AMENDMENT

The most important question from the perspective of personal liberty is the extent to which the government or its agents can invade our privacy against our will. As the Warren Court recognized in *Griswold v. Connecticut* (1965), much of the Bill of Rights can be read as establishing a "zone of privacy" into which the government is not permitted to intrude. The size of that zone has ebbed and flowed over the years as various issues have been presented to the Supreme Court; in particular, the legal force and effect of the "right to privacy" has come under attack due to its close association with the politically volatile issue of abortion (*Roe v. Wade*, 1973) and its lack of explicit grounding in the language of the Constitution itself. Nonetheless, as the Court convincingly demonstrated in *Lawrence v. Texas* (2003), in which the constitutionality of a Texas antisodomy statute was challenged, the core principle perseveres:

> The petitioners are entitled to respect for their private lives. The State cannot demean their existence or control their destiny by making their private sexual conduct a crime. Their right to liberty under the Due Process Clause gives them the full right to engage in their conduct without intervention of the government. It is a promise of the Constitution that there is a realm of personal liberty which the government may not enter. The Texas statute furthers no legitimate state interest which can justify its intrusion into the personal and private life of the individual.

The core of the constitutional right to privacy, the Fourth Amendment prohibition against unreasonable searches and seizures, is facing its gravest threat from advances in computer technology. Once an individual's hard drive has been seized, his or her entire life is essentially an open book to investigators and computer forensic specialists. Although computer information can be searched with some particularity, the potential for abuse is profound. Particularly disturbing are recent court decisions permitting random, warrantless searches of computer hard drives at the nation's borders. A Federal Privacy Protection Agency could play a valuable role in educating the courts about the privacy implications of new technologies, drafting legislation that balances national security and privacy, developing guidelines to minimize privacy intrusions if electronic searches are conducted, and educating both lawyers and the public about the Fourth Amendment issues raised by searches of computer data.

MONITORING AND REGULATING GOVERNMENT DATA PRACTICES

Supreme Court cases and law enforcement procedures are topics that attract a lot of attention, and the debates over the proper boundaries of the right to privacy are frequent and spirited. There is relatively little chance that significant diminutions in privacy in either sector would slide by unnoticed. The same cannot be said, however, about the steady erosion of privacy that has occurred—and continues to occur—as a result of governmental collection and sharing of personal information.

Despite the fact that the U.S. Constitution creates just one specific duty to collect information about Americans (the decennial census), federal and state government have become increasingly aggressive compilers of data. Much of that data collection is in connection with the provision of government services, which means that people are exchanging information in return for some benefit. And of course, citizens expect their government to function as efficiently as possible, which requires a certain amount of information for planning, analysis, and evaluation of results.

The fundamental question, which too often goes unasked, is whether a particular agency is collecting the minimum amount of information necessary for its mission and no more. Many more journalistic efforts like the *New York Times*'s investigation of the National Security Agency wiretapping (discussed in the introduction) are needed to help serve as a check on overzealous agencies. But that's merely a start.

Despite Congress's halfhearted efforts in the 1970s to protect privacy by limiting the amount of data sharing that could take place, federal and state agencies share massive amounts of information every day. In the wake of the USA PATRIOT Act, most of the restrictions on data sharing have been swept aside in favor of a concerted program of data mining aimed at learning as much information about people as possible.

There is a particularly compelling need for oversight of federal data mining and interagency sharing. Numerous federal regulatory agencies have enforcement powers, and there is no reason that a Privacy Protection Agency should be any different. The agency could have the power to fine or dismiss government employees who commit various privacy breaches, including the loss of personal data or the failure to take reasonable steps to secure it, failure to adopt effective privacy policies or to adhere to them, misuse of consumer information, and so on. The adoption and enforcement of consistent and publicized privacy standards throughout federal and state government would have the beneficial effect of making it easier for individuals to understand their privacy rights and play a role in protecting them.

MONITORING AND REGULATING CORPORATE DATA PRACTICES

Americans make the practice of data mining remarkably simple, not only for government agencies but also for companies with which we do business. As with the government, the invasions of privacy in the corporate realm stem from the combination of massive computer technology and the seemingly endless willingness of Americans to trade consumer data and personal information for the slightest iota of convenience.

Here too there is a rational relationship between the exchange of information and the benefit received. In general, a more efficient business is one that can charge lower prices than its competitors; collected and used carefully, information about consumers has a clear economic benefit to both a business and its customers.

The chief problem is that an individual may not be aware of the cumulative impact on his or her privacy for months or even years (absent a catastrophic impact such as identity theft). Moreover, our failure as individuals to take privacy into account in our dealings with businesses ignores the impact that such decisions have on the overall concept of privacy in this country. If everyone throws a single soda can out of the car window, it does not take long for a highway to look pretty hideous. But for decades, we've been casually tossing bits of personal information out into the world.

Businesses now are starting to see the benefit of tighter privacy policies. Ironically, much of the impetus comes from Web-based businesses, since consumers react quickly (and negatively) when loose handling of their information on the Internet results in a flood of spam in their inbox—or worse, large numbers of unexplained credit card charges. But it remains to be seen whether the marketing benefits of good privacy practices will outweigh the perceived benefits of data mining for most businesses. A Federal Privacy Protection Agency could play a powerful role in assisting in the protection of personal information.

EDUCATING THE PUBLIC

Admittedly, it is difficult to make a case for greater privacy protections when individuals are eagerly posting so much information about themselves online. With Web sites and blogs numbering in the hundreds of millions (quite a journey from Berners-Lee's solitary site seventeen years ago!), electronic exhibitionism is now a global activity. It would be inappropriate, paternalistic, and blatantly unconstitutional to argue that people should not be allowed to publish any personal information they feel is appropriate to share. But an argument can be made not only that everyone should be better educated about the consequences of electronic exhibitionism, but that they should not have such exhibitionism thrust upon them without their consent. Just as other federal agencies provide consumer education, a Federal Privacy Protection Agency could serve as a valuable source of institutional knowledge and curricula about the value of personal privacy and the risks inherent in the careless distribution of information.

But such education has a broader purpose as well. Understanding the concept of personal privacy and the challenges in preserving it requires a solid understanding of our history and our Constitution. One of the brilliant features of the Constitution is its delicate balancing of powers, a thoughtful approach that is wholly absent from the often chaotic and unruly marketplace. Adam Smith's "unseen hand" may be good for business, but increasingly it calls to mind a pickpocket that lifts from consumers their most deeply personal data.

Over the last three hundred years, the questions of privacy in our society have evolved from essentially two simple queries—"Is my home secure against governmental invasion?" and "Have my letters been opened?"—to a much broader and more open-ended puzzle: how can we protect our personal information and individual privacy in a world in which we are rapidly becoming prolific self-publishers, a world where copying is essentially free and data can live forever in a constantly expanding universe of hard drive space? The answer lies in a continued commitment to the spirit and intent of the U.S. Constitution—a document written long before computers and the Internet were ever conceived, but with an unwavering belief in the fundamental importance of individual autonomy and personal privacy.

ACKNOWLEDGMENTS

Publishing is undergoing some profound changes these days, and now more than ever the publication of a hardcover book is a leap of faith, both for authors and publishing houses. I am profoundly grateful to Beacon Press for its continued commitment to the written word and, more broadly, to the values and principles that are the foundation of a free society. It is an honor to work with the press and the people who each day perpetuate its fine tradition.

In particular, I would like to thank the Beacon Press publisher, Helene Atwan, for her steady enthusiasm for this project and her encouragement throughout; my editor, Allison Trzop, for her insightful comments and well-chosen edits, all of which helped to make this a much better book; Beacon Broadside editor Jessie Bennett, for putting together such a terrific blog for authors like myself to expand upon and publicize their works; and my former editor at Beacon, Brian Halley, for recommending to Beacon that they move forward with this project in the first place.

Once again, I would like to extend my thanks to my literary agent, Jessica Faust of BookEnds, LLC, for helping me to place this project with Beacon. I am very fortunate to have the opportunity to work with an agent who is so consistently thoughtful, enthusiastic, and prepared in her dealings with publishers and publishing houses.

During the course of this project, I have had the chance to write frequently on privacy-related topics for the technology news Web site, NewsFactor.com. I'd like to thank Lynda Geller, NewsFactor's cofounder and associate publisher, for giving me the opportunity to cover so many emerging issues and for being so patient with the ebbs and flows of a writer's workload. It has been enormously helpful to write frequently about the privacy implications of new technologies.

Through my work as a journalist for NewsFactor, I've had an opportunity to meet many of the people working tirelessly to promote and protect privacy in America. In particular, I'd like to acknowledge the efforts of Jeffrey Chester, executive director of the Center for Digital Democracy; Kathryn Montgomery, professor of communication at American University; Beth Givens, director of the Privacy Rights Clearinghouse; Marc Rotenberg, president and executive director of the Electronic Privacy Information Center; Allen Gilbert, executive director of the Vermont chapter of the American Civil Liberties Union; Lauren Weinstein, cofounder of People for Internet Responsibility; Ari Schwartz, deputy director of the Center for Democracy and Technology; Daniel Solove, associate professor of law at George Washington University School of Law; and Simson Garfinkel, associate professor of computer science at the Naval Postgraduate School.

During the course of my research on this book, I was invited by the Yale Law School Law and Media Program (LAMP) to participate in the Computers, Freedom, and Privacy 2008 conference in New Haven, Connecticut. I would like to thank LAMP for its sponsorship and for giving me the opportunity to meet so many of the leaders in the electronic privacy field. In particular, I would like to thank Tracey Parr, director of recruitment at Yale Law School, for her work in making all of the sponsored journalists feel so welcome.

Throughout the course of this project, I have had the pleasure of working in a number of wonderful libraries. I would like to thank the staffs at the Durrick Library at St. Michael's College, the Bailey-Howe Library at the University of Vermont, and Widener Library at Harvard University for their patient assistance and helpful suggestions.

Significant portions of this book were written in one of Burlington's great treasures, the Dobrá Tea shop. It is a haven for writers and an island of calm in a sometimes hectic world. My deepest appreciation to proprietor Andrew Snavely and the rest of the staff for creating such a terrific spot for creative work.

I am enormously fortunate to have the support and encouragement of my family as I pursue the often erratic and perpetually demanding writer's life. As always, my thanks and love to my parents, Warren and Anne Lane; my brother, Jonathan, and his wife, Allison; my sister Elizabeth and her husband, Jeremy; and my sister Katherine and her husband, Matt.

My deepest appreciation, love, and thanks to my sons, Ben and Peter, who will have to negotiate their own privacy boundaries as they grow up in a world of always-connected devices and increasingly sophisticated social networks. Above all, my thanks to my partner, Amy, for helping to make this book and so much else in my life possible. An invaluable editor and soon-to-be coauthor, her spirit and enthusiasm infuse every page of this book. I am deeply grateful.

SELECTED BIBLIOGRAPHY

The following are some of the resources that I found particularly useful while researching *American Privacy*.

INTRODUCTION

Meyer, Josh, and Joseph Menn. "U.S. Spying Is Much Wider, Some Suspect." *Los Angeles Times*, December 26, 2005.

Risen, James, and Eric Lichtblau. "Bush Lets U.S. Spy on Callers without Courts." *New York Times*, December 16, 2005.

Singel, Ryan. "Whistle-Blower Outs NSA Spy Room." *Wired*, April 7, 2006.

1: THE DECLARATION OF PRIVACY

Adams, Charles Francis. *The Works of John Adams, Second President of the United States*. Vol. 2. Boston: Little, Brown and Company, 1850.

Bradford, William. *Bradford's History "Of Plimoth Plantation."* Reproduced from the original manuscript. Boston: Wright & Potter, 1899.

Columbia Historical Society. *Records of the Columbia Historical Society*. Vol. 9. Washington, D.C.: Columbia Historical Society, 1906. (Includes a history of the early North American postal system.)

Flaherty, David H. *Privacy in Colonial New England*. Charlottesville: University Press of Virginia, 1972.

2: POSTAL POLITICS, PURITY, AND PRIVACY

Bates, David Homer. *Lincoln in the Telegraph Office*. New York: Century Company, 1907.

Hart, Albert Bushnell. *American History Told by Contemporaries*. Vol. 3, *National Expansion, 1783–1845*. New York: Macmillan, 1900.

Horowitz, Helen Lefkowitz. *Rereading Sex: Battles over Sexual Knowledge and Suppression in Nineteenth-Century America*. New York: Alfred A. Knopf, 2002.

Jones, S. Walter. *A Treatise on the Law of Telegraph and Telephone Companies.* Kansas City, Mo.: Vernon Law Book Company, 1916.

McPherson, Edward. *The Political History of the United States of America during the Great Rebellion, from November 6, 1860 to July 4, 1864.* Washington, D.C.: Philip & Solomons, 1864.

Standage, Tom. *The Victorian Internet: The Remarkable Story of the Telegraph and the Nineteenth Century's On-line Pioneers.* New York: Berkeley Trade Books, 1999.

3: POPULATION, PUNCH CARDS, AND PRIVACY

Alderman, Ellen, and Caroline Kennedy. *The Right to Privacy.* New York: Alfred A. Knopf, 1995.

Gajda, Amy. "What If Samuel D. Warren Hadn't Married a Senator's Daughter? Uncovering the Press Coverage that Led to *The Right to Privacy.*" Illinois Public Law and Legal Theory Research Paper Series, November 1, 2007.

Green, Martin. *The Mount Vernon Street Warrens.* New York: Charles Scribner's Sons, 1989.

Martin, T. C. "The Hollerith Electric Census System." *Technology Quarterly* (MIT) 5 (1892): 49–55.

Porter, Robert H. "Counting the World by Electricity." *Windsor Magazine,* January 1895, 452–56.

4: PRIVACY IN STATE COURTS AND LEGISLATURES

Brandeis, Louis D., and Samuel D. Warren. "The Right to Privacy." *Harvard Law Review* 4, no. 5 (1890): 193–220.

5: NO MORE GENTLEMEN: THE RISE OF GOVERNMENTAL ESPIONAGE

Fischer, Claude S. *America Calling: A Social History of the Telephone to 1940.* Berkeley: University of California Press, 1992.

Minutes and Testimony of the Joint Legislative Committee Appointed to Investigate the Public Service Commissions. Vol. 5. Albany, N.Y.: J. B. Lyon Company, 1916.

"Police Espionage in a Democracy." *The Outlook,* May 31, 1916, 235–36.

Yardley, Herbert O. *The American Black Chamber.* Indianapolis: Bobbs-Merrill, 1931.

6: THE PEEPING TOMS OF PUBLIC LIFE

Goodwin, Doris Kearns. *No Ordinary Time: Franklin and Eleanor Roosevelt: The Home Front in World War II.* New York: Simon & Schuster, 1994.

Newman, Roger K. *Hugo Black: A Biography*. New York: Fordham University Press, 1997.

Peterson, Julie K. *Understanding Surveillance Technologies: Spy Devices, Their Origins and Applications*. Boca Raton, Fla.: CRC Press, 2001.

Schlesinger, Arthur M. *The Politics of Upheaval, 1935–1936*. Boston: Houghton Mifflin, 1960.

7: THE GREAT RED THREATS TO PRIVACY: CREDIT CARDS AND COMMUNISM

Dash, Samuel F., Richard F. Swartz, and Robert E. Knowlton. *The Eavesdroppers*. New Brunswick, N.J.: Rutgers University Press, 1959.

8: PRIVACY'S GOLDEN HOUR: THE WARREN COURT

Miller, Arthur R. *The Assault on Privacy: Computers, Data Banks, and Dossiers*. Ann Arbor: University of Michigan Press, 1971.

Orwell, George. *1984*. New York: New American Library, 1949.

Packard, Vance. *The Naked Society*. New York: D. McKay, 1964.

Westin, Alan F. *Privacy and Freedom*. New York: Atheneum, 1967.

9: "TOWARD FREEDOM FROM FEAR": THE PRIVACY VERSUS SECURITY DEBATE INTENSIFIES

Doyle, William. *Inside the Oval Office: The White House Tapes from FDR to Clinton*. New York: Kodansha International, 1999.

Greenhouse, Linda. *Becoming Justice Blackmun: Harry Blackmun's Supreme Court Journey*. New York: Macmillan, 2005.

Toobin, Jeffrey. *The Nine: Inside the Secret World of the Supreme Court*. New York: Doubleday, 2007.

Woodward, Bob, and Scott Armstrong. *The Brethren: Inside the Supreme Court*. New York: Simon & Schuster, 1979.

10: THE PHANTOM DELETE KEY: THE INCREDIBLE DURABILITY OF DATA

Cringely, Robert X. *Accidental Empires: How the Boys of Silicon Valley Make Their Millions, Battle Foreign Competition, and Still Can't Get a Date*. Reading, Mass.: Addison-Wesley, 1991.

Woodward, Bob, and Carl Bernstein. *All the President's Men*. New York: Simon & Schuster, 1974.

11: NO PC IS AN ISLAND: THE RISE OF ONLINE COMMUNITIES

Brin, David. *The Transparent Society: Freedom vs. Privacy in a City of Glass Houses*. Reading, Mass.: Addison-Wesley, 1998.

Garfinkel, Simson. *Database Nation: The Death of Privacy in the 21st Century*. Cambridge, Mass.: O'Reilly Media, 2000.

12: ELECTRONIC EXHIBITIONISM AND VOYEURISM: PRIVACY IN A WEBBED WORLD

Rosen, Jeffrey. *The Unwanted Gaze: The Destruction of Privacy in America*. New York: Random House, 2000.

Rule, James B. *Privacy in Peril: How We Are Trading a Fundamental Right for Security and Convenience*. New York: Oxford University Press, 2007.

Solove, Daniel J. *The Digital Person: Technology and Privacy in the Information Age*. New York: New York University Press, 2004.

———. *The Future of Reputation: Gossip, Rumor, and Privacy on the Internet*. New Haven, Conn.: Yale University Press, 2007.

INDEX

abolitionist movement, 18–19

Abzug, Bella, 197

Acorn (code name for original IBM PC), 203

Adams, John, 2, 10, 11, 13

Adams, Rhonda, 232

Addressograph-Multigraph Corporation, 110

Administration of Justice Act (Great Britain, 1774). *See* Intolerable Acts

Advanced Research Projects Agency (ARPA), 147

Ahl, David H., 201

Al Qaeda, xi

Alderman, Ellen, 56

Alien and Sedition Laws of 1798, 130

Allen, Paul, 207

Altmeyer, Arthur J., 110

America Online (AOL), 211, 228, 240–41

American Association for the Advancement of Science (AAAS), 144, 145

The American Black Chamber, 91

American Civil Liberties Union (ACLU), xviii–xix, 170, 215, 222, 223, 258

American Credit Bureau Association, 127

American Express, 150, 242

American Liberty League, 105, 106

American Library Association, 250

American Newspaper Publishers Association, 107

Analysis, Dissemination, Visualization, Insight and Semantic Enhancement (ADVISE), 252–53

Anderson, Annelise G., 218

Anderson, Jack, 161–62

Anderson, Martin, 218

Andreessen, Marc, 230

Anne, Queen, 6

Anti-Federalists, 16

Apple Computer, 201–6

Apple II (personal computer), 202–3, 205–6

Arago, François, 21

Armstrong, Scott, 173

Arnold, Thelma, 241

ARPA. *See* Advanced Research Projects Agency

ARPANET, 147

Articles of Confederation, 38

Ashcroft, John, 247–48

AT&T, xiii, xvii, xix, 123

Attorney General's Commission on Pornography, 227–28

Austin, Warren, 114

Baird, William, 174

Bank Secrecy Act of 1970, 223, 248

Baran, Paul, 146, 147

Barbaro, Michael, 241

Barkan, Alexander E., 186